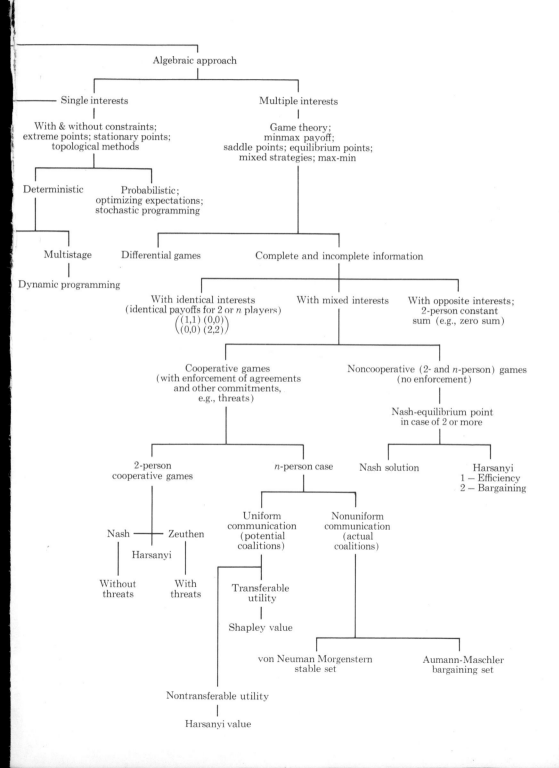

OPTIMIZATION IN INTEGERS AND RELATED EXTREMAL PROBLEMS

Optimization
in Integers and
Related Extremal
Problems

From a course given at the University of California, Los Angeles, and at the
George Washington University

Thomas L. Saaty
University of Pennsylvania

McGraw-Hill Book Company
New York St. Louis San Francisco London Sydney Toronto Mexico Panama

Optimization in Integers and Related Extremal Problems

Library of Congress Catalog Card Number 72-85169
54369

1234567890 MAMM 7654321069

This book was set in Modern by The Maple Press Company
and printed on permanent paper and bound by The Maple
Press Company. The designer was Merrill Haber; the
drawings were done by J. & R. Technical Services, Inc. The
editor was Donald K. Prentiss. Morton I. Rosenberg
supervised the production.

To

I. HELLER

"I cherish both faces of mathematics: the pure as a beautiful retreat from reality, the applied as an ardent hope for life."

Preface

There are few functions of modern life in which mathematics does not play a useful role. Many of these functions themselves involve the creation and use of mathematical thought. Much of this fertile thought is occupied with a fundamental mathematical idea—the concept of a maximum and a minimum.

Man is a perennial maximizer and minimizer. For brevity, we call him an *optimizer*. He optimizes because he needs to conserve his limited energies, capacities, and resources. In constructing his theories, he optimizes through simplicity and through a search for regularity and symmetry. He also shows a proclivity for optimization by constructing elegant mathematical proofs. He optimizes to leave time for leisure in life. The search for maxima and minima is interwoven into the fabric of man's idealism in his search for perfection and in his realism by greedily seeking the most without giving too much for it. But this goal is not contrived, because it has come to man through nature, and nature itself seems to be an optimizer. Nature also tells man to choose a strategy which maximizes his reward, assuming that he knows what reward he values most.

Three anecdotes serve to illustrate that sometimes the optimization strategy in problems subject to constraints is neither pure maximization nor pure minimization, but rather some optimum or prudent mixture.

The first story concerns three seamstresses, none of whom wants to sew less rapidly than the other two. The first greedily threaded her needle with a very long thread, which became entangled in the sewing and delayed her work. The second noted the difficulty of the first and frugally used a short thread, but had to keep rethreading her needle, also losing time. The third "prudently" cut a length of thread from her nose to the tip of the fingers of her outstretched arm. She had none of the problems encountered by the others.

The second anecdote concerns a dying rich man who offered each of his three sons as much land as he could circle in a simple closed path by starting at an appropriate point at sunrise and returning there at sunset. If any arrived after sunset, he lost his share. One son went out very far to start his tour and could not return before dark. The other son, not wanting to lose his share, made a short tour and was finished by noon. Now the third son was neither too greedy nor too conservative and used the entire day to pace off his land. He optimized under the constraint.

The third ancedote relates how, once upon a time, a certain mathematician was asked to estimate the number of beans in a large irregular container, whose volume he was able to estimate by imagined adjustment into a cylinder. By measuring and by treating the beans as spheres, he estimated their diameter; applying his knowledge of the greatest-known efficiency of the packing of spheres in 3-space, he obtained a very close answer and then corrected for the fact that the beans were not spherical in shape. He won a prize for his good judgment.

In the vernacular, the idea of an optimum is sometimes understood to be a balance of neither too much nor too little. On other occasions, it is understood as the best and "no better." One may associate with an optimum a notion referring to the worst and no worse, i.e., a pessimum.

On occasion, one refers to an optimum in-the-large as the *optimum optimorum*, or the *best of the best*, and to a *pessimum pessimorum*, or the *worst of the worst* outcomes, or *minimum minimorum*. Of course, all these notions have mathematical interpretations. For example, a continuous function on a closed bounded set in Euclidean space may have several local maxima, and the largest of these is sometimes referred to as the *optimum optimorum (maximum maximorum)*. Of course, this maximum need not be unique.

Some ordinary problems which require that a solution be shown to exist may be embedded in a corresponding maximization framework where the answer may be found.   For example, the possibility of covering an ordinary chessboard (from which the bottom-left-corner and top-right-corner squares have been removed) with dominoes, so that each covers two adjacent squares completely with no overlap, and so that no squares are left uncovered, may be stated in terms of the maximum number of dominoes which can be used to cover as many squares of the board as possible.   In this case, the optimization formulation is more difficult to solve but contains the answer to the original problem.   Conversely (and more usefully), a difficult maximization problem may be embedded in a more familiar framework.   For example, necessary conditions for the existence of maxima and minima are generally tied to the question of solvability of an equation or a system of equations.   In the calculus, these equations are algebraic; in the calculus of variations, they are differential.

The added twist of reasoning derived from embedding one problem in another may actually give insight into the solution of the original problem. For the chessboard problem in the maximization context, the number of dominoes cannot exceed 30 since it is easy to prove that each domino must cover two adjacent squares of different colors, and the board now has two more squares of one color than of the other (the two squares removed were of the same color) and hence cannot be covered with 31 dominoes.

In many ways it is regrettable that we have developed the habit of thinking about all problems through the continuous eye of analytic geometry.   Every problem involving surfaces is visualized in a continuous setting, thus losing the full impact of a different view of discrete problems. We must rethink through this ancient and beguiling approach.   Let us have two frameworks, the old one and a new one covering discrete problems.

Unlike the general area of continuous mathematics, discrete mathematics as yet has no unifying theory, and hence one is generally inclined to proceed through special cases.   Such an approach can generate broad insight into problems.   Creativity here might profit from analogy, and the development of an inclusive framework for preserving and building on such problems is a worthwhile goal.

An optimization problem may be modeled in geometric or in algebraic form.   An illustration of the geometric approach is the packing of a maximum number of identical spherical oranges into a rectangular crate. To obtain insight, one may construct a physical model of the problem to find ways of improving the packing.   One may also study the local relation between a small set of oranges and the effect of the boundary of the box on this relation.   A horizontal cross section through the centers of oranges in a well-defined layer (if there is such a layer) provides an idea of the packing of circles in that rectangular region.   Algebraic problems involve the explicit formulation of a problem in a framework where there is a function to be maximized or minimized, possibly subject to constraints given as equations or inequalities. For integer optimization, the variables are required to be integers, frequently nonnegative. Sometimes the maximum or minimum value must also be an integer. It would be desirable to reduce all optimization problems to an algebraic form. However, for some problems, it is more difficult to do so than to proceed by alternative treatment of the problem using geometric arguments.

There are two major new areas of optimization whose development is crucial to the solution of a number of theoretical and applied problems. The first is optimization over discrete sets, which is the subject treated in this book. The second area which occupies the attention of researchers is stochastic optimization, involving the use of expressions with stochastic elements. Here one would find answers to complex social and political problems. The chart on the inside back cover may help give the reader a wide orientation toward the mathematical methods of optimization.

This book is intended for undergraduate students in mathematics, science, engineering, social science, and operations research at the junior-senior level who have had background in advanced calculus and linear algebra. Some theorems are stated without proof. The purpose has been to stimulate the student's thinking along different lines of the subject. He is urged to look in the references for additional material.

This book, purposely small enough for a one-semester course, is the first of its kind and therefore has no precedents to draw on in its structure. Space restrictions limited the number of proofs to one that is adequate for teaching and for giving the student an idea of the kinds of proofs which occur in this general field.

There is a feeling of excitement, challenge, and sometimes even frustration in tackling problems of optimization *in integers*. In the continuous case, it is possible to make compromises in the interpretation of a problem and obtain good approximations to solutions. The demands of the discrete case are much stronger and lack flexibility. Here, from the whole space, one must single out comparatively few points and work with them. Thus, when the domain of optimization is less rich and more restrictive, the difficulties are multiplied. Sometimes the pursuit of an optimum is an obsession, not justified by the utility of the results. Frequently, good upper and lower bounds would suffice.

There are problems where it is possible to prove that a certain maximum as an *a priori upper bound* cannot be exceeded. In such a case, one must prove separately that the maximum is actually reached. For example, by using regular polygons and the fact that at least three of them meet at a vertex of a polyhedron, it is possible to prove that there are at most (there is a maximum possible number of) five regular convex polyhedra. However, a separate proof must be given to show that there are exactly five.

Other questions of interest in problems of maxima and minima take the form of *existence* and *uniqueness* theorems, *characterization* of the properties of a solution, its *construction, covergence* of the algorithm used, and *approximation* to the actual value of the desired solution.

This book is not intended to give a comprehensive account of all discrete optimization problems. Our purpose is a modest one—to stimulate and excite the reader's interest in the elementary methods and ideas of discrete optimization and related problems.

For helpful ideas and suggestions, I am grateful to Donald R. Chand (Secs. 5-5 and 5-6), Alan R. Curtis (Sec. 5-8), L. Few, Saul I. Gass, Michael Goldberg, Leo Moser, John Murchland, George Suzuki, and Marshall Waller. My thanks also go to my wife, Rozann, for careful reading and suggested improvements, and to Sue Ann White, for neatly typing the manuscript.

Thomas L. Saaty

Contents

Chapter 3
SOME ELEMENTARY APPLICATIONS 147

Chapter 4
OPTIMIZATION SUBJECT TO DIOPHANTINE CONSTRAINTS 163

Chapter 5
INTEGER PROGRAMMING 206

OPTIMIZATION IN INTEGERS AND RELATED EXTREMAL PROBLEMS

1

Basic Concepts: Examples of Methods and Problems

1-1 INTRODUCTION

When one considers a maximum or a minimum on sets, one has in mind a relation which compares their elements according to an ordering. To illustrate, we take a set whose elements are three real numbers, $E = \{a,b,c\}$, with the usual relation of order. If $a < b < c$, then a is the *minimum* or smallest element of E while c is its largest element or *maximum*. There is no element *in E* smaller than a. Also, there is no element *in E* greater than c. Note that b is neither a maximum nor a minimum since there is always some element which exceeds it and another element which it exceeds.

We are familiar with other types of order than the "less than" and "greater than" relation between numbers. Thus, a collection of sets may be ordered according to set inclusion. In that case, a maximal element would be the largest set in the collection, and a minimal element would be the smallest in the collection. For example, in a sequence of five concentric or nested circles, the outer circle can be considered the

1

largest and the inner circle the smallest because the first circle contains all others and the smallest is contained in all of them.

The notion of a maximum or a minimum is closely tied to the idea of a lower and an upper bound. An upper bound of a set of numbers E is a number c such that no element of E exceeds c. If, for example, $E = \{a,b\}$, $a < b$, then c is an upper bound if $a \leq c$ and $b \leq c$. A least upper bound of real numbers is an upper bound which does not exceed or majorize any other upper bound. One may assume that the set of upper bounds of E has a least element since it is bounded below (by b). This least element may or may not belong to the set E. If a set has a maximum, that maximum is a least upper bound of the set. A set E of real numbers has a maximum if it contains a number c such that $x \leq c$ for all $x \in E$. Thus, a maximum is a least upper bound but the converse is not true. If the least upper bound is in the set, it is a maximum. The set $\{1 - 1/n\}$, $n = 1, 2, \ldots$, tends to 1 as its least upper bound but does not contain it, and hence has no maximum. For a finite set of integers, the least upper bound and maximum coincide. Greatest lower bounds and minima are similarly defined.

From the above discussion, it is clear that some sort of ordering is necessary if we are to consider maxima and minima. But such a relation of order may only apply to a subset of the whole set. For example, the set of complex numbers, i.e., numbers of the form $a + ib$, where a and b are real numbers and where $i = \sqrt{-1}$, cannot be ordered by a simple use of $\leq$ without additional conditions on corresponding real and complex parts of ordered pairs. However, the real numbers which comprise a subset of the complex numbers can be totally ordered according to the relation $\leq$. More generally, for elements in n-dimensional Euclidean space E_n, it is not obvious whether it is possible to find an order relation between the elements in order to obtain a total ordering of the space. However, the situation is not hopeless. Lexicographic ordering is a common type of ordering in which the points $(x_1, \ldots, x_n)$ of E_n, whose coordinates $x_1, \ldots, x_n$ are real numbers, are ranked according to the magnitude of the first coordinate x_1; if they are tied, then they are ranked according to the magnitude of the second coordinate x_2, and so on. The smaller element or point is that which has the smaller first appearing coordinate. Thus, for example, (1,7,2) is smaller than (1,9,0) because, although they are tied in their first coordinates, in their second coordinates 9 exceeds 7. Naturally such an artificial ordering must be in harmony with the special case of E_1 which is the space of real numbers for which an order relation is already well defined.

However, it may only be possible to introduce order within each of several subsets of a set without being able to extrapolate the relation to the entire set. For example, one might consider a set whose elements dominate (are larger than, or precede) each other according to the disconnected directed graph whose arrows indicate the direction of hierarchy, from supervisor, or chief, to the supervised. The question, "Who is the commander-in-chief of this collection of two organizations?", cannot be answered, as we have no knowledge of the relation of dominance between the two separate parts. Such a set is only partially but not totally ordered (see the accompanying figure).

The majority of problems of maxima and minima involve finding a point of a set which maximizes or minimizes a function defined on the set whose image, or set of values, are the real numbers. Only because the real numbers are totally ordered do we consider such pursuit meaningful in general. If the image were a set of vectors, the problem of order presents itself, and maxima and minima would require special treatment.

The kind of optimization problems with which we are concerned here are related to finding maxima or minima of functions, defined over sets of points of the real line, the plane, and more generally E_n, whose coordinates have integer components. The sets over which the function may be defined in this case are *discrete* because their points are isolated. Thus, if spheres are chosen for neighborhoods in the underlying space to which the set belongs (i.e., the space in which it is embedded), then each point has a sphere about it that does not contain other points of the set. However, the concepts of optimization may also be applied to sets that are partially discrete. In this case, some of the points have spheres of the embedding space about them which do not contain other points of the set.

The function to be maximized or minimized will be assumed to take on real values. In some problems it may be required to assume only integer values, in others not. However, a maximum of the function that is an integer may be sought.

The remainder of this chapter is occupied with definitions, some useful ideas and theorems, and a brief, condensed, but useful presentation of some relevant material from the continuous case to which calculus treatment is applicable. Finally, examples of discrete optimization problems are given.

The remainder of the book is divided into two parts. Chapters 2 and 3 treat problems given in geometric or physical context. Chapters 4 and 5 are purely algebraic in approach. In Chap. 4 some elementary Diophantine problems are discussed. Chapter 5 is concerned with integer programming and a brief discussion of some useful algorithms.

To set the scene for the discussion and utilization of such ideas, we must provide some definitions but without being tedious, as most of the definitions can be found in standard elementary texts. Of course, our purpose is to develop the subject of maxima and minima over discrete sets where established calculus methods do not usually work. Some problems are given a geometric setting, others an algebraic one. It would be desirable to standardize the approach, but this seems difficult at present because the algebraic approach tends to rob a problem of its natural setting.

Throughout the book, the symbol $[x]$ will denote the greatest integer $\leq x$. There should be no problem in distinguishing the use of this symbol from that of ordinary brackets.

1-2 ELEMENTARY DEFINITIONS AND USEFUL THEOREMS

The following section may appear tedious, and it may be passed over. We include it for the sake of completeness.

ORDER

A relation is a primitive notion indicating correspondence between elements of sets.

A binary relation R in a set E can be regarded as a set of ordered pairs. Consider an ordered pair (x,y) in which x occupies the first position and y occupies the second position. (This arrangement defines the ordering of the pair x, y.) The element y is said to correspond to the element x under the relation R. Thus we write yRx. Since the set of all ordered pairs forms the cartesian set $E \times E$, it follows that a relation on E is a subset of $E \times E$. The set of first elements of the ordered pairs defined by a relation R is called its *domain set*, and the set of second elements is called its *image* or *range set*. Both these sets are subsets of the set E on which R is defined.

Just as we do for relations, we can define a function as a correspondence between two sets, its domain and range sets, such that to each point in its domain corresponds one point of its range.

An important class of binary relations are equivalence relations.

Definition   An equivalence relation on a set E is defined by the following properties:

1. xRx for every $x \in E$ (reflexive).
2. If xRy, then yRx for every $x, y \in E$ (symmetric).
3. If xRy and yRz, then xRz for all $x, y, z \in E$ (transitive).

Congruence and equality are examples of an equivalence relation.

Definition A preorder ($\leq$) on a set E is a relation on the elements of E such that for x, y, $z \in E$:

1. $x \leq x$ (reflexivity).
2. $x \leq y$, $y \leq z$ imply $x \leq z$ (transitivity).

Definition A set is said to be partially ordered if, in addition, the following is satisfied:

3. $x \leq y$, $y \leq x$ imply $x = y$ (antisymmetry).

The definition of partial ordering and of chains will be used in the discussion of local maxima and minima.

Definition The set E with a relation $\leq$ defined between some of its elements is said to form a partially ordered system.

It is possible that for some pair of elements $\bar{x}$, $\bar{y}$ neither $\bar{x} \leq \bar{y}$ nor $\bar{y} \leq \bar{x}$.

Definition A set E is said to be totally ordered, simply ordered, or ordered if, in addition, the following holds:

4. For every pair of elements x, $y \in E$, we have either $x \leq y$ or $y \leq x$.

Frequently, a totally ordered subset of a partially ordered set is called a *chain* when property 4 holds on any two elements which belong to the subset. It is a maximal (or connected) chain when it has the form $x_0 < x_1 < \cdots < x_n$, where x_i follows or covers x_{i-1} for all i.

Definition An ordered set E is said to be well ordered if every nonempty subset contains a smallest element.

The positive integers form a well-ordered set, but the reals do not.

Remark Note that the familiar principle of mathematical induction applies only to well-ordered sets. When well-ordering is appropriately interpreted, it gives rise to the principle of induction for a well-ordered set. Little is known about induction on partially ordered sets.

BOUNDS, MAXIMA, AND SUPS

Definition   If E is a set of real numbers, then by an upper bound of E we mean a number y such that, for every x in E, $x \leq y$. A least upper bound of E is an upper bound which is not greater than any other upper bound.

The integers are an example of a set which has no upper bound. A set cannot have more than one least upper bound because, if y_1 and y_2 are two such, then $y_1 \leq y_2$ and $y_2 \leq y_1$, and hence $y_1 = y_2$.

Definition   The maximum of a set E of real numbers is a member of E which is at the same time an upper bound of E. The maximum of E, if it exists, is unique and is the least upper bound of E.

Definition   A lattice is a partially ordered system in which every two elements x, y have a greatest lower bound (g.l.b.) and a least upper bound (l.u.b.)

A collection S of subsets of a set E is of *finite* character if, for every subset e of E, $e \in S$ if and only if $e_1 \in S$, where e_1 is any finite subset of e.

The maximality principle   A collection of subsets S of E of finite character has a maximal member with respect to partial ordering of S by set inclusion.

Many problems of optimization are confined to lattice points of E_n, which are points whose coordinates are all integers. The object there is to find a lattice point of E_n which maximizes or minimizes a given function subject to auxiliary equality or inequality constraints also defined over the lattice points.

If we let $\max (x_1, \ldots , x_n)$ denote the maximum of the set of real numbers $\{x_1, \ldots , x_n\}$, and if we let $|x|$ denote the absolute-value function defined by

$$|x| = \begin{cases} x & \text{if } x \geq 0 \\ -x & \text{if } x < 0 \end{cases}$$

then it is possible (though complicated) to express the maximum of a set of real numbers in closed form. In fact, not only maxima and minima, but also intermediate values may be represented in closed form.

Theorem 1-1 $max\ (x,y) = \frac{1}{2}(|x - y| + x + y)$.

Proof If $x \geq y$, then $x - y \geq 0$ and $|x - y| = x - y$, and the result follows since x is a maximum. If $x \leq y$, then y is a maximum; from $x - y \leq 0$ we have $|x - y| = -x + y$, and the right side is equal to y.

Theorem 1-2 $max\ (x,y,z) = \frac{1}{4}(|2z - |x - y| - x - y| + 2z + |x - y| + x + y)$.

Proof $\max (x,y,z) = \max [z, \max (x,y)]$, and, applying the previous result, we have

$$\max (x,y,z) = \frac{1}{2}\left(\left| z - \frac{|x - y| + x + y}{2} \right| + z + \frac{|x - y| + x + y}{2}\right)$$

from which the result follows.

Exercise 1-1 Give corresponding expressions for minima.

Exercise 1-2 Show that $\max (x_1, \ldots , x_n) = \max \{\max [\max (\cdots x_{n-1})], x_n\}$, and write down the expression for $\max (x_1,x_2,x_3,x_4)$. Show that $\min (x_1, \ldots , x_n) = - \max (-x_1, \ldots , -x_n)$.

Let int (x,y,z) be the second largest of the three numbers; we have [16] the following theorem.

Theorem 1-3 $int\ (x,y,z) = \frac{1}{4}(2x + 2y + |\ |x - y| - x - y + 2z| - ||x - y| + x + y - 2z|)$.

Proof

$$\begin{aligned}
\text{int } (x,y,z) &= -[\max (x,y,z) + \min (x,y,z) - x - y - z]\\
&= [x + y + z - \max (x,y,z) - \min (x,y,z)]\\
&= [x + y + z - \max (x,y,z) + \max (-x,-y,-z)]
\end{aligned}$$

and the result follows.

If we denote by $M_n{}^k(x_1, \ldots , x_n)$ the kth largest number of n numbers $(x_1, \ldots , x_n)$, then, for example, $M_3{}^2(x_1,x_2,x_3) = $ int (x_1,x_2,x_3).

Theorem 1-4 For $x_i \neq x_j$, $i, j = 1, \ldots , n$, $2 \leq k \leq n - 1$,

$$M_n{}^k(x_1, \ldots , x_n) = M_3{}^2[M_{n-1}^k(x_1, \ldots , x_{n-1}),$$
$$M_{n-1}^{k-1}(x_1, \ldots , x_{n-1}), x_n]$$

Proof

$$
\begin{aligned}
M_n{}^k &= M_{n-1}^k && \text{if } M_{n-1}^k > x_n \\
&= M_{n-1}^{k-1} && \text{if } M_{n-1}^{k-1} < x_n \\
&= x_n && \text{if } M_{n-1}^{k-1} > x_n > M_{n-1}^k
\end{aligned}
$$

We can complete these inequalities on x_n without difficulty. We obtain

$$
\begin{aligned}
M_n{}^k &= M_{n-1}^k && \text{if } M_{n-1}^{k-1} > M_{n-1}^k > x_n \\
&= M_{n-1}^{k-1} && \text{if } x_n > M_{n-1}^{k-1} > M_{n-1}^k \\
&= x_n && \text{if } M_{n-1}^{k-1} > x_n > M_{n-1}^k
\end{aligned}
$$

Thus we conclude that

$$ M_n{}^k = M_3{}^2(M_{n-1}^k, M_{n-1}^{k-1}, x_n) $$

Application   What are the sizes of rugs which can be laid flat on a given square floor? In other words, what is the condition on the sides a and b of a rectangle which ensure that it can be contained within the unit square?

Solution [20a]   The rug will fit if max $(a,b) \leq 1$. If max $(a,b) > 1$ and the rug fits, then it will also fit if moved to a position symmetric with a diagonal of the square, i.e., when $a + b \leq \sqrt{2}$. These two conditions can be summarized as

$$ \min\left[\max\ (a,b), \frac{a+b}{\sqrt{2}} \right] \leq 1 $$

or, using

$$ \max\ (x,y) = \frac{x + y + |x - y|}{2} $$

and

$$ \min\ (x,y) = \frac{x + y - |x - y|}{2} $$

we have

$$ (1 + \sqrt{2})(a + b) + |a - b| - |(1 - \sqrt{2})(a + b) + |a - b|\,| \leq 4 $$

EXAMPLES ILLUSTRATING THE USE OF BOUNDS

Problems are frequently encountered which use in their statements expressions such as "at most," "not more than," "an upper bound," "bounded above (by)," "least upper bound," "at least," "not less than," etc.

Upper and lower bounds are useful for estimating the number of solutions of equations and inequalities and for obtaining information on the range of values of a function. In the absence of formal methods for solving complex optimization problems, it may be necessary to try different values in search of the optimum. An upper bound on the number of possibilities helps one estimate the amount of effort needed in this search.

It is useful to have an order-of-magnitude estimate of the number of points comprising the set of constraints. A classic illustration of this type of analysis is the following simple example.

Find the number of integral solutions of [6]

$$x^2 + y^2 \leq n$$

where n is a given integer. This estimate is easy to compute for small values of n. In fact, one can list all the solutions. There is one for $n = 0$, five for $n = 1$, nine for $n = 2$, etc., and they are easily enumerated.

Points with integral coordinates are uniformly distributed in the plane. A unit square corresponds to exactly one such point. The area of a circle is approximately equal to the number of unit squares it contains and hence also to the number of solutions of the inequality because they lie on the corners of the squares.

Theorem 1-5   *The number of integral solutions N of*

$$x^2 + y^2 \leq n$$

with n an integer may be approximated as $N \approx n\pi$ with error $|N - \pi n| < 2\pi(\sqrt{2n} + 1)$.

Proof   Consider all points of the cartesian plane with integer coordinates. These points comprise the corners of unit squares. Associate with each unit square the point on its upper right-hand vertex. Let C_n be a circle with center at the origin which contains N integral points. Let S_n be the area of the corresponding squares. Let $C_n{}^1$ and $C_n{}^2$ be two circles concentric with C_n with radii $\sqrt{n} - \sqrt{2}$ and $\sqrt{n} + \sqrt{2}$, respectively. S_n lies completely within $C_n{}^2$ and contains in its interior $C_n{}^1$. Since the area of S_n is N, we have

$$\pi(\sqrt{n} - \sqrt{2})^2 < N < \pi(\sqrt{n} + \sqrt{2})^2$$

This gives

$$N \approx n\pi \qquad \text{and} \qquad |N - \pi n| < 2\pi(\sqrt{2n} + 1)$$

and completes the proof.

Exercise 1-3   Show by a geometric argument like the one given above that the number of integral solutions of

$$x^2 + y^2 + z^2 \leq n$$

is approximately equal to $\frac{4}{3}\pi n^{\frac{3}{2}}$.

We now give a second example illustrating the use of bounds.

Theorem 1-6   *A sufficient condition that at least two boxes contain the same number of objects among B boxes containing N objects is* [7]

$$N < \frac{B(B-1)}{2}$$

Proof   If no two boxes contain the same number of objects, then the total number of objects N is at least

$$0 + 1 + 2 + \cdots + (B-1) = \frac{B(B-1)}{2}$$

Thus, for at least two boxes to contain the same number of objects, it is sufficient that

$$N < \frac{B(B-1)}{2}$$

hold.

Definition   The Fibonacci number F_n is the greatest integer nearest to

$$\frac{[(1 + \sqrt{5})/2]^n}{\sqrt{5}}$$

Theorem 1-7   *The number of Fibonacci numbers not exceeding a given positive integer N is the greatest integer less than* [3]

$$\frac{\log (N + \tfrac{1}{2}) \sqrt{5}}{\log (1 + \sqrt{5})/2} - 1$$

Proof   We have $F_n \leq N$ if and only if

$$\frac{[(1 + \sqrt{5})/2]^n}{\sqrt{5}} < N + \tfrac{1}{2}$$

i.e., if and only if

$$n < \frac{\log [(N + \tfrac{1}{2}) \sqrt{5}]}{\log [(1 + \sqrt{5})/2]}$$

Since $F_1 = F_2 = 1$, the result follows.

The next two theorems provide yet two more examples of the use of bounds.

Theorem 1-8 $\Sigma_{i=1}^{n}\epsilon_i a_i$ *assumes at least* $\binom{n+1}{2} + 1$ *distinct values where*

$0 < a_1 < a_2 < \cdots < a_n$ *and* $\epsilon_i = \pm 1$.

Proof [20]   The smallest value is $C \equiv \Sigma_{i=1}^{n} -a_i$. Starting with this, we construct other possible values. Thus,

$$C < C + 2a_1 < C + 2a_2 < \cdots < C + 2a_n < C + 2a_n + 2a_1$$
$$< \cdots < C + 2a_n + 2a_{n-1} < C + 2a_n + 2a_{n-1} + 2a_1$$
$$< \cdots < C + 2 \left(\sum_{i=1}^{n} a_i \right) = \sum_{i=1}^{n} a_i$$

Thus, there is at least the following number of distinct values:

$$1 + n + (n-1) + (n-2) + \cdots + 2 + 1 = 1 + \frac{n(n+1)}{2}$$

Exercise 1-4   Prove the foregoing result, using induction. (Start with $S = \Sigma_{i=1}^{k-1}a_i \geq$ $\Sigma_{i=1}^{k-1}\epsilon_i a_i$, and suppose that the last sum has $\binom{k}{2} + 1$ distinct values. Consider the distinct values $a_k + S$, $a_k + S - a_{k-1}$, $a_k + S - a_{k-2}$, . . . , $a_k + S - a_1$. Thus there are at least $k + \binom{k}{2} + 1 = \binom{k+1}{2} + 1$ distinct values.)

Theorem 1-9   *If* $\Sigma_{i=1}^{n}a_i = A$, a_i *nonnegative integers, then*

$$\sum_{i=1}^{n-1} a_i a_{i+1} \leq \frac{A^2}{4}$$

Proof [19]   If $a_k = \max(a_1, \ldots, a_n)$, then

$$\sum_{i=1}^{n-1} a_i a_{i+1} = \sum_{i=1}^{k-1} a_i a_{i+1} + \sum_{i=k}^{n-1} a_i a_{i+1}$$
$$\leq a_k \sum_{i=1}^{k-1} a_i + a_k \sum_{i=k}^{n-1} a_{i+1}$$
$$= a_k(A - a_k)$$
$$= \frac{A^2}{4} - \left(\frac{A}{2} - a_k \right)^2 \leq \frac{A^2}{4}$$

Equality holds if and only if $a_k = A/2$.

We now turn to a discussion of maxima and minima of functions which map sets in E_n to the real line E_1. Sometimes the sets consist of lattice points, which may be mapped into the set of integer in E_1. In any case, the presence of constraints means that the function is defined on a subset rather than on the entire space.

1-3 MAXIMA AND MINIMA OF FUNCTIONS
ON n-DIMENSIONAL EUCLIDEAN SPACE E_n

THE CONTINUOUS CASE

Let $f(x_1, \ldots, x_n)$ be a twice-differentiable function with continuous second derivatives, which maps a domain D of Euclidean space E_n [the space of n-tuples $(x_1, \ldots, x_n)$ of real numbers x_i, $i = 1, \ldots, n$, with metric $(\Sigma_{i=1}^n x_i^2)^{\frac{1}{2}}$] into the reals. Let $f_{x_i}(x)$ and $f_{x_ix_j}(x)$, $i, j = 1 \ldots, n$, denote the first- and second-order partial derivatives of f.

Definition　$x^0 \equiv (x_1^0, \ldots, x_n^0) \in D$ is an absolute maximum point of f if

$$f(x) \leq f(x^0) \qquad \text{for all } x \in D, x \equiv (x_1, \ldots, x_n)$$

Definition　$x^0 \equiv (x_1^0, \ldots, x_n^0) \in D$ is a relative or local maximum point of f if $\epsilon > 0$ can be found so that f has an absolute maximum at x^0 for all $x \in D$ which satisfy

$$|x_i - x_i^0| < \epsilon \qquad i = 1, \ldots, n$$

Analogous definitions may be given for absolute and local minimum [at which $f(x) \geq f(x^0)$ is satisfied].

Exercise 1-5　Prove that the maximum point of $f(x)$ is the same as the minimum point of $-f(x)$.

Definition　A value of a function at either a maximum or a minimum point is called an *extreme value* or *extremum*. In a particular reference to one or to the other, it is called an *optimum*, e.g., the minimum value of a cost function or the maximum value of an output function.

Definition　$x^0 \in D$ is an extreme point of f if it is a maximum or a minimum point (absolute or relative).

Definition　$x^0 \in D$ with $f_{x_i}(x^0) = 0$, $i = 1, \ldots, n$, is a critical or stationary point of f.

Frequently, an investigation of extreme points and extreme values requires the analysis of critical points.

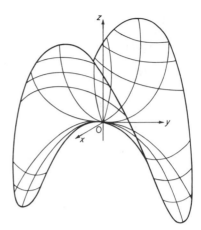

Fig. 1-1 Hyperbolic paraboloid, $z = x^2 - y^2$. In a small neighborhood of the point $(0,0)$, which is a saddle point, there are points at which the value of z is greater than its value at $(0,0)$, and there are points at which its value is less than that at $(0,0)$. Thus, the origin is neither a maximum nor a minimum, but a saddle point.

Definition $f(x_1, \ldots, x_n, y_1, \ldots, y_m)$ has a saddle point at (x^0, y^0) $\equiv (x_1^0, \ldots, x_n^0, y_1^0, \ldots, y_m^0)$ if and only if

$$f(x, y^0) \leq f(x^0, y^0) \leq f(x^0, y)$$

See Fig. 1-1.

Definition The jacobian determinant of a system of functions $f_i(x_1, \ldots, x_n)$, $i = 1, \ldots, n$, is the determinant of the matrix $\{\partial f_i / \partial x_j\}$ of first-order partial derivatives.

Definition The hessian matrix of $f(x)$ is the matrix $\{f_{x_i x_j}(x)\}$ of second-order partial derivatives of $f(x)$.

We shall need these ideas, for example, in characterizing convexity, which helps one to optimize some discretely valued functions by embedding.

Remark If $f(x)$ has a maximum in $x = (x_1, \ldots, x_n)$ then $\max_{x_1} \max_{x_2} \ldots \max_{x_n} f(x) = \max_{x_1, \ldots, x_n} f(x)$. This relation holds for any permutation of max on the left. To prove this in the two variable case we have

$$f(x, y) \leq \max_{x, y} f(x, y)$$

which implies

$$\max_{x} \max_{y} f(x, y) \leq \max_{x, y} f(x, y)$$

To prove the opposite inequality we note that

$$f(x,y) \leq \max_y f(x,y) = f[x,y^*(x)] \equiv g(x)$$

$$\max_{x,y} f(x,y) \leq \max_{x,y} g(x) = \max_x g(x) = \max_x \max_y f(x,y)$$

since $g(x)$ is independent of y. The proof of the general case is left as an exercise for the reader.

The following is a short digression to round out some of these ideas by extending them to the calculus of variations.

Definition A *functional* is a mapping which associates with each element of an abstract space, a real number.

An ordinary real-valued function is an example of a functional. A definite Riemann integral which associates with an integrable function (e.g., a continuous function), a real number, is another example of a functional.

Definition A relative extremum (maximum or minimum) of a functional is the smallest value of the functional among those values obtained from curves taken in a given neighborhood. If $y_0(x)$ gives an extremum among all curves for which $|y(x) - y_0(x)|$ is small (zero-order closeness), then the extremum is called *strong*. If the closeness is of the first order, i.e., if both $|y(x) - y_0(x)|$ and $|y'(x) - y_0'(x)|$ are small, then the extremum is called *weak*. Thus, a strong extremum is also weak, but the converse is not true.

We have already encountered the example of $\{1 - 1/n\}$ as n ranges over the positive integers. We said that it had no maximum. However, we can associate with it a notion which, for some purposes, could serve as a substitute. We shall employ these tools whenever appropriate.

Definition If f is a real-valued function, defined over a set E (which may be discrete), then by $\sup_{x \in E} f(x)$ we mean the least upper bound (or supremum) of the set F of all values of $f(x)$, that is, of the set F of all numbers y such that, for some $x \in E$, $y = f(x)$. Similarly, $\inf_{x \in E} f(x)$ denotes the greatest lower bound (or infimum) of the set F of all values of $f(x)$. (Note that $\sup_n \{1 - 1/n\} = 1$.)

It is easy to see that if the indicated bounds exist, then

$$\sup_{x \in E} [-f(x)] = - \inf_{x \in E} f(x)$$

and

$$\inf_{x \in E} [-f(x)] = - \sup_{x \in E} f(x)$$

We shall be frequently concerned with the case where D is a subset of the lattice points of E_n.

Definition $x \in D \subset E_n$, $x = (x_1, \ldots, x_n)$, is called a *lattice point* if x_j is an integer, $j = 1, \ldots, n$.   The totality of lattice points is called the *unit lattice* in E_n.

Remark   There are cases in which the domain D of a function f may also consist of points only some of whose coordinates are integers.   The values of f are sometimes restricted to the integers and in particular to the positive integers.   The domain D is usually defined by means of a system of constraints which are analytically given as equations and inequalities of the form $g_i(x) \leq 0$, $i = 1, \ldots, m$. D is the union of two sets (interior points and boundary points).   The boundary of D is the surface defined by $g_i(x) = 0$, $i = 1, \ldots, m$.   Each of the inequality constraints may be reduced to an equation by adding a nonnegative "slack" variable.   The resulting system defines a new domain in E_{n+m}. For example, the constraint $x + y \leq 0$ in E_2, on adding the slack variable $z \geq 0$, yields $x + y + z = 0$ in the upper half-space of E_3.

SPECIAL FUNCTIONS

We now introduce the notions of *monotonicity* and *convexity*, which sometimes occur in conjunction with the expressions to be optimized and in the constraints defining their domain of definition.

Definition   A function $f(x)$ of a single variable x is said to be monotone increasing (decreasing) if $f(x_1) \leq (\geq)f(x_2)$ whenever $x_1 \leq x_2$.   It is strictly increasing if strict inequality holds (see Fig. 1-2).

This definition may be extended to a function of several variables by requiring monotonicity with respect to each variable.   For a monotone everywhere-differentiable function, we have $df(x)/dx \geq 0$ if it is increasing and $df(x)/dx \leq 0$ if it is decreasing.

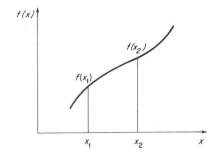

Fig. 1-2

Remark   If $f(x)$ is a differentiable function, then the stationary points of $f(x)$ (points at which the first derivative vanishes) at which $f(x)$ is not equal to zero are the same as those of $\log f(x)$.   The reason for this is that $d/dx \log f(x) = f'(x)/f(x)$, and the last expression is zero whenever $f'(x)$ is zero, provided that $f(x)$ is not zero at the same x.

Exercise 1-6   Let a_i, b_i, $i = 1, \ldots, n$, be positive numbers.   Show that

$$f(x) = \prod_{i=1}^{n} [xa_i + (1 - x)b_i] \qquad x \in [0,1]$$

is only maximized either at $x = 0$ or $x = 1$ if and only if

$$\left(\sum_{i=1}^{n} \frac{a_i - b_i}{a_i} \right) \left(\sum_{i=1}^{n} \frac{a_i - b_i}{b_i} \right) \geq 0$$

Hint: Consider $\log f(x)$, and impose monotonicity on it; i.e., either $f'(x)/f(x) \geq 0$ or $f'(x)/f(x) \leq 0$.   Both end points must satisfy whichever condition is to hold; thus, substitute $x = 0$ and $x = 1$ in each case.   Both cases yield the above condition.

Definition   A function $f(x_1, \ldots, x_n)$ is convex if

$$f[\theta x + (1 - \theta)y] \leq \theta f(x) + (1 - \theta)f(y)$$

where $0 \leq \theta \leq 1$, $x = (x_1, \ldots, x_n)$, $y = (y_1, \ldots, y_n)$.   A function is concave if $\geq$ holds instead of $\leq$ in the definition of convexity. Convexity and concavity are strict if the strict inequality holds. (Figure 1-3 illustrates convexity in E_2 for $\theta = \frac{1}{2}$.)

The convexity and concavity of a differentiable function may be tested for by using the principal minor determinants of the hessian matrix of f. They must be nonnegative for convexity and nonpositive for concavity. In the case of a function of a single variable $f(x)$, we have for convexity $d^2f/dx^2 \geq 0$ and for concavity $d^2f/dx^2 \leq 0$.   For a function of two

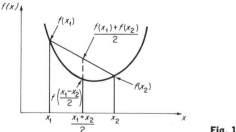

Fig. 1-3

Fig. 1-4

variables $f(x,y)$, we must have for convexity $f_{xx} \geq 0$, $f_{yy} \geq 0$; and $f_{xx}f_{yy} - f_{xy}^2 \geq 0$.

Exercise 1-7 Derive conditions in order that $f(x,y)$ be concave. Note that $-f$ must be convex.

Exercise 1-8 Show that

$$f(x,y) = \frac{1}{2\pi\sigma^2} \exp\left[-\frac{1}{2\sigma^2} (x^2 + y^2) \right]$$

which gives the normal distribution in two variables is concave over the disc $x^2 + y^2 \leq \sigma^2$.

Definition   A set E is said to be convex if whenever $x \in E$ and $y \in E$, then $\theta x + (1 - \theta)y \in E$, where $0 \leq \theta \leq 1$.

Thus E contains, with any two points x and y, the line segment joining them.   The set indicated by Fig. 1-4a is convex, but that of Fig. 1-4b is not because a part of the indicated line segment lies outside the set.

Definition   The convex hull of a set E is the least convex set containing E.

The convex hull of a star-shaped region is obtained by joining the vertices of the star with straight segments.

For maxima and minima on discrete sets, embedding the domain of definition in a convex set is sometimes useful for utilizing algorithms developed for that case and attempting to obtain solutions for the discrete problem.

It is easy to prove that if $x = (x_1, \ldots, x_n)$ and $f_i(x)$, $i = 1, \ldots, m$, are convex (concave) functions on a convex set E in E_n, then

$$f(x) = \sum_{i=1}^{m} f_i(x)$$

is also a convex (concave) function on E. To see this for the convexity of f, note that if $x^{(1)} = (x_1^{(1)}, \ldots, x_n^{(1)})$, $x^{(2)} = (x_1^{(2)}, \ldots, x_n^{(2)})$ are in E and if $0 \leq \theta \leq 1$, then

$$
\begin{aligned}
f[\theta x^{(1)} + (1 - \theta)x^{(2)}] &= \sum_{i=1}^{m} f_i[\theta x^{(1)} + (1 - \theta)x^{(2)}] \\
&\leq \sum_{i=1}^{m} \theta f_i(x^{(1)}) + (1 - \theta)f_i(x^{(2)}) \\
&= \theta \sum_{i=1}^{m} f_i(x^{(1)}) + (1 - \theta) \sum_{i=1}^{m} f_i(x^{(2)}) \\
&= \theta f(x^{(1)}) + (1 - \theta)f(x^{(2)})
\end{aligned}
$$

This is a useful result. If we are given a function which is the sum of several terms, each of which is known to be convex over the same convex set, we may conclude that the function is convex. If a minimum in integers is desired, we can then apply methods which will be discussed later.

Exercise 1-9 Show that a relation of the form $g(x_1, \ldots, x_n) \leq 0$, where g is convex, defines a convex set E; that is, if $x^{(1)} = (x_1^{(1)}, \ldots, x_n^{(1)}) \in E$ and $x^{(2)} = (x_1^{(2)}, \ldots, x_n^{(2)}) \in E$, then also $\theta x^{(1)} + (1 - \theta)x^{(2)} \in E$, $0 \leq \theta \leq 1$.

Exercise 1-10 Show that the intersection of convex sets is convex. Conclude that if in $g_i(x_1, \ldots, x_n) \leq 0$, $i = 1, \ldots, m$, all g_i are convex, then they jointly define a convex set.

Remark When does a function have a unique minimum? An example [20b] of a condition which a function must satisfy in order for a minimum to be unique is strict quasiconvexity; that is, if $f(x) < f(x^0)$, then $f(\theta x + (1 - \theta)x^0) < f(x^0)$ for $0 \leq \theta \leq 1$. Thus, a convex function has the property that every local minimum is a global minimum. This global minimum is unique if strict convexity or (the weaker) strict quasiconvexity holds.

THE DISCRETE CASE

Our definitions of a global maximum and minimum of a function $f(x_1, \ldots, x_n)$ remain the same if x_j, $j = 1, \ldots, n$, take on only integer values. However, for the definitions of local maxima and minima, greater care is required. Recall, for example, that the vanishing of the derivative of a differentiable function of a single variable at a maximum point x is obtained from

$$
\begin{aligned}
f(x) - f(x + \Delta x) \geq 0 \\
f(x) - f(x - \Delta x) \geq 0
\end{aligned}
\qquad \Delta x > 0
$$

Dividing the first inequality by Δx and then multiplying by -1 and passing to the limit with respect to Δx, we have $df/dx \leq 0$. If we multiply the second inequality by -1 and then divide by $-\Delta x$ and pass to the limit with respect to $-\Delta x$, we have $df/dx \geq 0$. Combining the two conditions, we obtain at the maximum $df/dx = 0$. When x takes on discrete values, one no longer can use arbitrarily small values for Δx. If x ranges over the integers, the smallest value that Δx can assume is $\Delta x = \pm 1$. Our problem now is to see when this approach makes sense. (Figure 1-5a illustrates a function defined over some lattice points of the plane. The corners of the small cubes of Fig. 1-5b are lattice points in E_3. Figure 1-6 shows what happens to a continuous function when only its values over lattice points are considered.)

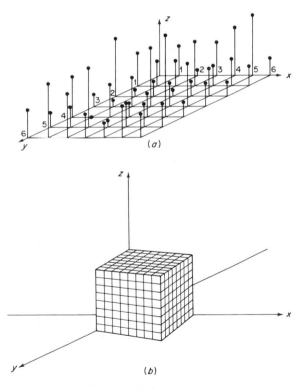

Fig. 1-5 (a) Example of a function defined over lattice points in the plane; (b) an illustration of a three-dimensional lattice whose points are the corners of the small cubes.

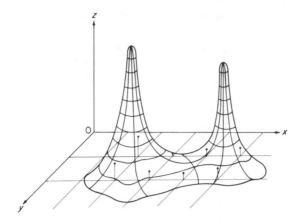

Fig. 1-6 Few points of a continuous surface remain when only its values over lattice points are considered. Its maxima and minima may be irretrievably lost.

LOCAL MAXIMA AND MINIMA ON DISCRETE SETS

When a function is defined on a discrete set and the set is partially ordered, from a general viewpoint it is meaningless to speak of a local maximum or minimum.   However, there is often an implicit underlying assumption on the nature of the function under consideration which makes the concept of local optimum meaningful even for the discrete set.   This happens when the function can be extended to a larger nondiscrete space into which the discrete space is embedded and the class of all extensions which preserve the nature of the function is such that any two members of that class are equivalent in the following sense: They assume their local minima and local maxima in the discrete space at the same places.   This is the reason why calculus methods, which work with the extension, sometimes apply.   The following is an example of this special case.

Suppose we have a function $f(x_1, \ldots, x_n)$ defined over the lattice points of E_n, and suppose that the special nature of f to which we have been referring consists of its being separable into monotone components. Thus, $f(x_1, \ldots, x_n) = \Sigma_{i=1}^n f_i(x_i)$.   In this case what we have said about embedding and extension (to all of E_n) applies, and calculus methods can be used, from which nearest-integer approximations are extracted for the desired answer.

DO LOCAL OPTIMA MAKE SENSE IN GENERAL?

One will note from the definition of a local maximum (or minimum) in the case of a continuous function, defined on E_n, that a choice of $\epsilon > 0$

was assumed possible.   In E_n we have a metric, and hence we can talk about selecting a positive ϵ.   A metric is a real-valued function defined for every pair of elements of E_n, denoted by $d(x,y)$, which satisfies $d(x,y) = 0$ if and only if $x = y$, $d(x,y) = d(y,x)$, $d(x,z) \leq d(x,y) + d(y,z)$. A metric may not exist on an arbitrary set, but the idea of a neighborhood is still usable.   A topology is defined on a set if a system of subsets (called *open sets*, e.g., open spheres in E_n) have been specified so that finite intersections and arbitrary unions of elements of the system, the entire space, and the null set belong to the system.   For an arbitrary set with a topology (called a *topological space*) a neighborhood of a point is any set which contains an open set that contains the point.   The kind of closeness that one is accustomed to in metric spaces may not exist.

Returning to maximization or minimization, in general, if a function is defined on an arbitrary set E, then not much can be done to define a local optimum of f unless some structure is given for E, using which, one can define a topology.   Two ways of obtaining such a structure are by embedding and by partial ordering.   For instance, if the set of points is just a set in E_n (i.e., it is embedded in the topological metric space E_n), then a natural way of defining a topology on E (called the *natural topology*) would be to use the relative topology induced on E by the standard topology of E_n.   The open sets of E are all those sets which are intersections of E with the open sets (open spheres defined by the metric) of the topology on E_n.   (If the set is discrete, every point would be open.)

Again, we may assume that there is a partial order on E.   Then we have a means for introducing a natural topology on it by considering all maximal chains.   Suppose we have a totally ordered set, consisting of an infinite sequence $a_1 \leq a_2 \leq \cdots \leq a_n \leq \cdots \leq a$.   The topology here is the order topology, where a neighborhood of a is the set of all points x such that $x \geq a_n$.   Thus, f has a local maximum at a if and only if there exists an n such that $f(x) \geq f(a_k)$ for all $k \geq n$.   The question now is how to introduce a topology on a partially ordered set. Naturally one would want to define the topology so that the neighborhoods for totally ordered subsets are the same as those just given for such sets.   This requirement furnishes a unique topology for any given partially ordered set.   Formally, restating what was just said, a topology is *defined* as follows: If P is a partially ordered set and S is a subset of P, then S is open if and only if the intersection of S with every maximal chain in P is open in the sense of the order topology on the chain.

What we have done here is the opposite of Euclidean-space embedding, discussed before.   There that subset inherited its natural topology from

the entire space.   Here, the partially ordered set is topologized in such
a way that totally ordered subsets inherit their natural topology.

In defining a topology on a chain, it is useful to introduce the idea of
a *subbase* and a *base*.   A subbase is a collection of open sets each of which
consists of all elements that are followers or predecessors of a given
element; in addition, the entire chain and the empty set are open.   A
base consists of all finite intersections of elements in the subbase.   A
set is said to be open if it is the union of elements in the base.   This
gives the topology.   This topology may now be used to define a local
maximum of a function in the usual manner, namely, using the foregoing
definition of an open set.

To illustrate, suppose that a function is defined over a finite partially
ordered set of points: $P = (a,b,c,d,e,f)$, whose chains are $(a \leq b \leq c;$
$d \leq e; f)$.   Clearly, the maximal chains are $P_1 = (a,b,c)$, $P_2 = (d,e)$,
$P_3 = (f)$.   If $S = (a,c,d)$, then $S \cap P_1 = (a,c)$, $S \cap P_2 = (d)$.   To see
if these intersections are open, we note that the chain (a,b,c) is open and
a is open because it is the set of predecessors or antecedents of b.   Similarly, c is open because it is the set of followers of b.   The union $a \cup c$
is open since a and c are open, and hence $S \cap P_1$ is open.   Similarly,
$P_2 = (d)$ is open.   Note that if a topology is defined on (f), then (f)
must be open.

Returning to the topology of the partially ordered set itself, we note
that if the order of P cannot be described in a finite number of sentences,
then defining the natural topology on P will be impossible because it
would require more than a finite number of sentences, and one would not
be able to define neighborhoods and local maxima.

The natural topology on any finite partially ordered set has the requirement that every point be open, and hence every subset is open.   Since
any point at which the function is defined is open, it is a neighborhood
of itself.   Therefore, the value of the function at every point is a local
maximum and a local minimum.   Thus, if a function is defined on a
discrete set of points and no extension is implicitly assumed, it is of little
use to speak of local maxima and minima.   However, if it is understood
that the function is to be extended, such as from the coordinate lattice
points to the entire Euclidean space, then there may be some practical
utility to defining local maxima and minima.

In many problems both extension of the function with subsequent use
of calculus methods and restriction to the given partially ordered set
(topologized as outlined above) are possible.   For an illustration consider a function $f(x_1, \ldots, x_n)$, defined over the lattice points of E_n.
Instead of extending f to all of E_n, we can stay with the lattice points
and use the induced-order topology; this leads to the following technique.
For a local maximum with respect to x_j at $x_j = x_j{}^0$ (that is, with respect

to the chain of lattice points on the line $x_i = $ constant, $i \neq j$), we may require the following to hold:

$$f(x_1, \ldots, x_j^0, \ldots, x_n) \geq f(x_1, \ldots, x_j^0 \pm 1, \ldots, x_n)$$
$$j = 1, \ldots, n$$

More generally, for a local maximum at $x = (x_1^0, \ldots, x_n^0)$, we have the stronger requirement

$$f(x_1^0, \ldots, x_n^0) \geq f(x_1^0 + \epsilon_1, \ldots, x_n^0 + \epsilon_n)$$

where $\epsilon_j = 0, 1, -1, j = 1, \ldots, n$.

Thus, the argument of f on the right actually assumes 3^n possible values (of which $(x_1^0 + 0, \ldots, x_n^0 + 0)$ is not new), and f evaluated at x must dominate its value at all the nearest neighboring lattice points. These are the lattice points just indicated. Similar definitions for a local minimum may be given.

It is easy to express the above condition for a local maximum for a function of a single variable. If we introduce the difference operator Δ (analogous to the derivative), which is defined by

$$\Delta f(x) = f(x + 1) - f(x)$$
$$\Delta^i f(x) = \Delta^{i-1} \Delta f(x) = \Delta^{i-1}[f(x + 1) - f(x)]$$

then a relative or local maximum at x_0 must satisfy the following necessary conditions

$$f(x_0) \geq f(x_0 - 1) \qquad \text{that is, } \Delta f(x_0 - 1) \geq 0$$
$$f(x_0) \geq f(x_0 + 1) \qquad \text{that is, } \Delta f(x_0) \leq 0$$

The two conditions together give as a necessary condition for a maximum

$$\Delta f(x_0) \leq 0 \leq \Delta f(x_0 - 1)$$

The analogous condition for a local minimum involves the reversal of the inequalities.

A sufficient condition for an absolute maximum at x_0 is given by

$$\Delta^2 f(x_0) \leq 0$$

The inequality should be reversed for an absolute minimum. A sufficient condition for an absolute maximum at $x = x_0$ is that $f(x)$ be monotone increasing for $x \leq x_0$ [that is, $f(x) \leq f(x_0)$, $x \leq x_0$] and monotone decreasing for $x \geq x_0$ [that is, $f(x) \geq f(x_0)$, $x \geq x_0$]. An example is given by those points of the range of a concave function whose corresponding domain is the integers.

Example   Consider the normal distribution function (see Fig. 1-7)

$$f(m,n) = \frac{1}{2\pi\sigma^2} \exp\left[-\frac{1}{2\sigma^2}(m^2 + n^2)\right]$$

with mean at the origin defined over the entire set of lattice points of the plane. We wish to determine if it has any maximum point. We write the $3^2 - 1$ inequalities

$$f(m,n) \geq f(m + \epsilon_1, n + \epsilon_2)$$

We then take logarithms on both sides. Since the logarithmic function is monotone increasing, the sense of the inequality remains unaffected. We obtain the following relations:

$\epsilon_1 = 1, \; \epsilon_2 = 0$	$x \geq -\frac{1}{2}$
$\epsilon_1 = 0, \; \epsilon_2 = 1$	$y \geq -\frac{1}{2}$
$\epsilon_1 = -1, \; \epsilon_2 = 0$	$x \leq \frac{1}{2}$
$\epsilon_1 = 0, \; \epsilon_2 = -1$	$y \leq \frac{1}{2}$
$\epsilon_1 = 1, \; \epsilon_2 = 1$	$x + y \geq -1$
$\epsilon_1 = -1, \; \epsilon_2 = -1$	$x + y \leq 1$
$\epsilon_1 = 1, \; \epsilon_2 = -1$	$x - y \geq -1$
$\epsilon_1 = -1, \; \epsilon_2 = 1$	$y - x \geq -1$

The first four relations limit (x,y) to a square whose corners are at $(\frac{1}{2},\frac{1}{2})$, $(\frac{1}{2},-\frac{1}{2})$, $(-\frac{1}{2},\frac{1}{2})$, and $(-\frac{1}{2},-\frac{1}{2})$. The point $(0,0)$ is the only lattice point which lies within this square and hence gives a local maximum. In this case, the last four relations are redundant. In general, they could contribute useful information, particularly if they are nonlinear in x and y.

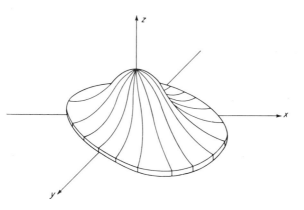

Fig. 1-7

Exercise 1-11   In the last example, prove that $(0,0)$ is a global maximum.

Exercise 1-12   Show that the elliptic paraboloid (Fig. 1-8)

$$\frac{x^2}{a^2} + \frac{y^2}{b^2} = z$$

has over the lattice points one minimum point at the origin.

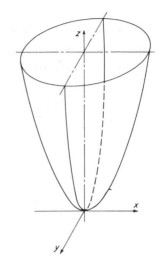

Fig. 1-8

Exercise 1-13 Show that the ellipsoid (Fig. 1-9)

$$\frac{x^2}{a^2} + \frac{y^2}{b^2} + \frac{z^2}{c^2} = 1$$

has one maximum and one minimum point over the lattice points. They are at the origin.

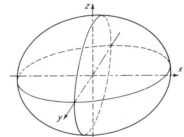

Fig. 1-9

Exercise 1-14 Show that the hyperbolic paraboloid (Fig. 1-10)

$$\frac{x^2}{a^2} - \frac{y^2}{b^2} = z$$

has no maxima or minima over the lattice points of the plane.

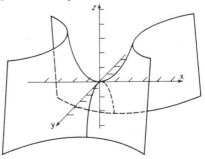

Fig. 1-10

1-4 CLASSIFICATION OF ALGEBRAIC PROBLEMS

Optimization techniques are dependent on the type of information available about the function to be optimized and may be classified as follows.

I. The case of an unconstrained function of a single or several variables.
   A. The function is not given in closed form.
      1. All functional values are given (if the function is finitely valued).
      2. The optimum is sought by taking samples of the values of a function. Thus, the search for the optimum suggests better ways of taking the samples with the purpose of obtaining a best estimate for the optimum value. If the function is known to be unimodal (i.e., to have one hump), the sequencing of the samples can be better designed than if the function were multimodal. The method of response surfaces and other experimental methods can be used to estimate an optimum value under these circumstances.
   B. The function is given in closed form.
II. The case of a constrained function.

For effective methods of solution, both the function and the constraints must be prescribed analytically. The constraints (which, for the purpose of the present discussion, are assumed to be given in algebraic form) may be given as equalities (Diophantine equations or systems of equations in discrete optimization) or inequalities. For discrete problems, calculus methods help provide estimates for the optimum, which must then be shown to yield the desired answer. However, mathematical-programming techniques give a direct approach to constrained optimization problems for which solutions in integers are desired. Frequently the search is for an optimum over the positive or nonnegative range of values of the variables.

In many geometric optimization problems, the optimum value is usually conjectured on the basis of information derived from the statement of the problem. Then a proof is given that the conjectured value is the desired optimum. For some geometric problems, symmetry plays a useful role in finding the optimum.

METHODS OF TREATMENT

If the expression to be optimized, together with the constraints, are given analytically in closed form, one resorts to the standard methods of the calculus, Lagrange multipliers, or programming to obtain a solution.   If the function is not known entirely but can be partly determined experimentally, then the approach to finding the optimum is more complicated and less certain.   In either case, an integral solution is hard to find, and the methods just mentioned generally do not work.   Whenever possible, integer programming is the standard procedure to follow for obtaining integer solutions.

CASE I*A*

A Function not in Closed Form: All Functional Values Given
Recall from Theorems 1-1 and 1-2 that it is possible, but complicated, to give a closed representation for the maximum of n real numbers $\alpha_1, \ldots, \alpha_n$.   In practice, it is easier to obtain the maximum by systematic comparison.

Theorem 1-10 *Exactly $n - 1$ comparisons are required to determine $max\ (\alpha_1, \ldots, \alpha_n)$, where $\alpha_1, \ldots, \alpha_n$ are real numbers.*

Proof   Compare α_1 successively with $\alpha_2, \ldots, \alpha_n$.   If $\alpha_1 \geq \alpha_i$, $i = 2, \ldots, n$, then max $(\alpha_1, \ldots, \alpha_n) = \alpha_1$, and $n - 1$ comparisons have been used.   If $\alpha_1 \geq \alpha_i$, $i = 2, \ldots, k$, but $\alpha_1 \leq \alpha_{k+1}$, then $\alpha_1, \ldots, \alpha_k$ are eliminated, and the process is repeated starting with α_{k+1}.   Continuing in this manner, exactly $n - 1$ comparisons would be made.

EXPERIMENTAL METHOD OF SEARCHING FOR THE MAXIMUM [11,13,28]
Assume that one is limited to exactly n samples of the values of a given discretely valued function of a single variable $f(x)$ in search of a maximum.   One starts by taking a sample of two values.   This provides an incentive to continue sampling near the larger of the two values.   Thus, the third sample is taken near the larger value.   A scheme is needed to decide where (to the left or to the right) and how far away from the previous value each subsequent sample is to be taken.

Suppose that the interval of uncertainty after $n - 1$ samples are taken is of length I_{n-1}; that is to say, the largest sampled value of $f(x)$ lies in I_{n-1}.   It is desired to place the final sample with respect to the preceding one so that the length of I_n, the next interval of uncertainty, is as small as possible.

We assume that we are dealing with a unimodal (one-hump) function $y = f(x)$.   Suppose that the samples are taken on the x axis, starting with x_1 and ending in x_n.   The x_k, $k = 1, \ldots, n$, need not be taken in increasing order.   Note that if, for example, a sample of three values, $x_1 > x_2 > x_3$, is taken on the unit interval where the maximum of $f(x)$ is sought, and if the corresponding functional values are y_1, y_2, and y_3, then if

$$y_1 > y_2 > y_3 \quad \text{the maximum lies in } [0, x_2)$$
$$y_1 < y_2 > y_3 \quad \text{the maximum lies in } (x_1, x_3)$$
$$y_1 < y_2 < y_3 \quad \text{the maximum lies in } (x_2, 1]$$

It would be desirable to make whatever interval contains the maximum as small as possible, so that when the last sample is taken, the estimate of the maximum will be as close as possible to the true value. Note that for each sample plan $x = (x_1, \ldots, x_n)$, there is an index α which is associated with x_α, for which $y(x_\alpha) \equiv y_\alpha$ is maximum.

Let $I_{n,\alpha}(x)$ be the length of the interval in which the maximum is located. Thus, $I_{n,\alpha}(x) = x_{\alpha+1} - x_{\alpha-1}$ and contains x_α in its interior. Let $L_n(x)$ be the longest of these intervals for any choice of x. Therefore,

$$L_n(x) = \max \{I_{n,\alpha}(x)\} \qquad \text{for all } x$$

From a theoretical point of view, with each arbitrary sample of size n there is associated an interval which contains the maximum of the function. We consider the largest of these intervals for all samples. Then our problem becomes that of finding the "best" choice of x, which we denote by $\bar{x}$ such that $\bar{L}_n \equiv L_n(\bar{x})$ is minimum.

In that case

$$\bar{L}_n = \min_x \max \{I_{n,\alpha}(x)\}$$

Without loss of generality, we assume that the function is defined on the unit interval $[0,1]$. Heuristically, to determine the optimum sampling procedure, consider an arbitrary interval $\bar{L}_j$, whose end points are a pair of x_k's, one or both of which may be an end point of the interval $[0,1]$. Exactly one of these end points must have belonged to $\bar{L}_{j-1}$. For a general algorithm to find x, whatever argument is used to decide the position of the next sample, which is placed inside $\bar{L}_{j-1}$, thus yielding $\bar{L}_j$, must now be symmetrically applied with respect to the other end point of $\bar{L}_{j-1}$, yielding $\bar{L}_{j+1}$. The reason for this is that in the absence of specific values of the function at the two end points, there is no reason to assume preference of one value over another, and hence two new samples must be taken. Thus, the two end points of $\bar{L}_{j-1}$ must be symmetric with respect to the largest value determined so far. This gives

$$\bar{L}_{j-1} = \bar{L}_j + \bar{L}_{j+1} \tag{1-1}$$

We have the following two cases:

1. The number of samples n is given. In this case, it is natural to take the nth or final sample in the middle of $\bar{L}_{n-1}$. Thus, $\bar{L}_{n-1} = 2\bar{L}_n$.

Combining this result with Eq. (1-1), we have

$$\bar{L}_{n-2} = \bar{L}_{n-1} + \bar{L}_n = 3\bar{L}_n$$
$$\bar{L}_{n-3} = \bar{L}_{n-2} + \bar{L}_{n-1} = 5\bar{L}_n$$

We note that the coefficients of $\bar{L}_n$ are the Fibonacci sequence 1, 2, 3, 5, 8, . . . , obtained from the recursive relation

$$F_k = F_{k-1} + F_{k-2} \qquad k \geq 1$$

with

$$F_0 = F_1 = 1$$

Thus, the foregoing iterations may be generally represented by

$$\bar{L}_{n-k} = F_{k+1}\bar{L}_n$$

Since

$$L_1 = 1 = F_n\bar{L}_n$$

we have

$$\bar{L}_n = \frac{1}{F_n}$$

2. The number of samples n is not given. Here we cannot apply the relation $\bar{L}_{n-1} = 2\bar{L}_n$. Instead, one attempts to keep the ratios of successive intervals constant. This gives

$$\frac{\bar{L}_{j-1}}{\bar{L}_j} = \frac{\bar{L}_j}{\bar{L}_{j+1}} = c \tag{1-2}$$

Dividing Eq. (1-1) by $\bar{L}_{j+1}$ gives

$$\frac{\bar{L}_{j-1}}{\bar{L}_{j+1}} = \frac{\bar{L}_j}{\bar{L}_{j+1}} + 1 \tag{1-3}$$

Since $\bar{L}_j{}^2 = \bar{L}_{j-1}\bar{L}_{j+1}$, on substituting for $\bar{L}_j$ in the middle expression of Eq. (1-2), we have

$$\left(\frac{\bar{L}_{j-1}}{\bar{L}_{j+1}}\right)^{\frac{1}{2}} = c$$

Thus Eq. (1-3) becomes

$$c^2 = c + 1$$

and $c = (1 + \sqrt{5})/2$ is the only positive root. Now $\bar{L}_1 = 1$, and hence we have from Eq. (1-2) $\bar{L}_2 = 1/c$ and recursively $\bar{L}_n = 1/c^{n-1}$. Wilde [28] calls this second method the "search by golden section."

One can show that

$$F_n = \frac{c^{n+1} - (-c)^{-(n+1)}}{\sqrt{5}} \approx \frac{c^{n+1}}{\sqrt{5}}$$

With this approximation, we can compare the result for $\bar{L}_n$ where n is given with the result when it is not. On taking ratios, we have

$$\frac{c^{n+1}}{\sqrt{5}\, c^{n-1}} = \frac{c^2}{\sqrt{5}} = 1.1708$$

Extensions to nonlinear integer programming are available [17a].

STEEPEST ASCENT ALONG FITTING SURFACES

Statistical methods of determining an optimum point for an unconstrained function of several variables, not given in closed form, also have been investigated [1,2]. The procedure will be briefly described here.

Suppose that the interactions of several factors $(x_1, \ldots, x_n)$ in an experiment are related by a function $f(x_1, \ldots, x_n)$ which is unknown. Assuming that this function has an optimum such as a maximum, it is desired to determine or estimate this optimum by experimental sampling and data fitting, without attempting to determine $f(x_1, \ldots, x_n)$ completely, which is usually an expensive and wasteful process.

The fitting of the data is done locally to determine a direction in which one may proceed toward the maximum; having followed a path of steepest ascent, one must stop somewhere and repeat the process.

One of the favorite attacks is the method of one factor at a time. By holding all controlled variables but one at prescribed values and allowing the latter to vary, a maximum is obtained; it is then used as a fixed value for this variable, and another variable is allowed to vary, etc.

A more reliable procedure leads to a maximum by following a path of steepest ascent in steps, assuming approximations by planes or quadratic surfaces in small regions as may be justified by series expansions. The plan is to predict the best-fitting plane in a small portion of the experimental region, using a least-squares procedure. A steepest-ascent path is indicated by changes in variables equal to the direction cosines which are proportional to the coefficients. Experiments are then performed along this path until a decrease in value is noted. Repetition of the procedure around this point can confirm whether a maximum has been reached or whether a new path of ascent should be determined. If the approximating surface indicates flatness, it does not imply that a maximum has been reached. The surface may contain a ridge which is stationary, or it may be slowly rising, or a saddle point may even have been reached. Further investigation is needed, depending on the type of solution in the practical problem.

It may be found that the linear and quadratic terms in the series expansion may be used as an approximation, and a least-squares method to determine the coefficients is then applied. Because of the increase in the number of coefficients, larger samples for their determination are required, since at least N observations are necessary to fit an approximating function containing N constants. Reduction to canonical form by a translation and orthogonal rotation facilitates the determination of the steepest-ascent path in terms of the latent roots of the associated characteristic equation.

CASE IB AND CASE II

If $f(x_1, \ldots, x_n)$ is twice differentiable in $x_j, j = 1, \ldots, n$, then a necessary condition for an optimum is given by [22]

$$\frac{\partial f}{\partial x_j} \equiv 0 \qquad j.= 1, \ldots, n$$

Sufficiency conditions can be given in terms of the principal diagonal determinants of the matrix of second-order partial derivatives, evaluated at the solution of the above system. All these determinants must be positive. (For the two-variable case, see the result given for convexity, and replace $\geq$ with $>$.)

If $f(x_1, \ldots, x_n)$ is to be optimized subject to constraints

$$g_i(x_1, \ldots, x_n) \leq 0 \qquad i = 1, \ldots, m$$

then one forms the lagrangian

$$F(x_1, \ldots, x_n; \lambda_1, \ldots, \lambda_m) = f - \sum_{i=1}^{m} \lambda_i g_i$$

The parameters $\lambda_1, \ldots, \lambda_m$ are called "Lagrange multipliers." For example, the lagrangian of $xyz = $ maximum subject to $x^2 + y^2 + z^2 = r^2$ is

$$F(x,y,z,\lambda) = xyz - \lambda(x^2 + y^2 + z^2 - r^2)$$

1. A necessary condition for a maximum for the case $g_i = 0$, $i = 1, \ldots, m$, is given by

$$\frac{\partial F}{\partial x_j} = 0 \qquad j = 1, \ldots, n$$

$$\frac{\partial F}{\partial \lambda_i} = 0 \qquad i = 1, \ldots, m$$

Elementary sufficiency conditions, for special cases, will be discussed later.

2. The case $g_i \leq 0$, $i = 1, \ldots, m$, occurs frequently, particularly when there are additional "nonnegativity" requirements

$$x = (x_1, \ldots, x_n) \geq 0$$

that is,

$$x_j \geq 0 \qquad j = 1, \ldots, n$$

These conditions may be written as

$$-g_{m+1} \equiv -x_1 \leq 0, \ldots, -g_{m+n} \equiv -x_n \leq 0$$

Suppose that the following condition holds for any point x^0 on the boundary and every sufficiently small displacement dx from x^0 such that

$$\nabla g_i(x^0) \, dx < 0 \qquad i = 1, \ldots, m$$

whenever

$$g_i(x^0) = 0 \qquad \nabla \equiv \left(\frac{\partial}{\partial x_1}, \ldots, \frac{\partial}{\partial x_n} \right)$$

and $dx_j \geq 0$ whenever $x_j{}^0 = 0$. Then dx lies in the constraint region. These conditions are designed to rule out degenerate situations such as might occur to a derivative at a cusp. Let $G(x)$ be the column vector of g_i, $i = 1, \ldots, m$. We have the following theorem.

Theorem 1-11 (Kuhn-Tucker) *A necessary condition that $f(x)$ attain its maximum at a boundary point $\bar{x}$ of $G(x) \leq 0$, with $\bar{x} \geq 0$, is that there exist $\lambda \geq 0$ and $\mu \geq 0$ such that* [17]

$$\nabla f(\bar{x}) = \lambda \, \nabla G(\bar{x}) - \mu$$

where, if $\bar{x}_j > 0$, then $\mu_j = 0$, and if $g_i(\bar{x}) < 0$ then $\lambda_i = 0$ (see Fig. 1-11).

Note that if $\bar{x}$ is in the interior of the region defined by the constraints, then $\bar{x} > 0$, $G(\bar{x}) < 0$, and hence $\mu = 0$, $\lambda = 0$, and the conditions reduce to those which require the vanishing of the derivatives of f.

We have seen that necessary conditions in optimization of a function subject to equality constraints under differentiability assumptions lead to the solution of a system of equations. It is sometimes possible to do the converse and hence go from the problem of solving a system of equations to an optimization problem.

Consider a function of two variables $F(x,y)$ that is linear in y. We can think of y as a Lagrange multiplier. We can then regard $F(x,y)$ as the lagrangian of an optimization problem in which the function to be

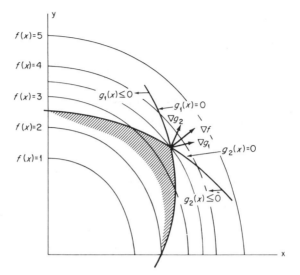

Fig. 1-11   An optimum on the boundary.

optimized is the part of $F(x,y)$, not involving y.   In that case, the coefficient of y is equated to zero as a constraint.   Of course, one may work up to such a function by integrating a system of algebraic equations which it is possible to consider as the necessary condition for an optimum obtained by differentiating the lagrangian.   This idea generalizes to the case of several variables in some of which the function is linear.

Example   The following example may be too simple, but it is intended only to illustrate the idea.   Consider the nonlinear system of equations

$$2x_i + y_i(\sin x_i + 1) = 0 \qquad i = 1, \ldots, n$$

We wish to assert whether this system has a real solution in x_i, $i = 1, \ldots, n$, for some y_i, $i = 1, \ldots, n$.   We form the lagrangian by integrating with respect to x_i, and, summing over i, we have

$$F(x_1, \ldots, x_n; y_1, \ldots, y_n) = \sum_{i=1}^{n} x_i^2 - \sum_{i=1}^{n} y_i(\cos x_i - x_i - c_i)$$

where c_i, $i = 1, \ldots, n$, are integration constants to be determined under specified conditions.   This lagrangian would have arisen from the optimization problem: Find

$$\max \sum_{i=1}^{n} x_i^2$$

subject to

$$\cos x_i = x_i + c_i \qquad i = 1, \ldots , n$$

This system has real bounded solutions, and thus a maximum exists. Consequently the original system has a real solution for some value of y_i, $i = 1, \ldots , n$.

GRADIENT AND GRADIENT METHOD

The gradient of the function $z = f(x_1, \ldots , x_n)$ is the vector

$$\nabla f = \left(\frac{\partial f}{\partial x_1}, \cdots , \frac{\partial f}{\partial x_n} \right)$$

Note that the normal line of the tangent plane to f at a point is a vector in $n + 1$-space, whereas ∇f is strictly in n-space since it is a vector of n components (see Fig. 1-12). The gradient ∇f points locally in the direction of maximum increase or steepest ascent along the contours of the surface $z = f(x_1, \ldots , x_n)$, and hence $-\nabla f$ points in the direction of maximum decrease or steepest descent. To see this, consider a small arbitary direction $dx = (dx_1, \ldots , dx_n)$, taken from a point of a contour. We wish to choose dx so that it points in the direction of maximum increase of f in the neighborhood of the point. First, note that total change in f is indicated by its total derivative

$$df = \frac{\partial f}{\partial x_1} dx_1 + \cdots + \frac{\partial f}{\partial x_n} dx_n = \nabla f \, dx = |\nabla f| \, |dx| \cos \theta$$

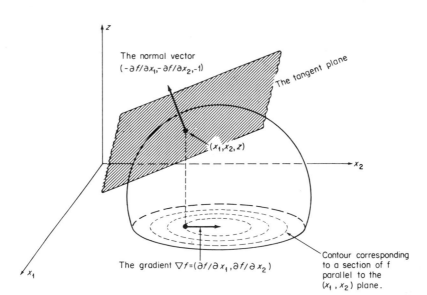

The normal vector $(-\partial f/\partial x_1, -\partial f/\partial x_2, -1)$

The tangent plane

(x_1, x_2, z)

z

x_2

x_1

The gradient $\nabla f = (\partial f/\partial x_1, \partial f/\partial x_2)$

Contour corresponding to a section of f parallel to the (x_1, x_2) plane.

Fig. 1-12

Thus df is largest when $\theta = 0$, and hence dx lies along the gradient. Thus, the gradient points in the direction of maximum increase in f.

The gradient may be used as a tool in an iterative method (known as the *gradient method*) for finding the maximum or minimum of a function. Thus, if we write

$$x^{(k)} = x^{(k-1)} - \lambda \, \nabla f(x^{(k-1)})$$

then the hope is to choose λ so that $x^{(k)}$ would be nearer to the optimum than $x^{(k-1)}$. The initial point $x^{(0)}$ is taken arbitrarily. Convergence can be proved for appropriate choices of λ and $x^{(0)}$. If we wish to minimize $f(x_1,x_2) = x_1^2 + x_2^2 - 2x_1x_2$, with $x^{(0)} = (x_1^{(0)},x_2^{(0)}) = (1,0)$, we have $\nabla f = (2x_1 - 2x_2, 2x_2 - 2x_1)$,

$$x^{(1)} = x^{(0)} - \lambda \, \nabla f(x^{(0)}) = (1,0) - \lambda(2,-2) = (1 - 2\lambda, \, 2\lambda)$$

If we substitute $x^{(1)}$ in f, the latter becomes a function of λ. We then minimize it as a function of λ by writing $df/d\lambda = 0$. This gives $\lambda = \frac{1}{4}$, $x^{(1)} = (\frac{1}{2},\frac{1}{2})$ which, using sufficiency tests (mentioned above), can be shown to yield the minimum.

Exercise 1-15   Determine the extrema (maxima and minima) of

$$f(x) = (x - 2)^2 \qquad 0 \le x \le 3$$

and prove that $x = 0$ is a global maximum, $x = 3$ is a local maximum, and $x = 2$ is a local minimum.

Draw a graph and interpret the results.

Exercise 1-16   Prove that

$$f(x_1,x_2) = \frac{x_1^2 + x_2^2}{2} \qquad \begin{array}{l} 0 \le x_1 \le 1 \\ 0 \le x_2 \le 1 \end{array}$$

has

a. a global minimum at $x_1 = x_2 = 0$
b. a global maximum at $x_1 = x_2 = 1$

Prove that $x_1 = 1$, $x_2 = 0$, and symmetrically $x_1 = 0$, $x_2 = 1$ are neither a maximum nor a minimum.

Draw a graph and interpret the results.

Exercise 1-17   Find the maximum of xy subject to $x^2 + y^2 = 25$.

Exercise 1-18   Find the maximum of xyz subject to

$$\frac{x^2}{a^2} + \frac{y^2}{b^2} + \frac{z^2}{c^2} - 1 = 0$$

Exercise 1-19   Find the dimensions of a rectangular box, without a top, with maximum value and a surface area of 108 sq in.

Exercise 1-20   Find the maximum and minimum values of

$$f(x,y) = 2x^2 + 2xy + 3y^2 \quad \text{in the region } x^2 + y^2 \leq 1, \, x + y \geq 0$$

Exercise 1-21   Maximize

$$f(x,y) = \int_0^x e^{-t^2/2} \, dt + \int_0^y e^{-t^2/2} \, dt$$

subject to $g(x,y) \equiv x + y \leq c, \, c > 0, \, x \geq 0, \, y \geq 0$.

Hint: First show that the maximum is not in the interior of the region.   Prove that f is concave.   (The criterion for proving convexity is to show that the principal minor determinants of the matrix of second-order partial derivatives are nonnegative for all x and y.   For concavity, multiply by -1 and test for convexity.) Hence the maximum is on the boundary.   Apply the Kuhn-Tucker theorem.

Exercise 1-22   (Josiah Willard Gibbs)   Let $f(x_1, \ldots, x_n) = \Sigma_{i=1}^n f_i(x_i)$, and let $\Sigma_{i=1}^n x_i = C$, $x_i \geq 0$.   Using Theorem 1-11, prove that a necessary condition for $(x_1^0, \ldots, x_n^0)$ to maximize f subject to the constraints is the existence of a real number λ such that

$$f_i'(x_i^0) \equiv \frac{\partial f_i(x_i)}{\partial x_i}\bigg|_{x_i = x_i^0} = \lambda \quad \text{if } x_i^0 > 0$$

$$f_i'(x_i^0) \equiv \frac{\partial f_i(x_i)}{\partial x_i}\bigg|_{x_i = x_i^0} \leq \lambda \quad \text{if } x_i^0 = 0$$

Prove that this condition is also sufficient if $f_i(x_i)$, $i = 1, \ldots, n$, are concave; that is, $f_i''(x_i) \leq 0$.   After λ has been found, and assuming concavity of the functions, prove that a sufficient condition is given by

$$f_i'(0) > \lambda \quad \text{if and only if } x_i^0 > 0$$
$$f_i'(0) \leq \lambda \quad \text{if and only if } x_i^0 = 0$$

Write down the necessary condition for a minimum for the above problem.   Assuming convexity, give the corresponding sufficiency conditions.

Exercise 1-23   Using the conditions for convexity from Exercise 1-22, show that convexity holds and minimize

$$\sum_{i=1}^n a_i e^{-b_i x_i} \qquad a_i, b_i > 0$$

subject to

$$\sum_{i=1}^n x_i = 1 \qquad x_i \geq 0$$

Exercise 1-24   Apply the gradient method to obtain the minimum point of the ellipsoid

$$\frac{x^2}{a^2} + \frac{y^2}{b^2} + \frac{z^2}{c^2} = 1$$

Hint: Solve for z and use the lower lobe.

Exercise 1-25 Show that the problem of solving the system $f_i(x_1, \ldots, x_n) = 0$, $i = 1, \ldots, n$, is equivalent to that of finding $(x_1, \ldots, x_n)$, which minimizes the expression $\Sigma_{i=1}^n f_i^2$. Obviously the minimum value of this expression is zero.

NEWTON'S METHOD

The Lagrange-multiplier approach requires the solution of a set of $m + n$ equations, $f_i = 0$, $i = 1, \ldots, m + n$ in $m + n$ unknowns. As indicated in Exercise 1-25, to solve these equations, they may be squared, added together, and minimized to zero by the gradient method. Alternatively, they may be solved by Newton's method, which, starting at an arbitrary initial point,

$$x^{(0)} = (x_1^{(0)}, \ldots, x_n^{(0)}; \lambda_1^{(0)}, \ldots, \lambda_m^{(0)}) \equiv (x_1^{(0)}, \ldots, x_{m+n}^{(0)})$$

gives

$$x^{(k)} = x^{(k-1)} - [f_1(x^{k-1}), \ldots, f_{m+n}(x^{k-1})]J^{-1}(x^{k-1})$$

obtained by applying Cramer's rule to solve for x in the linear system obtained by truncating the series expansion of each f_i around $x^{(k-1)}$ up to linear terms. (The term $J^{-1}(x)$ is the inverse of the matrix of first-order partial derivatives.) Thus,

$$f_i(x) = f_i(x^{(k-1)}) + \sum_{j=1}^{m+n} \frac{\partial f_i}{\partial x_j}\bigg|_{x^{(k-1)}} (x_j - x_j^{(k-1)}) \qquad i = 1, \ldots, m + n$$

Note that $f_i(x)$ is zero. Solving for x_j, and writing it as a new iteration $x_j^{(k)}$, we have the above expression for Newton's method. (For convergence, see Ref. 22.)

Exercise 1-26 Consider the system

$$2x^3 - y^2 - 1 = 0$$
$$xy^3 - y - 4 = 0$$

Start with $x^{(0)} = (1.2, 1.7)$ and show that Newton's method gives $x^{(1)} = (1.23, 1.66)$.

1-5 EXAMPLES OF DISCRETE OPTIMIZATION OF FUNCTIONS IN CLOSED FORM: SUFFICIENCY CRITERION

Here we shall illustrate some methods of treating discrete problems. This section may be properly included with Chap. 4, but it is included here for introductory purposes.

Theorem 1-12 $\Sigma_{i,j=1}^n a_i b_j$ *is maximized by taking* $i = j$, *where* a_i *and* b_j *are given and satisfy* $a_1 > a_2 > \cdots > a_n > 0, b_1 > b_2 > \cdots > b_n > 0$.

Remark   In the foregoing sum, each a_i and each b_j appears precisely once.

Proof [27]   We proceed by induction. The result is trivially valid for $n = 1$. For $n = 2$ we have

$$(a_1b_1 + a_2b_2) - (a_1b_2 + a_2b_1) = (a_1 - a_2)(b_1 - b_2) > 0$$

From this we have

$$a_1b_1 + a_2b_2 > a_1b_2 + a_2b_1$$

Assume the theorem is true for $i = 1, \ldots, k; j = 1, \ldots, k$; let us show that it is true for $k + 1$. We may write $a_i = a_{k+1} + p_i$, $b_i = b_{k+1} + q_i$ with $p_i > 0$, $q_i > 0$, $p_{k+1} = q_{k+1} = 0$. Substitution gives

$$\sum_{i;j=1}^{k+1} a_i b_j = a_{k+1}b_{k+1} + \sum_{i=1}^{k+1} b_{k+1}p_i + \sum_{j=1}^{k+1} a_{k+1}q_j + \sum_{i;k=1}^{k+1} p_i q_j$$

The first three expressions on the right are constant and hence independent of whether or not $i = j$. By assumption,

$$a_{k+1} + p_i = a_i > a_{i+1} = a_{k+1} + p_{i+1}$$

and hence $p_i > p_{i+1}$. Similarly, $q_i > q_{i+1}$. Now if $\Sigma_{i;j=1}^{k+1} p_i q_j$ has the term $p_{k+1} q_{k+1}$ (which is zero) appearing, then

$$\sum_{i;j=1}^{k+1} p_i q_j = \sum_{i;j=1}^{k} p_i q_j$$

is by induction maximum when $i = j$. Consider now the case when two terms appear, one having the form $p_{k+1}q_s$, $1 \le s \le k$, and the other having the form $q_{k+1}p_t$, $1 \le t \le k$, both of which are zero. Our sum can then be written as follows:

$$\sum_{i;j=1}^{k+1} p_i q_j = \sum_{i;j=1}^{k} p_i q_j - p_t q_s$$

By induction, the sum on the right is maximum when $i = j$, and since $p_t q_s > 0$ we have

$$\sum_{i=1}^{k+1} p_i q_i = \sum_{i=1}^{k} p_i q_i > \sum_{i;j=1}^{k} p_i q_j - p_t q_s = \sum_{i;j=1}^{k+1} p_i q_j$$

Thus, the last sum is maximum when $i = j$. This completes the proof.

Exercise 1-27   A man has $n \equiv 0 \bmod 5$ shirts which he uses at the rate of one per working day (five per week). The number of shirts to be laundered for minimum cost is a multiple of five. He can take his shirts to be laundered and pick up clean shirts only on Saturdays. It takes a calendar week for the laundry to be completed.   How should he arrange to take his shirts to be laundered if he wishes to minimize the number of trips to the laundry?   Characterize the solution.   Is there a unique solution to this problem?   Give proofs.

Exercise 1-28   Show that [15]

$$\sum_{m=1}^{M} \sum_{n=1}^{N} \min\,(m,n) = \frac{N(N+1)(3M-N+1)}{6}$$

Observe that

$$\sum_{m=1}^{M} \sum_{n=1}^{N} \min\,(m,n) = \sum_{n=1}^{N} \sum_{m=1}^{n} m + \sum_{m=n+1}^{M} n$$

from which the result follows.

For some optimization problems, it is not easy to obtain the optimum directly.   Instead, one uses one type of argument to give a lower bound to the optimum.   Another argument may give an upper bound.   If the two are the same, it is the desired maximum; otherwise, the maximum lies between its upper and lower bounds.

Sometimes calculus methods lead to a conjectured value of an optimum of a discrete function.   Thus, one begins by embedding the problem of maximizing $f(x_1, \ldots, x_n)$, where the x_i's take on integer values in the more general or extended form in which the x_i's are real.

Theorem 1-13   *The positive integer m which minimizes*

$$f(m,n) = 2m + 3 + \frac{n}{m}$$

is the integer nearest to $\sqrt{n/2}$.

Proof 1   Using our definition of a local minimum in the discrete case, we have

$$f(m,n) - f(m+1, n) = -2 + \frac{n}{m} - \frac{n}{m+1} \leq 0$$

$$f(m,n) - f(m-1, n) = 2 + \frac{n}{m} - \frac{n}{m-1} \leq 0$$

from which we obtain

$$m(m-1) \leq \frac{n}{2} \leq m(m+1)$$

or

$$\left| \frac{n}{2m} - m \right| \leq 1$$

To find m, which satisfies this inequality, we put $(n/2m) - m = 0$, from which we have $m = \sqrt{n/2}$; and since m is an integer, we take $m = [\sqrt{n/2}]$.

Proof 2   Regarding f as continuous and differentiable in m, we have

$$\frac{df}{dm} = \frac{m(4m + 3) - (2m^2 + 3m + n)}{m^2}$$

$$= \frac{4m^2 + 3m - 2m^2 - 3m - n}{m^2} = 0$$

or

$$2m^2 - n = 0$$

Thus $m = \sqrt{n/2}$.

This suggests taking m as the nearest integer to $\sqrt{n/2}$. Let us denote this integer by $[\sqrt{n/2}]$. Substituting in f, we have

$$2\left[\sqrt{\frac{n}{2}}\right] + 3 + \frac{n}{[\sqrt{n/2}]}$$

We now prove that

$$f\left(\left[\sqrt{\frac{n}{2}}\right], n\right) \le f(m,n) \qquad \text{for all } m$$

Thus we show that

$$2\left[\sqrt{\frac{n}{2}}\right] + 3 + \frac{n}{[\sqrt{n/2}]} \le 2m + 3 + \frac{n}{m}$$

or

$$2\left[\sqrt{\frac{n}{2}}\right] + \frac{n}{[\sqrt{n/2}]} \le 2m + \frac{n}{m} \qquad \text{for all } m$$

Simplifying, we have

$$2\left\{\left[\sqrt{\frac{n}{2}}\right] - m\right\} \le n\left\{\frac{[\sqrt{n/2}] - m}{m\,[\sqrt{n/2}]}\right\}$$

which we show holds.   Now if $m < [\sqrt{n/2}]$, then we must show that

$$2 \le \frac{n}{m[\sqrt{n/2}]}$$

or

$$2m\left[\sqrt{\frac{n}{2}}\right] \le n$$

or

$$m \left[\sqrt{\frac{n}{2}} \right] \leq \frac{n}{2} = \sqrt{\frac{n}{2}} \sqrt{\frac{n}{2}}$$

or

$$m \left(\sqrt{\frac{n}{2}} + \theta \right) \leq \sqrt{\frac{n}{2}} \sqrt{\frac{n}{2}} \qquad |\theta| \leq \frac{1}{2}$$

Since this must hold for any $-\frac{1}{2} \leq \theta \leq \frac{1}{2}$, we must have $m \leq [\sqrt{n/2}]$. If $m > [\sqrt{n/2}]$, the same type of argument holds in proving that

$$2 \geq \frac{n}{m[\sqrt{n/2}]}$$

Thus $m = [\sqrt{n/2}]$ gives the minimum of f.

Exercise 1-29   Using the second derivative test, show that $f(m,n)$ as a continuous and differentiable function of m is convex in m.   Hence, deduce that the minimum of f as a discrete function of m is given at one of the two integer values on each side of that value of m which minimizes $f(m,n)$.

A SUFFICIENCY CRITERION

In Fig. 1-13 we have a convex function $z = f(x,y)$, defined over the lattice points in the plane.   The point $(\bar{x},\bar{y})$ yields the minimum for the continuous embedding.   Values at the four surrounding lattice points

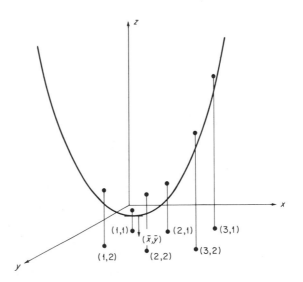

Fig. 1-13

must be compared for the minimum.   In E_n, 2^n lattice points surround the continuous solution point and must all be tried unless an alternative shortcut which omits some of these points is used.   The criterion developed below has this purpose in mind.

The following is a sufficiency condition for the Lagrange-multiplier approach in the case of maximizing $f(x_1, \ldots, x_n)$ subject to [4b]

$$g_i(x_1, \ldots, x_n) \leq 0 \qquad i = 1, \ldots, m$$

It involves no differentiability assumptions and no restrictions on the domain of definition D which may be discrete.   Using the lagrangian function $F(x;\lambda) \equiv F(x_1, \ldots, x_n; \lambda_1, \ldots, \lambda_m)$, we prove the following theorem.

Theorem 1-14   (Everett)   *Given* $\bar{\lambda}_i \geq 0$, $i = 1, \ldots, m$, *and given* $\bar{x}$, *which maximizes* $F(x;\lambda)$ *for all* $x \in D$, *then* $\bar{x}$ *maximizes* $f(x)$ *for all* $x \in D$ *which satisfy*

$$g_i(x) \leq g_i(\bar{x}) \qquad i = 1, \ldots, m$$

Remark   This theorem says that $\bar{x}$ maximizes the constrained problem if, when evaluated at $\bar{x}$, the resulting value of each $g_i(x)$, $i = 1, \ldots, m$, is a constant which is an upper bound on the corresponding $g_i(x)$.

Proof   By assumption

$$F(\bar{x};\bar{\lambda}) \geq F(x;\bar{\lambda})$$

Thus,

$$f(\bar{x}) \geq f(x) + \sum_{i=1}^{m} \bar{\lambda}_i[g_i(\bar{x}) - g_i(x)]$$

for all $x \in D$.   Since the second term on the right is nonnegative, we have $f(\bar{x}) \geq f(x)$, and the proof is complete.

The foregoing theorem may be generalized to the case where the lagrangian has the form $f(x) - G[g_1(x), \ldots, g_m(x); \lambda_1, \ldots, \lambda_m]$ and where if $g_i(x^1) \leq g_i(x^2)$, $i = 1, \ldots, n$, then

$$G[g_1(x^1), \ldots, g_m(x^1); \lambda_1, \ldots, \lambda_m]$$
$$\leq G[g_1(x^2), \ldots, g_m(x^2); \lambda_1, \ldots, \lambda_m]$$

for all λ_i, $i = 1, \ldots, m$.   This is the requirement that G be monotone on the directed set of constraint vectors partially ordered under set inclusion.   A vector includes another if it dominates it componentwise.

We now prove that a solution which produces a value of the lagrangian $F(x;\lambda)$ near the maximum must also nearly maximize $f(x)$ subject to the constraints $g_i(x) = g_i(\bar{x})$, $i = 1, \ldots, m$.

Theorem 1-15 *If*

$$F(\bar{x};\bar{\lambda}) \geq F(x;\bar{\lambda}) - \epsilon \qquad for\ small\ \epsilon > 0$$

then

$$f(\bar{x}) \geq f(x) - \epsilon$$

for

$$g_i(x) = g_i(\bar{x}) \qquad i = 1, \ldots, m$$

Proof The proof is identical to the previous proof but incorporates ϵ.

In general, different values of $\lambda = (\lambda_1, \ldots, \lambda_m)$ yield different maxima. However, it is useful to investigate the effect on the solution of changes in the values of λ or in some of its components.

Theorem 1-16 *If $\bar{x}^1$ and $\bar{x}^2$ are two solutions corresponding to $\bar{\lambda}^1$ and $\bar{\lambda}^2$, respectively, and if $g_i(\bar{x}^1) = g_i(\bar{x}^2)$, $i \neq k$, and $g_k(\bar{x}^1) > g_k(\bar{x}^2)$, then the components $\bar{\lambda}_k^1$ and $\bar{\lambda}_k^2$ satisfy*

$$\bar{\lambda}_k^2 \geq \frac{f(\bar{x}^1) - f(\bar{x}^2)}{g_k(\bar{x}^1) - g_k(\bar{x}^2)} \geq \bar{\lambda}_k^1$$

Proof

$$f(\bar{x}^1) \geq f(x) + \bar{\lambda}_k^1[g_k(\bar{x}^1) - g_k(x)] + \sum_{i \neq k} \bar{\lambda}_k^1[g_k(\bar{x}^1) - g_k(x)]$$

Substituting $\bar{x}^2$ for x, this relation still holds, and, using the hypothesis for $i = k$, we have

$$\frac{f(\bar{x}^1) - f(\bar{x}^2)}{g_k(\bar{x}^1) - g_k(\bar{x}^2)} \geq \bar{\lambda}_k^1$$

Interchanging the roles of $\bar{x}^1$ and $\bar{x}^2$, we have the other side of the inequality, which completes the proof.

Example Given: A system of m stages which are connected in series. The ith stage consists of n_i components connected in parallel as indicated in Fig. 1-14. The probability that an ith-stage component would function is p_i, and its cost is c_i. The system can function only if at least one component in each stage is operable.

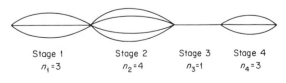

Stage 1   Stage 2   Stage 3   Stage 4
$n_1 = 3$ $n_2 = 4$ $n_3 = 1$ $n_4 = 3$

Fig. 1-14

It is desired to develop a curve which gives a tradeoff between the maximum reliability of the system and the minimum cost of the system.

Since the probability that a component of the ith stage is operable is p_i, $1 - p_i$ is the probability that it is inoperable, and $(1 - p_i)^{n_i}$ is the probability that no component of the ith stage is operable. Hence $1 - (1 - p_i)^{n_i}$ gives the probability that at least one component of the ith stage is operable. Since the stages are in series, we take the product of these probabilities to obtain the probability $P(n_1, \ldots, n_m)$ that the system is operable, and we have

$$P(n_1, \ldots, n_m) = \prod_{i=1}^{m} 1 - (1 - p_i)^{n_i}$$

The cost of the system is given by $C = \Sigma_{i=1}^{m} c_i n_i$. One may proceed by maximizing P for a given value of C, or by minimizing C for a given value of P.

Now P is a concave function of n_i, $i = 1, \ldots, m$. To see this, note that $1 - (1 - p_i)^{n_i}$ is monotone nondecreasing in n_i. Hence, the product P is a monotone-nondecreasing function of $n = (n_1, \ldots, n_m)$. Furthermore, if regarded as a continuous function of n, P is concave. Hence, we can start by using calculus methods to determine the maximum of P as a continuous function of its argument and then look for the nearest lattice point (which is one of the 2^m possible lattice-point vertices of the cube surrounding the computed value of P). One of these gives the maximum. However, 2^m may be a large number, and it is preferable to find a better procedure for arriving at the maximum. This is accomplished by judicious choices of the lagrangian parameter. Recall that if we assume differentiability, a necessary condition for maximizing a function is the same as that for maximizing its logarithm. Thus we take $\log P$, add $\lambda \Sigma_{i=1}^{m} c_i n_i$ to it, put

$$\frac{\partial \log P}{\partial n_i} = 0$$

and solve for n_i. This gives

$$n_i = \frac{\log \{1/[1 - \log (1 - p_i)/\lambda c_i]\}}{\log (1 - p_i)}$$

By fixing λ, we obtain an estimate for n_i, $i = 1, \ldots, m$, expressed by this formula, from which $[n_i]$ one of the two integers nearest to n_i for each i is used as a trial solution.

As a more efficient approach, we use the above sufficiency theorem (Theorem 1-14). We first guess at a value of λ and obtain a solution $\bar{n}_i$, which is maximum for all n_i which satisfy

$$\Sigma c_i n_i \leq \Sigma c_i \bar{n}_i \leq C$$

Then we can pick or guess at another λ and improve the constraint condition, obtaining yet a better maximum. We continue this process, generating a reliability-vs.-cost curve which enables a decision-maker to choose according to a tradeoff between cost and reliability. By choosing the λ's sufficiently small so that only one n_i changes from one trial to another, we can tell where the best improvement in cost occurs. Note that if several n_i's change each time a new λ is chosen, it would be difficult to decide where the most favorable improvement in the n_i's toward the maximum is occurring. For problems involving a large number of variables, trial procedure is more economical than evaluating P at every corner of the cube.

Remark Relating to the foregoing example, one can show that a duality relation exists between maximizing

$$\prod_{i=1}^{m} f_i(n_i) \qquad \text{subject to} \qquad \sum_{i=1}^{m} C_i(n_i) = C$$

and minimizing

$$\sum_{i=1}^{m} C_i(n_i) \qquad \text{subject to} \qquad \prod_{i=1}^{m} f_i(n_i) = P$$

the latter being easier to treat since its objective function is a sum.

Exercise 1-30 Consider the problem of finding nonnegative integers x_i, $i = 1, \ldots, n$, which maximize

$$f(x_1, \ldots, x_n) = \sum_{i=1}^{n} \log \frac{a_i x_i}{a_i + x_i}$$

subject to

$$\prod_{i=1}^{n} x_i = C$$

Does f have properties which permit taking integer values nearest to the solution obtained through differentiation? Can Lagrange multipliers be used? Explain your approach to the solution of this problem. What would the situation be if one were to minimize $\prod_{i=1}^{n} x_i$ subject to $f(x_1, \ldots, x_n) = C$, thus interchanging the role of the constraint expression and f?

1-6 ASYMPTOTIC RESULTS

It is sometimes necessary and useful to work out the solution of a problem under the assumption that one or more variables are allowed to take on arbitrarily large values. Such an approach permits comparison of the limiting solutions of a discrete problem and those of its continuous embedding, should there be such embedding. The use of asymptotic expressions is illustrated by the problem of a mailman who must distribute the mail on both sides of an ordinary city street. If there are few houses and they are far apart he may cross the street back and forth in attempting to minimize the total distance traveled. However, as the number of houses becomes large on both sides, it is apparently better for the mailman to service all houses on one side first and then cross over to the other side to deliver his mail. His strategy ultimately depends only on the house positions. It would be an interesting exercise for the reader to work out his shortest route for a few typical configurations. In this problem the asymptotic case provides good ground for the use of intuition, giving twice the length of the street plus its width as the shortest distance traveled. This length is also an upper bound for the distances covered in all other cases. Several examples will occur in the book which illustrate the derivation and use of asymptotic results.

The following notation is sometimes found useful in connection with asymptotic and other limit problems. $f(x) = O(g(x))$ as $x \to x_0$ means that $|f(x)| < Ag(x)$ as $x \to x_0$ for some positive constant A. When no statement is given regarding $x \to x_0$, then the O notation means that the second statement holds everywhere. Thus $f(x) = O(1)$ means that $f(x)$ is a bounded function. We have

$$\sin x = O(|x|) \qquad (x+1)^2 = O(1) \qquad \text{as } x \to 0$$
$$\sin x = O(1) \qquad (x+1)^2 = O(x^2) \qquad \text{as } x \to \infty$$

To say that $f(x) = o(g(x))$ as $x \to x_0$ means that $f(x)/g(x) \to 0$ as $x \to x_0$. Thus for example

$$\sin x = o(x^2) \qquad x - 1 = o(x^2) \qquad \text{as } x \to \infty$$

The expression $o(1)$ denotes a function which tends to zero as $x \to x_0$. To say that $f(x) \sim g(x)$ as $x \to x_0$ means that $f(x)/g(x) \to 1$ as $x \to x_0$.

Example [15a] Suppose we are given a positive integer n and are asked to determine N, the maximum number of disjoint couples of positive integers with distinct sums all less than n. For example if $n = 10$ we have the three couples $(1,8)$, $(2,6)$, and $(3,4)$. None of the members of a couple occur in any other couple, and hence they are disjoint.

Solution In general since we have N couples, we have $2N$ numbers whose total sum is at least $1 + 2 + \cdots + 2N = N(2N + 1)$. Also from the statement of the problem this total sum is at most

$$(n - 1) + (n - 2) + \cdots + (n - N) = \frac{N}{2}(2n - N - 1)$$

These two relations give $N(2N + 1) \leq (N/2)(2n - N - 1)$ or $N \leq (2n - 3)/5$. Now if k is the largest integer in $n/5$, then the couples $(1,4k)$, $(3, 4k - 1)$, $(5, 4k - 2)$, $\ldots$, $(2k - 1, 3k + 1)$, and $(2,3k)$, $(4, 3k - 1)$, $(6, 3k - 2)$, $\ldots$, $(2k - 2, 2k + 2)$ are disjoint and have different sums. The sum of any couple is

$$2k - 1 + 3k + 1 = 5k < n$$

Since we have $2k - 1$ couples satisfying the conditions of the problem we conclude that

$$N \geq 2k - 1 \geq 2\left(\frac{n}{5} - 1\right) - 1 = \frac{2n}{5} - 3$$

This gives

$$\frac{2n}{5} - 3 \leq N \leq \frac{2n - 3}{5}$$

Now as n becomes arbitrarily large, N behaves as $2n/5$.   Thus we write

$$N = \frac{2n}{5} + O(1)$$

where $O(1)$ indicates a bounded function, which is constant in this case.   More strongly, we may also write $N \sim 2n/5$ as $n \to \infty$, since the ratio of these two quantities approaches 1 as $n \to \infty$.

1-7 EXAMPLES OF PROBLEMS

There are two general ways in which an optimization problem, particularly one in integers, may be stated.   The first is to present it in general qualitative terms as in the description of a physical or geometric problem.   For example, find the maximum number of dominoes, each covering two squares, needed to cover a chessboard with its bottom left-hand square and top right-hand square cut out.   For brevity, we shall classify such problems, which involve spacial relations between objects, as *geometric*.   Sometimes, it is possible to formulate such a problem algebraically, at other times not.   The second way in which an optimization problem may be stated is in an algebraic setting.   Here, the relations are reduced in terms of algebraic variables.   There is no clear line of demarcation between the two types.   Generally, one may prefer the algebraic formulation, but often geometry provides deeper insights.

PROBLEMS IN GEOMETRIC SETTING

The line-division problem   Divide a line, whose length is N units, into n segments with $n \leq N$, such that the length of each segment is an integral number of units and the product of the lengths of the segments is maximum.   Algebraically, if $x_1, \ldots, x_n$ are the lengths of the n parts, then the problem asks for positive integers x_i, $i = 1, \ldots, n$, which maximize $\Pi_{i=1}^{n} x_i$, subject to $\Sigma_{i=1}^{n} x_i = N$.   (See Chap. 4 for the solution of this problem.)

A coin-packing problem   What is the maximum number of identical coins, each of 1-in. diameter, which can be laid to cover the surface of a square table of 1 yd on the side so that no two coins overlap?

The coconut problem   There are n sailors who one night decide to divide a pile of coconuts in the morning.   During the night, a sailor wakes up and decides to take his share by himself.   He discards d_1 coconuts so that he can divide the rest by n and takes his share.   Later, another sailor wakes up and discards d_2 coconuts from the remaining pile, divides by n, and takes his share.   The process is repeated.   In all, $m - 1$

sailors took their share at night, sailor i, $i = 1, \ldots, m - 1$, discarding d_i coconuts to make the rest divisible by n. In the morning the n sailors together discarded d_m coconuts from the remaining pile and divided the rest among themselves equally. What is the minimum number of coconuts that could have been in the pile originally so that at the end each sailor would get at least one coconut [14]? (See Chap. 3 for the treatment of this problem.)

The bomber problem Given: n targets, distributed over a wide terrain. Each target has any one of three possible values, 1, 2, 3; the greater number corresponds to the higher value. An airplane with fixed gasoline capacity and a maximum payload of 8,000 lb wishes to bomb targets on a single mission and return to its base. There are three types of bombs: a 500-lb bomb, which can only destroy targets of value 1; a 1,000-lb bomb, which can destroy targets of value 1 or 2; and a 2,000-lb bomb, which can destroy targets of value 1, 2, or 3. The plane can carry no more than 12 bombs. The fuel consumption is proportional to the weight of the airplane, which depends on the weight of the unexpended bomb load and on the remaining fuel. It is assumed that a bombed target is completely destroyed. The optimum selection of targets determines the order in which bombs are loaded and later dropped. What type of bombs and what order of loading would produce the maximum total value of targets destroyed?

The counterfeit-coin problem Given: An equal-arm or equal-beam balance and a set of coins in which there is a single counterfeit coin. A weighing consists of balancing coins on one side against the same number of coins on the other side in search of the counterfeit coin. One must also determine whether the counterfeit coin is heavier or lighter. For a fixed number of weighings n, find the maximum number of coins from which the counterfeit may be identified and determined as heavier or lighter [5]. (See Chap. 3 for the treatment of this problem.)

The four-color problem What is the minimum number of colors needed to color the regions of an arbitrary planar map so that no two regions which have a boundary segment (not just a point) in common have the same color? What is the maximum number of regions which can be colored with four colors? (See Chap. 5 for an algebraic formulation of this problem, and see Chap. 2 for greater detail.)

The minimum-intersection problem A complete graph on n vertices drawn in the plane is the graph obtained by connecting every pair of the n vertices by a simple curve. Among all possible drawings, find the one with a minimum number of intersections of simple curves at points other than the n given vertices. Two simple curves may intersect at no more than a single point which is not a vertex. (See Chap. 2 for a treatment of this problem.)

PROBLEMS IN ALGEBRAIC SETTING

The personnel-assignment problem [26]   Given m persons, n jobs, and the expected productivity c_{ij} of the ith person on the jth job, find an assignment x_{ij} of the ith person to the jth job (whose value is either zero or one) for all i and j such that the total productivity $\Sigma_{j=1}^{n} \Sigma_{i=1}^{m} c_{ij}x_{ij}$ of the persons assigned is a maximum, subject to

$$\sum_{j=1}^{n} x_{ij} \leq a_i \qquad i = 1, \ldots, m$$

$$\sum_{i=1}^{m} x_{ij} \leq b_j \qquad j = 1, \ldots, n$$

where a_i is the number of persons in personnel category i, and b_j is the number of jobs in category j.

The transportation problem   Suppose that a homogeneous product is to be shipped from m origins to n destinations, each origin furnishing a stated amount of the item, and each destination requiring a stated amount, so that the total supply and total demand are equal. Let a_i be the amount available for shipment from origin i $(i = 1, \ldots, m)$, and let b_j be the amount required at destination j $(j = 1, \ldots, n)$; these are known quantities. Then

$$\sum_{i=1}^{m} a_i = \sum_{j=1}^{n} b_j$$

with $a_i, b_j \geq 0$ for all i and j.

Let x_{ij} be the unknown quantity to be shipped from the ith origin to the jth destination. Then

$$\sum_{j=1}^{n} x_{ij} = a_i \qquad i = 1, \ldots, m$$

$$\sum_{i=1}^{m} x_{ij} = b_j \qquad j = 1, \ldots, n$$

$$x_{ij} \geq 0 \qquad \text{for all } i \text{ and } j$$

Let c_{ij} be the cost of shipping a unit amount of the item from the ith origin to the jth destination. These values are also given. The problem is to find x_{ij} satisfying the above constraints which will minimize

$$\sum_{j=1}^{n} \sum_{i=1}^{m} c_{ij} x_{ij}$$

(See Chap. 5, for the solution of an example.)

The caterer's problem A caterer knows that in connection with the meals he has arranged to serve during the next n days, he will need $r_j(\geq 0)$ fresh napkins on the jth day, with $j = 1, 2, \ldots , n$. Laundering normally takes p days; i.e., a soiled napkin sent for laundering immediately after use on the jth day is returned in time to be used again on the $(j + p)$th day. However, the laundry also has a higher-cost service which returns the napkins in $q < p$ days (p and q are integers). Having no usable napkins on hand or in the laundry, the caterer will meet his early needs by purchasing napkins at a cents each. Laundering expense is b and c cents per napkin for the normal and high-cost service, respectively. How does he arrange matters to meet his needs and minimize his outlays for the n days [9]?

A procurement problem [23] Each naval ship has certain functions which it must perform with electronic equipment. We call a specific combination of a function and a ship an *activity*. Each activity j is authorized to receive up to its allowance of equipment units b_j, and, although a unit may be capable of performing more than one function, once installed, a unit is assumed to fill only one allowance position. There are m equipment types, and each type i is available for assignment in quantities a_i. The problem, then, is how should these available types be assigned to the fleet in the best way?

Suppose we hypothesize a set of values c_{ij} for each possible assignment situation, such that these values represent in an acceptable manner the military worth of the assignment of equipment of type i to activity j. These values are determined such that $c_{ij} > c_{kh}$ implies that assignment of one set of model i to activity j is preferable to the assignment of one set of model k to activity h and, furthermore, such that $c_{ij} = wc_{kh}, w > 0$, implies that the assignment i, j is w times more desirable than the assignment k, h.

Given a sum of money M and unit prices p_i for each unit of a type of equipment, how should the money be allocated to the equipment types to effect an optimum purchase? A good procurement plan must, of course, consider equipment which is in stock or on order and the manner in which the purchased equipment is to be used by the fleet. Thus procurement and allocation must be considered simultaneously. The problem is formulated as a linear program as follows: Find

$$\max \sum_i \sum_j c_{ij} x_{ij}$$

subject to the restraints

$$\sum_j x_{ij} \leq a_i + y_i$$

$$\sum_i x_{ij} \leq b_j$$

$$\sum_i p_i y_i \leq M$$

$x_{ij}, y_i \geq 0$ nonnegative integers

$i = 1, 2, \ldots, m$

$j = 1, 2, \ldots, n$

The y_i's represent quantities of each model that are to be purchased.

Smooth progression rule for optimal gradings in telephony [24,25]   The rule of "smooth progression" in telephone trunking for the determination of the best grading was proposed by G. F. O'Dell in 1927, and the grading schedules based on it were adopted by most telephone administrations throughout the world.

The grading arrangement consists of n groups, each with k contacts ("availability" k) and the total number R of trunks. The contacts in each group are ordered as first, second, . . . , and last (that is, kth) "choices." Contacts from different groups are interconnected along those choices to form individual, partial-common, and common trunks shared by one, more than one, and all groups, respectively (see Fig. 1-15).

This structure implies that $k \leq R \leq kn$, where the boundary cases $R = k$ and $R = kn$ correspond to the simple full availability groups and to n separate groups, respectively.

In order to determine the actual execution of grading, for given parameters n, k, and R, the number n of groups is factorized to give q factors f_i $(i = 1, \ldots, q)$, arranged in the increasing order

$$1 = f_1 < f_2 < \cdots < f_{q-1} < f_q = n$$

The choices are ordered into q classes according to the magnitude of f_i, all choices in the ith class having the same f_i, and each f_i is taken to be the number of contacts per trunk in the ith class $(i = 1, \ldots, q)$.

Fig. 1-15   Diagram for $n = 6$, $k = 10$, $R = 20$.

Hence, each choice within the ith class contains the same number of trunks (f_i-tuples), namely, n/f_i.

Let x_i ($i = 1, \ldots, q$) be the number of choices having f_i-tuples. Consequently, the total number of trunks is

$$\sum_{i=1}^{q} x_i \frac{n}{f_i} = R \quad \text{and} \quad \sum_{i=1}^{q} x_i = k$$

where $0 \le x_i \le k$, $i = 1, \ldots, q$. According to the rule of smooth progression, the best (optimum) grading is defined such that the sum of absolute consecutive differences

$$D = |x_1 - x_2| + |x_2 - x_3| + \cdots + |x_{q-1} - x_q|$$

is a minimum.

Tables of optimal solutions (for given k, n, R) were published by O'Dell, but the possibility of nonunique solutions was not mentioned. The existence and uniqueness of optimal solutions were examined by Syski. (See Chap. 4.)

An airline-crew-allocation problem An airline wishes to minimize the costs involved in allocating its crew to nonstop flights of airplanes between pairs of cities. The problem is to find the optimal allocation. The payoff matrix may be exhibited as follows

	Crew 1	Crew 2	Crew m
Flight 1	1	0	$\cdots$
Flight 2	0	1	$\cdots$
Flight 3	1	0	$\cdots$
$\cdots$			
Flight n	1	0	$\cdots$

Here we use 1 or 0 to indicate whether a crew is allocated to a flight or not, respectively. The cost of allocating crew j on the n flights is c_j, $j = 1, \ldots, m$. Since each flight requires just one crew, the sum of the elements in each row must equal unity. This type of problem has been solved by the method of cutting planes. According to H. Schipper, the typical solution time for a matrix of 350 rows and 3,000 columns on the IBM 7094 was about 45 min.

Tankers to meet a fixed schedule [4] The problem of determining the minimum number of tankers needed to meet a fixed schedule can be interpreted as a linear-programming problem of the transportation type.

The scheduling problem may be stated as follows:

Discharge points

		1			2			$\cdots$		j		
Pickup stations	1	t_{11}^1	t_{11}^2	$\cdots$ t_{11}^{k11}	t_{12}^1	t_{12}^2	$\cdots$ t_{12}^{k12}	$\cdots$	t_{1j}^1	t_{1j}^2	$\cdots$	t_{1j}^{k1j}
	2											
	p	t_{p1}^1	t_{p1}^2	$\cdots$ t_{p1}^{kp1}	t_{p2}^1	t_{p2}^2	$\cdots$ t_{p2}^{kp2}	$\cdots$	t_{pj}^1	t_{pj}^2	$\cdots$	t_{pj}^{kpj}

where p represents the pickup station, j represents the discharge point, k_{pj} represents the last entry in pj, and t_{pj} represents the time at which a tanker is to load fully at pickup point p and deliver to j. The t_{pj}'s are finite in number. Two arrays of positive numbers a_{pj} and b_{pj} are given, where a_{pj} represents the loading—traveling time from p to j—and b_{pj} represents the unloading—traveling time from j to p.

The problem is to arrange the numbers t_{pj} into S sequences, where each sequence is a schedule for one tanker such that the following conditions are met:

1. Each sequence is monotone increasing.
2. If $t_{p_1 j_1}^{k_1} < t_{p_2 j_2}^{k_2}$ are consecutive numbers in any one of the S sequences, then $t_{p_2 j_2}^{k_2} - t_{p_1 j_1}^{k_1} \geq a_{p_1 j_1} + b_{p_2 j_2}$, which says that the time used by a tanker loading at p_1 and traveling to j_1, plus the time used in unloading at j_1 and getting over to pickup point p_2, cannot be larger than the difference of the two pickup times.
3. S must be minimal.

The tanker problem can be reformulated as a linear-programming problem as follows: For convenience, let t_{pj}^k, a_{pj}, and b_{pj} be positive numbers. Define

$$T_{pj}^k = (t_{pj}^k + a_{pj})$$

as the time when a tanker loaded at p will arrive at j. Let $n_{\alpha p}$ be the number of tankers loading at p at time α, $N_{\beta j}$ be the number of tankers arriving at j at time β, and $X_{\alpha p \beta j}$ be the number of reassignments from j at time β to loading point p at time α. Then, for any schedule, the following inequalities will hold:

$$\sum_{\alpha, p} X_{\alpha p \beta j} \leq N_{\beta j}$$

$$\sum_{\beta, j} X_{\alpha p \beta j} \leq n_{\alpha p} \tag{1-4}$$

$$X_{\alpha p \beta j} \geq 0 \tag{1-5}$$

where $b_{pj} > \alpha - \beta$ implies that $X_{\alpha p \beta j} = 0$. Inequalities (1-4) can be made into system of equalities which is of the transportation type by introducing nonnegative slack variables $X_{\alpha p}$, $Y_{\beta j}$, and $Z = \Sigma_{\alpha,p}\Sigma_{\beta,j}X_{\alpha p \beta j}$. Inequalities (1-4) can now be written as

$$
\begin{aligned}
\sum_{\alpha,p} X_{\alpha p \beta j} + Y_{\beta j} &= N_{\beta j} & Y_{\beta j} &\geq 0 \\
\sum_{\beta,j} X_{\alpha p \beta j} + X_{\alpha p} &= n_{\alpha p} & X_{\alpha p} &\geq 0 \\
\sum_{\alpha,p} X_{\alpha p} + Z &= \sum_{\alpha,p} n_{\alpha p} & Z &\geq 0 \\
\sum_{\beta,j} Y_{\beta j} + Z &= \sum_{\beta,j} N_{\beta j}
\end{aligned}
\qquad (1\text{-}6)
$$

Thus, any schedule leads to an integral solution of inequalities (1-5) and Eqs. (1-6). Conversely, a schedule can be constructed from any integral solution of (1-5) and (1-6). The tanker-scheduling problem can be reduced to the problem of minimizing $\Sigma_{\alpha,p}X_{\alpha p}$ over the set of integral solutions of (1-5) and (1-6).

A schedule can be constructed from an integral solution in the following manner: $X_{\alpha p}$ is the number of tankers that start their individual schedules at time α from p; there will be $X_{\alpha p}$ sequences in the rearrangement, which have $t_{pj}{}^k = \alpha$ as a first member. Delete one such $t_{p_0 j_0}^{k_0} = \alpha_0$ from t; let $\beta_0 = T_{p_0 j_0}^{k_0} = \alpha_0 + a_{p_0 j_0}$. Since $N_{\beta_0 j_0} > 0$, at least one of the variables $X_{\alpha p \beta_0 j_0}$, $Y_{\beta_0 j_0}$ has a positive value. Select one of them.

Case 1   If $X_{\alpha_1 p_1 \beta_0 j_0} > 0$ is selected, then some $t_{p_1 j_1}^{k_1} = n_{\alpha_1 p_1} > 0$. Assign α_1 as a second member of the sequence. Strike out α_1 from t and reduce $X_{\alpha_1 p_1 \beta_0 j_0}$, $N_{\beta_0 j_0}$, $n_{\alpha_1 p_1}$ by one.

Case 2   If $Y_{\beta_0 j_0} > 0$ is selected, the sequence ends with α_0. Reduce $Y_{\beta_0 j_0}$, $N_{\beta_0 j_0}$ by one.

In case 1 let $\beta_1 = T_{p_1 j_1}^{k_1} = \alpha_1 + \alpha_{p_1 j_1}$, and examine the values of the variables $X_{\alpha p \beta_1 j_1}$, $Y_{\beta_1 j_1}$; one of these must be positive. Apply either case 1 or case 2, with α_1 playing the role of α_0. Repetition of this procedure must eventually end with the selection of some $Y_{\beta_k j_k} > 0$, thus completing one of the sequences. The other sequences can be obtained in the same manner.

The problem of satellite communication   Consider Telstar-type relay satellites, whose time of availability over any communication complex of cities is given according to a schedule. (The Syncom-type fixed-satellite problem is an easier special case of this model [21].)

The problem is to allocate satellite time to pairs of stations for communication purposes. Each such pair is referred to as a *link*. The times in which a satellite, for each of its orbits, is visible to a link are given. The satellites consist of a given number of duplex (two-way-communication) transmitters, where each transmitter has an assigned channel capacity. The communication requirements of a link are given in terms of transmitters and the time of day. A station can use a satellite for communication with another station through the use of any number of the satellite's transmitters. However, the satellite may be simultaneously used by other links through the remaining transmitters. A satellite is tracked by a radar antenna, and a single antenna cannot track two satellites simultaneously. More than a single satellite may be used simultaneously by a single link if additional tracking equipment is available. An extra antenna is prepared to track the next-assigned satellite coming into radar view if it is necessary to continue communication. We assume that each link has an adequate number of antennas, and that each has an adequate number of transceivers to meet the allocation program. (This problem will be formulated in Chap. 5 as an integer-optimization problem.)

REFERENCES

1. Box, G. E. P., and K. B. Wilson: On the Experimental Attainment of Optimum Conditions, *J. Roy. Stat. Soc.*, ser. B, p. 13, 1951.
2. Box, G. E. P.: The Exploration and Exploitation of Response Surfaces, *Biometrics*, vol. 10, 1954.
3. Cloud, J. D., and William D. Jackson: Number of Fibonacci Numbers Not Exceeding N, *Am. Math. Monthly*, p. 798, September, 1964.
4. Dantzig, G. B., and D. R. Fulkerson: Minimizing the Number of Tankers to Meet a Fixed Schedule, *Naval Res. Log. Quart.*, vol. 1, no. 3, September, 1954.
4a. Dorn, W. S.: Lagrange Multipliers and Inequalities, *Operations Res.*, vol. 9, no. 1, pp. 95–104, January–February, 1961.
4b. Everett, III, Hugh: Generalized Lagrange Multiplier Method for Solving Problems of Optimum Allocation of Resources, *Operations Res.*, vol. 11, no. 3, pp. 399–417, May–June, 1963.
5. Fine, N. J.: The Generalized Coin Problem, *Am. Math. Monthly*, pp. 489–491, October, 1947.
6. Gelfand, I. M.: "The Method of Coordinates," Library School of Mathematics, The M.I.T. Press, Cambridge, Mass., 1966.
7. Golomb, S. W., and M. S. Klamkin: N Objects in B Boxes, *Am. Math. Monthly*, vol. 60, pp. 552–553, October, 1953.
8. Hadwiger, Hugo, and Hans Debrunner: "Combinatorial Geometry in the Plane," Holt, Rinehart and Winston, Inc., New York, 1964.
9. Jacobs, W. W.: The Caterer Problem, *Naval Res. Log. Quart.*, vol. 1, pp. 154–165, 1954.
10. Johnson, R. A.: Relating to a Problem in Minima, *Am. Math. Monthly*, vol. 24, pp. 243–244, 1917.
11. Johnson, S. M.: Optimal Search for a Maximum is Fibonaccian, *Rand Corp. Rept.* P-856, 1956.
12. Kaplan, Seymour: Solution of the Lorie-Savage and Similar Integer Programming

Problems by the Generalized Lagrange Multiplier Method, *Operations Res.*, vol. 14, no. 6, pp. 1130–1136, 1966.

13. Kiefer, J.: Sequential Minimax Search for a Maximum, *Proc. Am. Math. Soc.*, vol. 4, p. 502, 1953.

14. Kirchner, Roger B.: The Generalized Coconut Problem, *Am. Math. Monthly*, pp. 516–518, June–July, 1960.

15. Klamkin, M. S.: Quickie Number 264, *Math. Mag.*, pp. 175–176, 1960.

15a. Klamkin, M. S., and D. J. Newman: Some Combinatorial Problems of Arithmetic, *Math. Mag.* vol. 42, pp. 53–56, March, 1969.

16. Konhauser, Joseph D. E., J. L. Brown, and David Chale: Greatest of Three, *Math. Mag.*, pp. 187–189, May–June, 1962.

17. Kuhn, H. W., and A. W. Tucker: Non-linear Programming, in J. Neyman (ed.), "Proceedings of the Second Berkeley Symposium on Mathematical Statistics and Probability," University of California Press, Berkeley, Calif., 1951.

17a. Krolak, D. Patrick: Further Extensions of Fibonaccian Search to Nonlinear Programming Problems, *SIAM J. Control*, vol. 6, no. 2, 1968.

18. Lennes, N. J.: Note on Maxima and Minima by Algebraic Methods, *Am. Math. Monthly*, vol. 17, pp. 9–10, 1910.

19. MacDonald, Jr., J. E., and J. Cohen: An Inequality, *Am. Math. Monthly*, pp. 914–915, October, 1964.

20. Moser, Leo, and B. R. Toskey: Minimum Number of Distinct Values Assumed by a Sum, *Am. Math. Monthly*, p. 670, June–July, 1963.

20a. Newman, D. J., and D. L. Silverman: Rectangular Rugs in a Square Room, *Am. Math. Monthly*, pp. 209–210, February, 1964.

20b. Ponstein, J.: Seven Types of Convexity, *SIAM Rev.*, vol. 9, no. 1, January, 1967.

21. Saaty, T. L., and G. Suzuki: A Nonlinear Programming Model in Optimum Communication Satellite Use, *SIAM Rev.*, vol. 7, pp. 403–407, July, 1965.

22. Saaty, T. L., and Joseph Bram: "Nonlinear Mathematics," McGraw-Hill Book Company, New York, 1964.

23. Suzuki, George: Procurement and Allocation of Naval Electronic Equipments, *Naval Res. Log. Quart.*, vol. 4, no. 1, pp. 1–7, March, 1957.

24. Syski, R.: *Algebraic Properties of Optimum Gradings*, 3d Intern. Teletraffic Cong., Paris, 1961.

25. Syski, R.: "Introduction to Congestion Theory," Oliver and Boyd Ltd., London, 1960.

26. Votaw, D. F.: Methods of Solving Some Personnel-Classification Problems, *Psychometrika*, vol. 17, no. 3, pp. 255–265, 1952.

27. Wagstaff, Ronald: The Maximum of $\Sigma_{i,j=1}^{n} a_i b_j$, *Am. Math. Monthly*, pp. 46–47, January–February, 1964.

28. Wilde, Douglass J.: "Optimum Seeking Methods," Prentice-Hall, Inc., Englewood Cliffs, N.J., 1964.

2
Methods of Geometric Optimization

2-1 INTRODUCTION

Optimization or extremal problems may be regarded abstractly in terms of sets and transformations on sets. The usual problem is to find, for a specified domain of a transformation, a maximal element of the range set. The range set is frequently a set of real numbers. Sometimes the problem is the opposite one: Given certain constraints on the range set, it is desired to determine a certain maximal or minimal property, in some sense, of the domain set which allows it to be mapped into the range set. Naturally, all transformations may be applied to map a set into itself or into subsets.

The reader may wish to familiarize himself with some general topics where extremal problems occur in geometry by examining Table 2-1, which, for the most part, is self-explanatory. Some discussion will be provided at the beginnings of the sections throughout this chapter.

Our purpose here, of course, is to study problems involving discrete optimization—i.e., queries of the type: there are at least or at most (a minimum or a maximum) so many objects of a certain kind—and to indicate methods for determining such values, whether exactly, approximately, or asymptotically.   Thus, in general, we shall be seeking upper and lower bounds and minimum and maximum values of a function given on appropriately defined sets to the reals.   Needless to say, rarely is such a function given in explicit form.   By appropriate estimation procedures, one is able to converge on the exact answer.   (See, for example, Sec. 2-8 on the packing of circles in the plane.)

In Sec. 2-2 we give some examples which utilize symmetry arguments to deduce the optimum.   Apart from the special use of symmetry or the casting of a problem (whenever possible) in one of the standard algebraic forms, there is no single direct method for formulating and solving a geometric problem which involves optimization.   The analysis of a variety of examples is itself a powerful tool for treating newly arising problems.

Not all the extensive topics given in Table 2-1 can be adequately treated in one chapter.   Since variety and a broad view are our purpose, we shall proceed by using interesting examples.   A wide list of references is included for those who wish to pursue the subject further.

2-2 SYMMETRY IN OPTIMIZATION

The presence of symmetry is basic to the solution of many problems which otherwise would be difficult to solve.   On occasion, a problem without symmetry may be embedded in a larger problem which has symmetry properties and which leads to the solution of the nonsymmetric problem.   The embedded problem inherits its solution from the larger problem, which may be regarded as an extension of it.   Perhaps a useful motto to remember is: *To maximize or minimize, symmetrize.*

Example   Consider a game on a rectangular board.   Two players alternate in placing a penny on the board without overlap.   Whoever, in his turn, places the last penny in an available space wins.   How?

Solution   It is clear that whoever goes first and places his penny at the center can win.   He does this by thereafter placing each penny in a symmetric position with the other player's last-placed penny, that is, on a line passing through the centers of the board and of the last-placed penny, and at an equal distance on the other side of the center.   Of course, there are other types of symmetry which also enable him to win.

Exercise 2-1   Mention two other strategies, utilizing symmetry, to win this game.

Example   Given an equilateral triangle, consider a simple curve which must start at some point on one side and terminate at some point on another side.   It is desired to determine the shape of the curve of minimum length, which bisects the area of the triangle [85].

Table 2-1 Optimization in discrete geometry

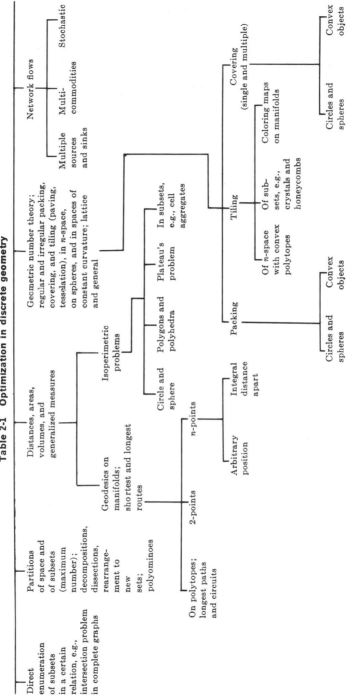

Solution   Suppose we draw the bisecting curve.   We reflect the triangle about one of the two sides containing an end point of the curve.   Next we reflect the image about the side containing the other end point, and then reflect this image, and so on, obtaining a hexagon.   The curve now becomes a closed curve inside the hexagon (see Fig. 2-1).   This curve divides the area of the hexagon in two equal halves. The curve of minimum length which contains half the area of the hexagon is a circle concentric with it.   Thus the desired curve is an arc of a circle.   (See Theorem 2-6 for this property of the circle.)

Exercise 2-2   Determine the shape of a simple, closed curve of minimum length, contained inside an equilateral triangle, which encloses half the area of the triangle. Use an argument of continuity with respect to the area enclosed by the curve.

Yet another example of symmetry in optimization is given by the fair-division problem (treated in Chap. 3), where a cake is to be divided into n pieces among n people so that each one receives what he considers his fair share.   This is indeed an example of optimization, although at first glance it does not seem to be either a maximization or a minimization problem.

Example   (Neither too much nor too little)   Given: A cup of coffee and a cup of milk, each having the same amount of liquid.   A spoonful of milk is transferred into the coffee cup, and, after mixing thoroughly until the mixture is homogeneous, a spoonful of this mixture is transferred back into the milk cup.   Show that there is the same amount of milk in the coffee cup as there is coffee in the milk cup.
Solution   One can give an analytical proof, involving the fraction of milk in the coffee cup (which is also the fraction in the spoonful to be transferred) and the fraction of coffee in the milk cup.

An easy symmetric proof which does not depend on the homogeneous mixing is as follows: Since at the end both cups have the same amount of fluid, whatever amount of milk has replaced coffee in the coffee cup must have been replaced by an equal amount of coffee in the milk cup.

Example (application of a reflection principle [43,44])   Suppose we are given a polygon and some point on one of its sides, and are asked to find the shortest path which starts at the given point, touches some or all other sides, and then returns to the starting point.   How would we find the path?
Solution   The answer is not obtained by dropping successive perpendiculars, but rather by reflecting the polygon about the first side to be touched after the starting point, and then reflecting the image about the second side to be touched, and so

Fig. 2-1

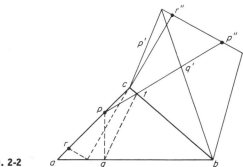

Fig. 2-2

on, to the last side to be touched.   If we consider the figure obtained by the original polygon and all its reflections, and mark the image of the starting point in the last polygonal image, we can obtain the answer.   We draw a straight line joining the starting point with its final image.   If the line intersects each image polygon, we can take the reflection of this line back in the original polygon and obtain the desired answer.   If this procedure misses some polygon, or if part of the line falls outside the configuration, shortest-line segments are drawn appropriately from the initial point to its terminal image.

The same procedure may be applied to drawing a shortest path touching different faces of a polyhedron by appropriate reflections of the polyhedron about the faces in the required sequence.   In Fig. 2-2 the triangle abc has been reflected, first about bc, then about the image of ab.   The segment pp'' lies inside the figure, and its reflection in abc gives the desired shortest path which locates the point t on the original triangle.   If the starting point had been r, then the segment rr'' would lie outside the figure.   In that case, the shortest path would consist of the segment rc, followed by the reflection of the segment cr''.

Exercise 2-3   Assign coordinates to the vertices of the above triangle, and use the calculus to formulate the foregoing problem in order to see how messy things can get.

Exercise 2-4   Tackle the problem of finding the shortest path which starts at a given point of a polygon and touches a prescribed number of sides, without returning to the starting point.

Exercise 2-5 [54a]   How would one find the shortest distance between two points on the surface of a polyhedron (for a definition, see Sec. 2-3), a cone, and a cylinder. (For the cylinder, the answer is an arc of a helix which winds around the cylinder, passing through the given points.)
Hint: Flatten the figures out on the plane.

SYMMETRY IN COUNTING

The use of symmetry in counting is powerfully illustrated by the following elementary example.

Example   Find the number of paths in the array in Fig. 2-3 which spell the word "MATHEMATICIAN" [66].

```
                              M
                            M A M
                          M A T A M
                        M A T H T A M
                      M A T H E H T A M
                    M A T H E M E H T A M
                  M A T H E M A M E H T A M
                M A T H E M A T A M E H T A M
              M A T H E M A T I T A M E H T A M
            M A T H E M A T I C I T A M E H T A M
          M A T H E M A T I C I C I T A M E H T A M
        M A T H E M A T I C I A I C I T A M E H T A M
      M A T H E M A T I C I A N A I C I T A M E H T A M
```

Fig. 2-3

Solution 1 One may count paths "backward" from the N. In counting the left half of the array, including the center column, there are two choices for each backward step. Thus, this portion yields 2^{12} paths. Doubling this number and subtracting the center column, which was counted twice, yields $2^{13} - 1 = 8{,}191$ paths.

Solution 2 Every path must originate on a "boundary M" and terminate at the unique N. The paths lying completely in the left half of the array (including the vertical path) correspond one-to-one with the words of twelve letters, each of which is chosen from the pair (H,V), where H stands for *horizontal* and V for *vertical*. The number of these is $2^{12} = 4{,}096$. Similarly, the paths lying completely in the right half of the array (excluding the vertical path) are found to number $2^{12} - 1 = 4{,}095$. Thus, the total number of distinct paths is 8,191, since every path lies completely in one-half of the array.

Example An elementary example of the use of symmetry is given by Gauss' derivation of the sum of n numbers which form an arithmetic series. Thus,

$$1 + 2 + 3 + \cdots + n$$

plus (by writing the sum backward)

$$n + (n - 1) + (n - 2) + \cdots + 1$$

yield, on adding each term of the lower sum to the term immediately above it in the upper sum,

$$(n + 1) + (n + 1) + \cdots + (n + 1) = n(n + 1)$$

from which the sum itself is given by $n(n + 1)/2$.

Geometrically, symmetry may be used to transform a nonsymmetric convex figure into a symmetric one. This process is usually done with respect to a point, a line, a plane, etc., if one goes to higher dimensions. In the plane, symmetry with respect to a line or fixed axis of symmetry L replaces a convex figure by a new one as follows: Each chord C (line segment whose end points lie on the convex boundary curve) of the figure that is perpendicular to L is displaced along its length to a new position that is symmetric with respect to L, i.e., until it intersects L

at its midpoint. The result is a figure which is symmetric with respect to L.

A method frequently used to symmetrize a convex figure with respect to a point is to consider the strip determined by two parallel lines tangent to the boundary of the figure and replace it by a new strip which is perpendicular to it, whose lines are equidistant from some point used for establishing symmetry. If the process were to be repeated for the infinite number of possible pairs of parallel strips, the intersection of these would yield a convex figure which is symmetric with respect to the point. (Other concepts of symmetry will occur throughout this chapter in different contexts.)

2-3 POLYGONS AND POLYHEDRA

In this section we are mainly concerned with definitions of polygons and polyhedra, concepts which will occur frequently throughout the chapter. We shall also take this opportunity to examine Euler's formula, which will be needed in several places, particularly in relation to graphs and maps. We also exploit this knowledge to give bounds on iterations of linear-optimization problems, for which the constraint set is polyhedral in shape. A number of optimization questions relating to polyhedra will be examined in the appropriate sections, relating to Table 2-1.

Definition A polygon is a finite set of segments such that exactly two segments meet at every end point of each segment and no subset of segments has this property. The segments are called the *sides* or *edges* of the polygon, and the end points are called its *vertices*. In a plane polygon one can associate with each vertex an angle describing the change in direction of a point moving along the edges and returning to its starting position.

Definition A polygon is regular if all its edges and angles are equal.

Definition A polyhedron in 3-space is a finite set of polygons such that every edge of a polygon belongs to exactly one other polygon and no subset of polygons has the same property. The polygons are the faces of the polyhedron; their edges and vertices are the edges and vertices of the polyhedron.

With each vertex of a polyhedron, we can associate a figure (which generally is a skewed polygon), generated by the lines joining the midpoints of each pair of edges of a face, meeting at that vertex. A polyhedron is regular if all such vertex figures and all the faces of the polyhedron are regular.

Definition   A set of points in n-space whose coordinates satisfy a linear equation

$$a_1x_1 + \cdots + a_nx_n = b$$

where not all a_i, $i = 1, \ldots, n$, are zero, a_i and b real, is called a *hyperplane* or an $(n-1)$-*dimensional subspace*.

Definition   A convex polytope in n-space is the convex hull of a finite set of points, not all of which belong to a hyperplane.

Definition   A simplex is the convex hull of $(n + 1)$ points in n-space, not all of which belong to a hyperplane.

We have already encountered (in the preface) ideas leading to the following theorem.

Theorem 2-1   *There are, at most, five regular convex polyhedra in three-dimensional space.*

Figure 2-4 shows that there are at least five such polyhedra.

Exercise 2-6   Prove this theorem by considering regular triangles, squares, and pentagons which have a vertex in common.   How many can be crowded around such a point without overlap?   Can one do with less at each vertex of a regular polyhedron?

Tetrahedron   Octahedron   Hexahedron

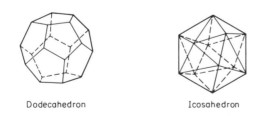

Dodecahedron   Icosahedron

Fig. 2-4   The five regular convex polyhedra in three dimensions.

Remark   There are four nonconvex regular polyhedra.   The faces in each are regular triangles.

Some properties of convex polyheda are useful in the analysis of optimization problems.   The constraints of a problem may give rise to such a convex set.   For example, in linear programming the set S, defined by the constraints

$$\sum_{j=1}^{n} a_{ij}x_j \leq b_i \qquad i = 1, \ldots, m$$

$$x_j \geq 0 \qquad j = 1, \ldots, n$$

is the intersection of half-spaces.   It is a convex polyhedral set. (See also Chap. 5.)

Exercise 2-7   Demonstrate that the intersection of half-spaces whose boundaries are linear is a convex set whose boundary is a polyhedron which may be open.

EULER'S RELATION

We will now examine some bounds on the relationships between the vertices V, edges E, and faces F of a closed polyhedron in 3-space.   It is easy to prove that Euler's formula

$$V - E + F = 2$$

always holds for such a polyhedron.

Exercise 2-8   Prove this relation by cutting out a face, flattening on a plane without overlap, and noting that $V - E + F$ does not change if two vertices in a region are connected by an edge or if a new vertex is added and connected to each of two existing vertices with an edge.   The inverse operations of the foregoing also do not change $V - E + F$.   Reduce to a triangle, for which $V - E + F = 1$.   The cut-out face makes the right side equal to 2 for the polyhedron.

Euler's relation gives a functional dependence of the number of faces of a dimension on the number of faces of the other two dimensions.   Note that, in order to have a polyhedron, at least three edges must meet at a vertex.   Since each edge joins two vertices it follows that

$$3V \leq 2E$$

i.e., twice the number of edges is at least equal to three times the number of vertices.   This bound is fine and cannot be improved.   Equality holds for the tetrahedron with $V = 4$ and $E = 6$.   Since $V = E + 2 - F$, we have $3(E + 2 - F) \leq 2E$ or

$$E \leq 3F - 6$$

Similarly, each face of a polyhedron is bounded by three edges, and each edge is on the boundary of two faces. This gives

$$3F \leq 2E$$

Again we have

$$E \leq 3V - 6$$

Finally, from $3V \leq 2E$ and $E \leq 3F - 6$, we have

$$V \leq 2F - 4$$

Similarly,

$$F \leq 2V - 4$$

Thus we have six fine bounds and one exact relation between the faces of a polyhedron.

A polyhedron must have *at least* one face, with no more than five edges. Otherwise, if every face has at least six, then $6F \leq 2E$; thus, because $E \leq 3F - 6$, we have $-6 \geq 0$—a contradiction. If a polyhedron has less than 12 faces, then *at least* one face has less than five edges. Otherwise, $5F \leq 2E$; thus, because $E \leq 3F - 6$, we have $F \geq 12$, which is a contradiction.

If F_i, $i = 0, 1, \ldots, n - 1$, denotes the number of ith-dimensional faces of a polytope in n-space, then Euler's formula has the following generalization:

$$\sum_{i=0}^{n-1} (-1)^i F_i = 1 - (-1)^n \qquad n = 1, 2, \ldots$$

One of the methods used to solve a linear-programming problem in n variables is the simplex process (see Chap. 5). It is a systematic method of seeking a vertex of the polyhedral set in n-space, which yields the optimum of a linear form. Thus, an upper bound on the number of vertices may serve as a useful estimate for the maximum amount of time which may be needed to solve such a problem. Since the number of constraints determines the number of faces of the polyhedral set, it is useful to give the upper bound on the number of vertices F_0 in terms of the number of highest-dimensional faces F_{n-1}. We have, as a partly proved (for some n), partly conjectural bound, given in the form of binominal coefficients [32],

$$F_0 \leq \binom{F_{n-1} - \left[\frac{n+1}{2}\right]}{F_{n-1} - n} + \binom{F_{n-1} - \left[\frac{n+2}{2}\right]}{F_{n-1} - n}$$

As a reminder, here $[x]$ is the greatest integer $\leq x$.

Problem   Find a polyhedral solid, of uniform material, with the smallest number of faces, which is stable on one face only; i.e., it can rest on only one face without falling under the influence of gravity.   M. Goldberg has found one with 21 faces. Roughly, it is a cylinder sliced at both ends at a skewed angle, and its cylindrical surface is gently flattened along its length into 19 polygons of gradually decreasing sizes.   The example has not been published at the date of this writing.

2-4 PARTITIONS OR DECOMPOSITIONS

This section will be occupied with several elementary examples of geometric problems involving partitions.   The object is either to find the maximum number of parts produced by a partition or to find the minimum number of partitions which yield a prescribed number of parts. A wide class of related problems, which are briefly described here, are not optimization problems.   In these one seeks to determine conditions under which one configuration may be decomposed or dissected into another.

The statement of such optimization problems frequently requires finding an extremum without being directly asked for it.   For our purpose, we shall turn the statements of these problems to direct statements of optimization.   To illustrate, consider the following problem: "What is the number of parts obtained by dividing 3-space with n planes in arbitrary position?   Any three of these planes meet at exactly one point, but four or more do not."   This problem may be stated along the following lines [50a].

Theorem 2-2   *The maximum number of parts into which n planes in general position divide 3-space is $(n + 1)(n^2 - n + 6)/6$.*

Two lemmas are needed.   The proof of the first lemma is obvious.

Lemma 2-1   *A straight line is divided by n points into $n + 1$ parts.*

Exercise 2-9   Supply the proof of this lemma.

Lemma 2-2   *The maximum number of parts into which n lines divide a plane is $(n^2 + n + 2)/2$.*

Proof   If x_n is the maximum number of parts into which n lines divide a plane, and if x_{n+1} is the maximum for $n + 1$ lines, then since any line intersects the remaining n lines in n points, by Lemma 2-1 a line is divided into $n + 1$ parts by the other n lines.   Since each of these parts must be the boundary of two planar parts—an old one generated by the n lines and a new one generated by adding the $n + 1$st line—

we have $n + 1$ new planar parts. This gives

$$x_{n+1} = x_n + n + 1$$

from which we have

$$x_n = x_{n-1} + n$$
$$x_{n-1} = x_{n-2} + n - 1$$
$$\cdot \ \cdot \ \cdot \ \cdot \ \cdot \ \cdot \ \cdot \ \cdot \ \cdot \ \cdot \ \cdot \ \cdot$$
$$x_2 = x_1 + 2$$

It is clear that $x_1 = 2$. Thus,

$$x_n = x_1 + n + (n - 1) + \cdots + 2 = 1 + \sum_{i=1}^{n} i$$
$$= 1 + \frac{n(n + 1)}{2} = \frac{n^2 + n + 2}{2}$$

Proof of Theorem 2-2   Let y_n be the maximum number of parts into which n planes divide 3-space, and let y_{n+1} be the corresponding number for $n + 1$ planes. Any of the planes intersects the remaining n in n lines. By Lemma 2-2, these lines divide the plane into $(n^2 + n + 2)/2$ parts, each of which is the boundary of an old and a new part of space. This gives $(n^2 + n + 2)/2$ additional parts of space. Thus,

$$y_{n+1} = y_n + \frac{n^2 + n + 2}{2}$$

and because $y_1 = 2$ we obtain, by recursion and simplification,

$$y_n = \frac{(n + 1)(n^2 - n + 6)}{6}$$

Exercise 2-10   Prove that a straight line is divided into $2n + 1$ parts by n circles (i.e., by n pairs of points), and that n pairs of points divide a circle into $2n$ parts.

Exercise 2-11   Prove that a plane and the surface of a sphere are each divided by n pairwise intersecting circles into $n^2 - n + 2$ parts.

Exercise 2-12   Prove that space is divided by n spheres into a maximum of $n(n^2 - 3n + 8)/3$ parts. Instead of asking for the maximum, one may require that every pair of spheres should intersect.

Exercise 2-13   Six points are in general position in 3-space (no three in a line, no four in a plane). Each of the 15 line segments joining them in pairs is drawn with either a red or a blue color. Prove that some triangle has all its sides of the same color.

Alternative statement   Prove that at a gathering of any six people, three of them are either mutual acquaintances or complete strangers to each other.

Consider n points in a plane, no three of which are collinear. Let each of these points correspond to one of n individuals. If two individuals are acquainted, the corresponding pair of points is joined by a line segment, otherwise not. A full triangle is a triangle, all of whose vertex pairs are connected, indicating that every pair corresponds to individuals who are acquainted. An empty triangle is a set of three points, none of which are connected, indicating that every pair corresponds to individuals who are strangers. We have the following theorem.

Theorem 2-3 (Goodman) *Let E and F be the number of empty and full triangles, respectively. Then, in any configuration of n points* [31],

$$
E + F \geq
\begin{cases}
\dfrac{u(u-1)(u-2)}{3} & \text{if } n \geq 2u \\[2mm]
\dfrac{2u(u-1)(4u+1)}{3} & \text{if } n \geq 4u+1 \\[2mm]
\dfrac{2u(u+1)(4u-1)}{3} & \text{if } n = 4u+3
\end{cases}
$$

where u is a nonnegative integer. This lower bound is sharp for each positive integer n.

This theorem has not been generalized as yet to the case of full and empty quadrilaterals and figures of a higher number of sides.

A cube problem Suppose it is desired to divide a cube, whose side is p in., into p^3 small cubes, each with 1-in. sides by planar cuts of a knife. The cut pieces may be arranged side by side in any convenient manner before the next cut is made. What is the minimum number of cuts? Note that if $p = 2$, then three cuts are needed. If $p = 3$, six cuts are needed. If $p = 4$, one cut may be made vertically along a middle line of the top face, and then the two pieces are stacked for the next cut; thus, one obtains four slabs, each of dimension 4^2, etc., giving six cuts [89].

This problem is a special case of the following theorem.

Theorem 2-4 *The minimum number of planar cuts of a rectangular parallelepiped of dimensions p, q, and r into pqr unit cubes is $\alpha + \beta + \gamma$, where α, β, and γ are the minimum integers such that*

$$
2^{\alpha-1} \leq p \leq 2^{\alpha} \qquad 2^{\beta-1} \leq q \leq 2^{\beta} \qquad 2^{\gamma-1} \leq r \leq 2^{\gamma}
$$

Proof Note, by considering similar cuts of a straight line, that at least n cuts are necessary to obtain 2^n distinct segments. This is done by cutting in half, stacking the two pieces, then cutting in half and stacking the remaining pieces, cutting in half, and so on. Now if $p = 2^\alpha$, $q = 2^\beta$, $r = 2^\gamma$, then, to obtain $pqr = 2^{\alpha+\beta+\gamma}$ pieces, at least $\alpha + \beta + \gamma$ cuts are necessary. In general, if any of p, q, or r is not expressible as a power of 2, the parallelepiped may be considered as a part of a larger one, whose sides are the nearest powers of 2, which are, of course, α, β, and γ. Thus, at most $\alpha + \beta + \gamma$ cuts are required for the given parallepiped. To show that it is minimal, we reason by induction. Assume that it is true for every parallelepiped which is smaller than the given one. Suppose that the first optimal cut of the given parallelepiped divides p into two parts, p_1 and p_2, as equal as possible. Then the minimum number of cuts [denoted by $A(x,y,z)$ for a parallelepiped with sides x, y, z] satisfies the following relation (at least):

$$A(p,q,r) \geq 1 + \max \{A(p_1,q,r), A(p_2,q,r)\}$$
$$= 1 + A\left(\left[\frac{p}{2}\right], q,r\right) = 1 + [(\alpha - 1) + \beta + \gamma]$$
$$= \alpha + \beta + \gamma$$

where $[p/2]$ is the nearest integer greater than $p/2$. Since $A(p,q,r)$ is at most and at least $\alpha + \beta + \gamma$, we have equality. This completes the proof.

Exercise 2-14 Trivially conclude the result for cutting rectangles.

Exercise 2-15 Attempt a generalization to a four-dimensional cube.

EQUIDECOMPOSITION [7]

A polygon is cut (decomposed) along a straight line into two pieces. Each piece may then be similarly cut. A polyhedron is cut into two pieces by a planar section.

If a figure can be decomposed and rearranged into another figure, the two figures are said to be *equidecomposable*. A theorem of Bolyai-Gerwin asserts that two polygons whose areas are equal are equidecomposable.

To produce a figure which has a central symmetry with respect to another figure, we choose a point called the *center* outside the given figure and draw a line from each point of the figure through the center. We determine a point whose distance on the opposite side of the center is the same as that of the given point from which the line is drawn. The totality of such points yields a figure which is centrally symmetric with respect to the original figure. The theorem of Hadwiger-Glur asserts that any two polygons whose areas are the same may be so decomposed that each piece of one may be obtained from a corresponding piece of the other by a translation in a parallel direction or by central symmetry.

A necessary and sufficient condition that equidecomposability hold between a convex polygon and a square is that the polygon be symmetric about a point.

A dihedral angle in a polyhedron is the angle subtended between two faces inside the polyhedron at their common edge. The angle is measured between the two lines of intersection of the faces with a plane perpendicular to this edge.

Let α_i, $i = 1, \ldots, p$, denote the radian measure of the dihedral angles of a polyhedron P, $d_1, \ldots, d_p$, the lengths of the corresponding edges, and define $f(P) = \Sigma_{i=1}^{p} d_i f(\alpha_i)$ for some choice of $f(\alpha_i)$, where f satisfies the special additivity relation $\Sigma_{i=1}^{p} k_i f(\alpha_i) = 0$, whenever $\Sigma_{i=1}^{p} k_i \alpha_i = 0$ is satisfied (i.e., whenever the α_i are linearly dependent for some choice of nonzero integers k_i, $i = 1, \ldots, p$). The function $f(P)$ is called an invariant of P. It depends on P and on the choice of $f(\alpha_i)$, $i = 1, \ldots, p$. Hadwiger proved that two polyhedra P and Q, with corresponding dihedral angles $\alpha_i (i = 1, \ldots, p)$ and $\beta_j (j = 1, \ldots, q)$, are not equidecomposable if there is an f which is additive on $\alpha_1, \ldots, \alpha_p$, $\beta_1, \ldots, \beta_q$, π and satisfies $f(\pi) = 0$, $f(P) \neq f(Q)$. This theorem can be generalized to polyhedra in n-space, where the dihedral angle is defined at each $(n - 2)$ dimensional face. Every such face is the intersection of exactly two $(n - 1)$-dimensional faces.

Theorem 2-5   (Dehn)   *A regular tetrahedron cannot be cut with planar cuts into a finite number of pieces and reassembled into a cube* [7].

Remark   There are some irregular tetrahedra which can be so divided and reassembled.

Proof   The dihedral angle of a cube is equal to $\pi/2$. We denote the dihedral angle of the regular tetrahedron by φ. To use Hadwiger's theorem we need the angles $\pi/2$, φ, π. If $k_1 \pi/2 + k_2 \varphi + k_3 \pi = 0$ where $k_i = 1, 2, 3$ are integers, then also $(k_1 + 2k_3)\pi + 2k_2 \varphi = 0$ and we have a linear dependence between π and φ. However, it is known that for a tetrahedron $\cos \varphi = \frac{1}{3}$ and consequently it can be shown that π and φ are incommensurable (i.e., cannot be rational multiples of each other). Thus $k_1 + 2k_3 = 0$, $k_2 = 0$, and substituting above we have $k_3 \pi + (-2k_2)\pi/2 = 0$ and there is no other linear dependence between $\pi/2$, φ, and π. Let $f(\pi) = f(\pi/2) = 0$, $f(\varphi) = 1$. Thus f is additive since $k_3 f(\pi) + (-2k_3)f(\pi/2) = 0$. We must finally show that $f(\text{cube}) \neq f(\text{tetrahedron})$. Let the length of each of the 12 edges of the cube be d. Then $f(\text{cube}) = 12df(\pi/2) = 0$. If b is the length of each edge of the tetrahedron then $f(\text{tetrahedron}) = 6bf(\varphi) \neq 0$. This completes the proof.

This theorem may be generalized to n-space. In that case one uses the fact that an angle A for which $\cos A = 1/n$ is not commensurable with π.

Problem Given n equal unit squares, dissect each of these in exactly the same way with straight cuts into $p(n)$ parts such that $np(n)$ pieces may be assembled to form a square of edge $\sqrt{n}$. Investigate $k(n)$, the minimal values of $p(n)$, and show that $k(n) \leq 5$ for all n.

Solution [26] Let $[\sqrt{n}]$ be the integral part of $\sqrt{n}$. Then, if $\sqrt{n} - [\sqrt{n}] > \frac{1}{2}$, take $[\sqrt{n}]$ as the edge of a basic square. If $\sqrt{n} - [\sqrt{n}] < \frac{1}{2}$, take $[\sqrt{n}] - 1$ as the edge of a basic square. Then, if the basic square is placed in the corner of a square of edge $\sqrt{n}$, as shown in Fig. 2-5. it will be bordered by an L-shaped region of width w. This width is restricted by the relation $\frac{3}{2} > w > \frac{1}{2}$. By a single cut, this L-shaped region can be changed into a rectangle of width w.

Fill the basic square with the required number of given unit squares. The remainder of the unit squares must now be transformed by dissection into rectangles of width w. Since $\frac{3}{2} > w > \frac{1}{2}$, this transformation never requires more than three pieces, as shown by the solid lines. (See separate demonstration of this construction.) The dotted lines forming the required cut in the rectangle of width w to transform it back into the L-shaped region will, with proper orientation of the division of a fundamental rectangle, divide one of the fundamental rectangles into, at most, five pieces. All other fundamental rectangles and squares should then be cut into the same five pieces.

Dissection of the unit square A unit square can be cut into three pieces to form a rectangle of width w, where $\frac{3}{2} > w \geq 1$, as shown in Fig. 2-6. The top edge of piece 1 is never more than half the horizontal dimension of the rectangle. Therefore, a vertical cut dividing this rectangle into any desired ratio can always be selected so that it cuts pieces 2 and 3 without cutting piece 1. Therefore, only five pieces will be formed.

If $1 \geq w > \frac{1}{2}$, the same dissection is used, except that that w is now the short edge of the rectangle. A horizontal cut, dividing the rectangle into any desired ratio, can always be selected so that piece 1 is not cut. Therefore, at most five pieces will be formed. If only piece 3 is cut, then only four pieces will be formed.

Goldberg and Stewart [28] have shown that $k(n) \leq 4$, and that this number

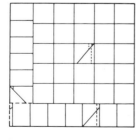

Fig. 2-5

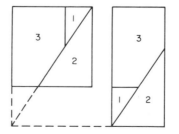

Fig. 2-6

Table 2-2

	0	1	2	3	4	5	6	7	8	9
0		1	2	3	1	2	3	4	2	1
1	2	4	3	2	3	3	1	3	2	4
2	2	3	4	4	3	1	3	3	3	3
3	3	4	2	3	3	3	1	3	4	4
4	2	2	3	4	3	2	4	4	3	1
5	2	4	2	3	3	3	3	3	3	4
6	3	2	4	3	1	3	3	4	3	3
7	3	4	2	3	2	3	3	3	3	4
8	2	1	3	4	3	2	4	4	3	3
9	2	3	3	3	4	3	3	3	2	3

cannot be improved. They give Table 2-2 for the first 99 squares. The number of squares is obtained by using the first digit from the left column and the second digit from the top row. For example, 25 squares require no cuts, and hence each small square is left as one piece. They point out that the problem may be analogously investigated for the equilateral triangle, the regular hexagon, and the L-shaped region, formed by deleting a corner quarter of a square.

2-5 EXAMPLES OF ISOPERIMETRIC AND SHORTEST-DISTANCE PROBLEMS

This section involves optimization, but most of it requires finding a solution having a certain property. There is not much enumeration involved, except perhaps in some special cases. However, the methods used in the proofs are interesting and useful. Some facts are simply stated. A few proofs are also provided.

In his interesting monograph, Kazarinoff [47] treats a large number of elementary problems, involving closed perimeters and the area contained in them in the plane. In some cases the perimeter is given, and the area is to be maximized; in others the area is given, and the perimeter is to be minimized.

Problems which seek, among all simple closed figures of a certain kind, having a fixed perimeter, one which contains the largest area in the plane are called *isoperimetric* (the same perimeter) problems. For example, of all plane figures with a given perimeter, the circle encloses the greatest area (for proof see proof of Theorem 2-6 below).

If the area is given, then the circle has the minimum perimeter. Analogously the sphere contains the largest volume for a given surface area. Of all triangles with a common base and perimeter, the isosceles triangle has the largest area. The equilateral triangle has the largest area among all triangles with a given perimeter.

Exercise 2-16 Prove that if the angles of an n-gon, inscribed in a circle of radius r, are $\alpha_1, \ldots, \alpha_n$, then its area is given by

$$\frac{r^2}{2} \sum_{i=1}^{n} \sin 2\alpha_i$$

Hint: Prove that $\sin x$ is concave on $[0,\pi]$, and hence show that this area is dominated by

$$\frac{r^2}{2} \sin \frac{2\alpha_1 + \cdots + 2\alpha_n}{n} = \frac{nr^2}{2} \sin \frac{2\pi}{n}$$

which is the area of a regular n-gon [7].

We now give a sketch of Steiner's famous proof of the general iso-perimetric problem in the plane, which, of course, can be solved, using the calculus of variations (see below).

Theorem 2-6 *Among all simple closed curves C of given length, the circle encloses the largest area* [11].†

Proof (sketch) Although the following reasoning has an aesthetic appeal, there is an error in its assumption of the existence of a solution. However, a solution can be shown to exist by other methods.

Steiner first shows that a solution to the problem exists by proving that for a given perimeter, of all even-sided polygons, a regular even-sided polygon has the maximum area. He then shows that all the vertices of this regular polygon lie on a circle. By allowing the number of vertices of the polygon to increase indefinitely, the polygon tends to a circle in the limit. Thus, he concludes that the problem has a solution.

Now, to see how one obtains a circle from an arbitrary simple closed curve C, he first shows that the region enclosed by C is convex. If it is concave anywhere, it is possible to reflect the portion of the perimeter where it is concave so that one has convexity and, in addition, a larger area. Then C is divided into two arcs of equal length, and a straight line is passed through the division points. That half which contains the larger area is taken. It is then shown that in order to contain the maximum area it must be a semicircle (the other half may be obtained by reflection). This is demonstrated by selecting a point on the half-perimeter under consideration and joining it to the end points, which have a line connecting them. This gives a triangle. The angle subtended at the point is then increased or decreased, using the point as a hinge, as is required to produce a right angle. This gives another (right-angle) triangle whose area can easily

† See also Steiner's collected works, Berlin, 1881–1882.

be seen to be greater than that of the first triangle. This increases the area under the curve. Since the point chosen was arbitrary, and since a right triangle is subtended at any point of the circumference of a circle by a diameter, one can obtain a right triangle at any point of the perimeter. This yields a semicircle. By symmetric reflection, one has the entire circle. This completes the proof.

Note that if the circumference of the circle has length c, then the area A of any figure, the length of whose perimeter is also c, satisfies the inequality

$$A \leq \pi \left(\frac{c}{2\pi} \right)^2 = \frac{c^2}{4\pi}$$

which is the isoperimetric inequality in the plane.

Exercise 2-17 Prove by contradiction that the simple closed curve with minimum perimeter which encloses a given area in the plane is a circle. This is the converse isoperimetric problem for the circle.

Remark The variational approach to the foregoing problem (for necessity) requires [42] maximizing $\int_0^1 y \, dx$, subject to $y(0) = y(1) = 0$, $\int_0^1 (1 + y'^2)^{\frac{1}{2}} \, dx = L$, where L is given. Using Euler's equation on the lagrangian $y + \lambda(1 + y'^2)^{\frac{1}{2}}$, we have

$$\lambda \frac{d}{dx} \left[\frac{y'}{(1 + y'^2)^{\frac{1}{2}}} \right] - 1 = 0$$

which, after integration, solving for y', and a second integration, gives $y = \pm [\lambda^2 - (x - c_1)^2]^{\frac{1}{2}} + c_2$, simplifying to an expression for a circle. The conditions $y(0) = y(1) = 0$ and the given L determine c_1, c_2, λ. If $L > \pi/2$, the solution is no longer single-valued in x.

Exercise 2-18 Prove by a symmetry argument that among all rectangles of a given area, the square has the smallest perimeter.

Exercise 2-19 Generalize the proof of Exercise 2-18 to the parallelepiped and the cube in n dimensions, using volume instead of area, but still minimizing the perimeter. (The answer to this exercise will be also worked out algebraically in Chap. 4.)

Theorem 2-7 *A regular n-gon has the smallest area among all n-gons circumscribed about a circle* [83].

Proof Let P_n be an arbitrary n-gon, and let $\bar{P}_n$ be the regular n-gon, both circumscribed about a circle c. Consider the circle C circumscribed about $\bar{P}_n$. Let $P_n C$ be the part common to P_n and to C, let $s_1, s_2, \ldots, s_n$ be the circular sections of C cut off by consecutive sides of P_n, and let s be the circular section of C cut off by a tangent to c.   Then

$$P_n C = C - ns + (s_1 s_2 + s_2 s_3 + \cdots + s_n s_1)$$

Hence

$$P_n C \geq C - ns$$

Consequently

$$P_n \geq P_n C \geq C - ns = \bar{P}_n$$

Equality holds in $P_n \geq P_n C$ (in $P_n C \geq \bar{P}_n$) only if no vertex P_n lies outside (inside C).

Remark   Using Lagrange multipliers, Demir [16] has proven: The maximum area of the plane region bounded by a simple closed polygon with given sides occurs when the polygon can be inscribed in a circle. In the proof, the polygon is divided into triangles, all new edges issuing from one vertex to the remaining vertices. The polygonal edges meeting at this vertex are labeled r_1 and r_n, and the new edges between them are consecutively labeled r_2, r_3, . . . , r_{n-1}. The angles at the vertex are all measured from r_1 and denoted by θ_1, θ_2, . . . , θ_{n-1}. The area of the polygon to be maximized with respect to θ_2, . . . , θ_n, r_2, . . . , r_{n-1} is

$$S = \tfrac{1}{2} \sum_{i=1}^{n-1} r_i r_{i+1} \sin \Delta \theta_i$$

where

$$\Delta \theta_i = \theta_{i+1} - \theta_i \qquad i = 1, \ldots, n-1$$

subject to the constraints on the r_i,

$$g_i \equiv r_i{}^2 + r_{i+1}^2 - a_i{}^2 - 2 r_i r_{i+1} \cos \Delta \theta_i = 0 \qquad i = 1, \ldots, n-1$$

where a_i, $i = 0$, . . . , n, is the ith edge of the polygon, starting from $a_0 = r_1$ and terminating at $a_n = r_n$.

Exercise 2-20   Find four triangles such that the sum of their perimeters is a minimum, subject to the following constraints [60]:

1. All sides of all triangles have integral lengths.
2. Each triangle has a side of length k.

ISOPERIMETRIC PROBLEMS IN 3–SPACE

The sphere generalizes the circle problem to three dimensions by enclosing the maximum volume for a given surface area. Another isoperimetric problem in 3-space is the following: Among all curves of a given length joining two points, find one which, upon revolution around a given axis, generates the minimal surface. Here the catenary (in standard position) gives the desired answer [54a]. Plateau's problem is a generalization of this idea by seeking the surface of minimum area bounded by prescribed space curves.

Exercise 2-21 If n is the number of faces of a polyhedron in 3-space, show that for every $n > 4$ there is (1) a pyramid, whose base is a polygon with $(n - 1)$ edges, and whose side faces are triangles, and (2) a prism, whose base and top are polygons of $(n - 2)$ edges each, and whose side faces are quadrilaterals. There are infinitely many such pyramids and prisms for each n. For $n = 4$ we only have pyramids.

Exercise 2-22 If n is the number of faces of a polyhedron, with $4 \leq n \leq 8$, give all possible polyhedra which can be constructed according to the number of edges of each face, i.e., using a mixture of triangles, quadrilaterals, pentagons, and so on.

AN ISOPERIMETRIC PROBLEM FOR POLYHEDRA

What are the shapes of the convex polyhedra which possess the greatest volume V for a given number of faces and a given surface area S? One immediately thinks of regular polyhedra for the relevant number of faces. However, neither the octahedron nor the icosahedron is in the solution class. The answers are known only for polyhedra with 4, 5, 6, 7, and 12 faces.

In general, let P denote a polyhedron with n faces such that for its surface area S, its volume V is a maximum. We may call such a polyhedron optimal. It also has the property that for its volume V, S is a minimum (the proof is left to the reader). Conversely, this property also implies the previous one. Thus an optimal polyhedron can be defined in two ways which can be combined in this definition: P is optimal if and only if the isoperimetric quotient S^3/V^2 is minimal (obvious).

A theorem of Lindelöf asserts that the faces of the optimal polyhedron for any number of faces are all tangent at their centers of gravity to an inscribed sphere [82]. Hence the problem reduces to this: among all polyhedra of n faces circumscribed about a unit sphere find the optimal one. Since for these polyhedra $S^3/V^2 = 27V$ (obtained by dissecting the polyhedron into pyramids with common vertex at the center of the sphere), the optimal polyhedra will be those with minimum volume. Goldberg [27] first gave the following result for a general polyhedron with F faces circumscribed about a sphere:

$$\frac{S^3}{V^2} \geq 54\,(F - 2)\,\tan \omega_F (4 \sin^2 \omega_F - 1) \qquad \omega_F = \frac{F}{F - 2}\frac{\pi}{6}$$

Equality holds for the tetrahedron, cube, and dodecahedron. This result was independently discovered by Fejes Tóth and proved by Florian [82].

For the case of eight faces for which the answer is not yet known, Goldberg has developed an experimental chart, shown below, which leads to the conjecture that the double-skew pyramid is the desired answer. The problem may be stated as follows:

What is the shape and volume of the octahedron of smallest volume which can be circumscribed about a sphere of unit radius? Examples of octahedra are listed in Fig. 2-7.

THE MALFATTI PROBLEM (UNSOLVED)

Another example of a constrained optimization problem in geometry which is yet unsolved is the Malfatti problem, posed in 1803. We shall give only a statement of this problem.

Given a right-triangular prism of any sort of material, such as marble, how shall three circular cylinders each of which has the same height as the prism be related to one another inside the prism and leave over the least possible amount of material?

This reduces to the plane problem of cutting three circles from a given triangle so that the sum of their areas is maximized [29].

TWO DISTANCE PROBLEMS

On the shortest distance through n points in the plane   A well-known and now classical problem of combinatorial mathematics is the traveling-salesman problem. The salesman must make a tour of n cities and return to his starting point, visiting each city only once, and covering the minimum total distance on his tour (see Chap. 5 for an algebraic formulation). If the n cities are given in the unit square of the Euclidean plane so that their distances are the actual distances measured in the plane, then the following theorem gives an interesting bound on the total distance to be traveled, provided the salesman is not required to return to his starting point. This estimate does not apply if the distances between pairs of points are assigned arbitrarily. (Such problems will be examined in Sec. 2-6.)

Remark   In this regard, it is interesting to note that the shortest closed route connecting n points in a plane not all on a straight line is a simple polygon. In particular, if the convex hull of the set contains none of the n points in its interior, then its boundary is the shortest closed route. (Thus, there need not be any crossing of routes in the corresponding traveling-salesman problem.) To prove this fact, we connect the n points by any closed path and note that a shorter path is obtained by

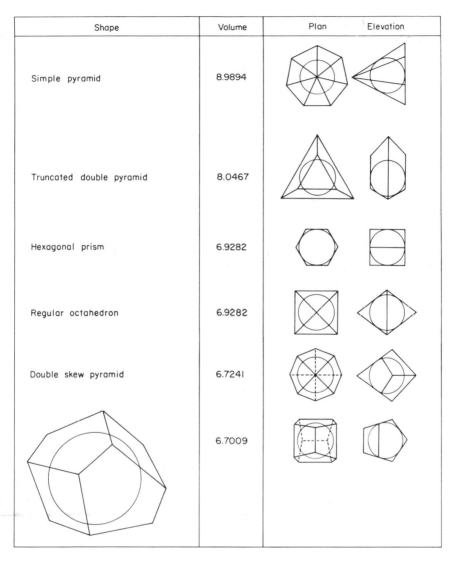

Shape	Volume	Plan	Elevation
Simple pyramid	8.9894		
Truncated double pyramid	8.0467		
Hexagonal prism	6.9282		
Regular octahedron	6.9282		
Double skew pyramid	6.7241		
	6.7009		

Fig. 2-7

connecting the points in the same order by straight-line segments, with the given points as the only vertices. If the segments $v_i v_{i+1}$ and $v_j v_{j+1}$ intersect in a point, we suppose that the path followed is $v_i v v_{i+1} \cdots v_j v v_{j+1} \cdots v_i$. If v is not one of the given points, then $v_i v_j \cdots v_{i+1} v_{j+1} \cdots v_i$ is a shorter polygonal path which does not contain the intersection v. If, on the other hand, v is in the set of given points, then $v_i v v_j$

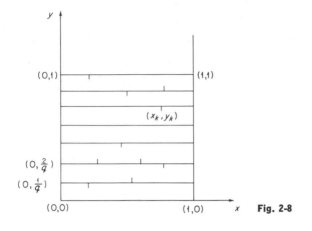

Fig. 2-8

$\cdots v_{i+1}v_{j+1} \cdots v_i$ is a polygonal path which does not contain v as an intersection point. (A sketch will clarify the argument [86].)

The following theorem is due to L. Few [23].

Theorem 2-8 *Given any $n(\geq 2)$ points in a unit square, there is a path through the n points which does not exceed $(2n)^{\frac{1}{2}} + 1.75$ in length.*

Proof Consider the unit square $0 \leq x \leq 1$, $0 \leq y \leq 1$, and let the coordinates of the n points be (x_1,y_1), . . . , (x_n,y_n). Consider q horizontal lines, $y = 0$, $1/q$, $2/q$, . . . , 1, with q arbitrary, and draw from each of the n points a perpendicular to the nearest of the $q + 1$ lines (see Fig. 2-8). Repeat the construction, using the q lines, $y = 0$, $1/2q$, $3/2q$, . . . , $(2q - 1)/2q$.

Each construction gives a path consisting of suitable portions of the lines, $x = 0$, $0 \leq y \leq 1$, and $x = 1$, $0 \leq y \leq 1$, together with each perpendicular line counted twice—once from a horizontal line to a point and then back to the horizontal line—thus continuing the path through the n points. If we denote these two paths by L_1 and L_2, respectively, we have

$$L_1 = q + 1 + 2 \sum_{i=1}^{n} q^{-1}\|qy_i\| + 1$$

$$L_2 = q + 2 \sum_{i=1}^{n} q^{-1}\|qy_i - \tfrac{1}{2}\| + 1$$

where $\|\alpha\|$ denotes the absolute difference between α and the nearest integer. Note that

$$\|\alpha\| + \|\alpha - \tfrac{1}{2}\| = \tfrac{1}{2}$$

We have

$$L_1 + L_2 = 2q + 3 + 2q^{-1}\frac{n}{2} = 2q + 3 + nq^{-1}$$

We choose the integer q to minimize this value. It is the integer nearest to $(n/2)^{\frac{1}{2}}$. Thus $n = 2(q + \theta)^2$, with $|\theta| \le \frac{1}{2}$. Substituting for n, we have

$$L_1 + L_2 = 2q + 3 + nq^{-1} \le 2(2n)^{\frac{1}{2}} + \tfrac{7}{2}$$

Consequently the length of one of the two paths does not exceed $(2n)^{\frac{1}{2}} + 1.75$.

Exercise 2-23 Using a construction similar to the above, show that if the vertical line to each point is counted only once, then the length of one of the two constructed "roads" does not exceed $n^{\frac{1}{2}} + 1.75$.

If we generalize the construction of the last exercise we can show:

Theorem 2-8a *Given n points in a unit k-dimensional cube, there is, for fixed k and $n \to \infty$, a road (no repetition of line segments) through the n points whose length does not exceed*

$$k[8(k - 1)]^{(1-k)/2k}n^{1-1/k} + O(n^{1-2k})$$

Proof As in the estimate of the proof of the exercise which follows closely the proof of the theorem preceding it, we find in the k-dimensional case a road whose length does not exceed

$$(q + 1)^{k-1} + q^{-1}[(q + 1)^{k-1} - 1] + \tfrac{1}{2}nq^{-1}\left(\frac{k - 1}{2}\right)^{\frac{1}{2}}$$

Choosing $q = \{[n^2/8(k - 1)]^{1/2k}\} + 1$ gives for an upper bound to the length of the road the expression given in the statement of the theorem.

An asymptotic result for the length of the shortest path between n points contained in a unit cube in k dimensions is that it is at least equal to

$$\left[\Gamma\left(1 + \frac{k}{2}\right)\right]^{1/k} \pi^{-\frac{1}{2}}n^{1-1/k}$$

To see this, note that the volume of a sphere of radius r in k dimensions is

$$V_k = \frac{\pi^{k/2}r^k}{\Gamma\left(\dfrac{k}{2} + 1\right)}$$

Consider n points in a k-dimensional unit cube so arranged that the distance apart of any two is at least $2r$. Thus if each point is the center of a sphere of radius r, then the spheres form a packing (see later in this chapter). The density of this packing for k fixed and as $n \to \infty$ is $\delta = nV_k'$. It is the ratio of the sum of the volumes of the spheres to the volume of the cube. The length of a path is $2r(n - 1)$. Solving for r in terms of δ, substituting in this expression, and noting from the discussion given later in the chapter that $\delta \geq 1/2^k$, we obtain our result.

A max-min problem   If C is a configuration of five points P_i, $i = 1, \ldots, 5$, in a closed domain D, show that [15]

$$\max_{C} \min_{i \neq j} \overline{P_i P_j} = \begin{cases} 2^{-\frac{1}{2}} & \text{if } D \text{ is the unit square} \\ \dfrac{1}{2} & \text{if } D \text{ is the unit equilateral triangle} \\ 2 \sin \dfrac{\pi}{5} & \text{if } D \text{ is the unit circle} \\ \dfrac{\pi}{2} & \text{if } D \text{ is the surface of the unit sphere} \end{cases}$$

where $\overline{P_i P_j}$ is the distance from P_i to P_j.

Solution   1. Divide the unit square into four $\frac{1}{2}$-unit squares. At least one of these contains two of the five points. In it, the maximum spacing $2^{-\frac{1}{2}}$ between two points is obtained when the points are diagonally opposite. This is also the value obtained for the unit square when the five points are the vertices and center of the square.

2. Partition the triangle into four $\frac{1}{2}$-unit equilateral triangles, and locate the points at any five of the six vertices of the $\frac{1}{2}$-unit triangles.

3. Partition the circle into five congruent sectors, and space the points equidistant about the circumference. If two points are in a sector of arc ϕ ($\phi \leq 2\pi/5$), their greatest separation would be

$$\max \left(1, \, 2 \sin \frac{\phi}{2} \right) \leq 2 \sin \frac{\pi}{5}$$

4. Place one point P_1 at the north pole and the others 90° apart on the equator. If the four points are located more than $\pi/2$ from P_1, they would lie in the southern hemisphere; if this area is partitioned into four congruent regions, then the max-min for these four points would be less than $\pi/2$.

2-6 GRAPHS AND NETWORKS

Shortest-distance problems generalize to shortest-path problems. It is convenient at this point to introduce graphs and examine a variety of optimization problems associated with them. Some applications are then made to polyhedra.

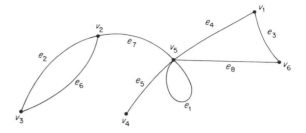

Fig. 2-9 An undirected graph.

A graph is a set of points called *vertices* and a set of simple curves called *edges* such that every closed edge contains precisely one vertex, every open edge contains precisely two vertices, which are its end points, and no edges have points in common other than vertices (Fig. 2-9). With each edge, one may associate a direction indicated by an arrow. The resulting graph is then called a *directed graph*, and its edges are called *arcs* (Fig. 2-10).

A graph is called *bipartite* if the vertices can be divided into two disjoint sets such that the only edges in the graph are those which connect vertices from one set to those of the other.

A simple chain (path) in an undirected (directed) graph is a succession of edges (arcs) and vertices in which no vertex is repeated; a circuit (cycle) is a chain (path) whose initial and terminal vertices coincide. A graph is said to be connected in the undirected sense if there is a simple chain between any pair of vertices. A graph of $n + 1$ vertices is n-tuply connected if the removal of $n - 1$ or less vertices does not disconnect it. Two chains are said to be disjoint if they have no vertices in common, except perhaps for their end points. A tree is a connected subgraph which has no circuits. A spanning tree is a (maximal) tree which contains all the vertices of the graph. An edge of the graph that is in the tree is called a *branch*. An edge of the graph that is not in the tree is known as a *chord*. Figure 2-10 shows a spanning tree for a directed graph. The tree is rooted at v_0, from which all paths that are in the tree begin.

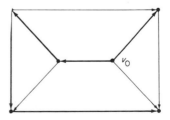

Fig. 2-10 A directed graph with a tree indicated.

A network is a connected graph such that a nonnegative number called a *capacity* is associated with every edge and every vertex [2,9]. Frequently two vertices v_α and v_ω are distinguished in a network; v_α is called the *source*, and v_ω is called the *sink*. A pair consisting of a path from v_α to v_ω and a nonnegative number (which cannot exceed the capacity of any vertex or edge along the path), representing the flow along this path from v_α to v_ω, is called a *path flow from v_α to v_ω*.

A flow in a network is a collection of path flows such that the sum of the numbers of all path flows through any vertex or edge of the network does not exceed the capacity of that vertex or edge. The value of the flow is the sum of the numbers of the collection of path flows which compose it. A disconnecting set in a network is a collection of edges and vertices whose removal disconnects v_α and v_ω. The sum of the capacities of these edges and vertices is the value of the disconnecting set.

We give, without proof, the max-flow min-cut theorem of Ford and Fulkerson [25]. We will not discuss additional extremal problems in network flows. (For further information, consult Ref. 25a which pursues maximum flow and related problems in great depth.)

Theorem 2-9   *The maximum of the values of all flows (called max-flow) from the source v_α to the sink v_ω of a network is equal to the minimum of the values of all disconnecting sets (called min-cut).*

In Chap. 5 an algebraic formulation of a network-flow problem is given.

The vertices and edges of a polytope may be regarded as the vertices and edges of a corresponding graph in n-space. Because of this, one may be interested in examining related problems in graph theory.

Returning to our discussion of linear programming in Sec. 2-3, we note that the simplex process need not evaluate the linear function to be maximized at all the vertices of the constraint polytope, but only at some of them. In that case there may be different, distinct paths which it follows from the initial to the final vertex. It may be useful to know the bounds on how many such paths there may be for some practical considerations. The corollary to Theorem 2-11, given below, provides such information. We give, without proof, the following theorem.

Theorem 2-10   (Balinski)   *The vertices considered as points and the edges considered as lines of the convex polyhedral set S [of a linear-programming problem the convex hull of whose vertices is S which lies within no $(n - 1)$-dimensional hyperplane] form an n-tuply connected graph.*

Theorem 2-11   (Whitney)   *A graph G is n-tuply connected if and only if there exist n disjoint paths between any pair of points* [88].

Proof   The following proof, due to Balinski, utilizes ideas from the theory of network flows.

Introduce a network by denoting any pair of points by v_α and v_ω. Assign capacity 1 to each vertex of G, except for v_α and v_ω, and capacity $n + 1$ to each edge of G, except for any edges which join v_α and v_ω. If there are such edges, assign them capacity 1.   In the resulting network, assume that max-flow $< n$.   Then min-cut $< n$.   Since this contradicts the fact that G is n-tuply connected, we must have max-flow $\geq n$.   No vertex can have two unit-path flows passing through it.   Thus there are n disjoint paths from v_α to v_ω.   This proves necessity.   Sufficiency is obvious.

Corollary   *There are at least n disjoint paths between any pair of vertices of the polyhedral convex set S.*

Remark   The degree of a vertex is equal to the number of edges incident with it.   Dirac [18] has proven that if every vertex of a graph of at most $2n$ vertices has least degree $n > 1$, then the graph has a cycle which passes through every vertex exactly once.

EXAMPLES OF POLYHEDRAL AND OTHER EXTREMAL PROBLEMS, UTILIZING IDEAS FROM GRAPH THEORY

Definition   The diameter of a polyhedron is the greatest number of edges on any path between any two vertices.

Exercise 2-24   Find the diameters of all five regular polyhedra with unit edges in 3-space.

Theorem 2-12   *The maximum diameter d of all three-dimensional convex polyhedra with n vertices is given by*

$$d = \left[\frac{n + 1}{3} \right]$$

Proof [45]   By Balinski's theorem, the corresponding graph is 3-connected; and by Whitney's theorem, any pair of vertices is connected by three disjoint paths.   If a pair of vertices have their distance equal to the diameter d, then the length of each of the three paths is $\geq d$; hence each path has at least $d - 1$ vertices other than the given pair.   Since the vertices are all different, we have

$$3(d - 1) + 2 \leq n$$

or since d is an integer

$$d \le \left[\frac{n+1}{3}\right]$$

Equality holds for a triangular prism with tetrahedral caps on the top and bottom triangles in case $n \equiv 2 \bmod 3$. One or both caps may be removed for the other cases.

Definition   The smallest integer r such that the path length from some vertex to any other vertex does not exceed r is called the *radius of a polyhedron*.

Conjecture (Jucovič and Moon)   *The maximum radius of all three-dimensional convex polyhedra with $n \ge 6$ vertices is not less than $[(n+4)/4]$.*

Moon and Moser [58] have studied the following problem in k-dimensional space. Call the maximum number of vertices on any simple path of a polytope whose $n(n \ge k+1)$ vertices do not all lie in a $(k-1)$-space, the *path length*. If $p(n,k)$ denotes the minimum path length of all such polytopes, then $p(n,3) \le (2n+13)/3$ is proved in Ref. 8a. In general we have [58]:

Theorem 2-13 $p(n,k) < (2k+3) \ \{[1-2/(k+1)]n - (k-2)\}^{\log 2/\log k}$
       $-1 < 3kn^{\log 2/\log k}$

Theorem 2-14   (Erdös)   *Let the maximum and minimum distances determined by n points in a plane be denoted by r and r', respectively. Then r can occur at most n times, and r' at most $3n - 6$ times* [21].

Proof   If $\overline{P_1P_2} = r$ and $P_3P_4 = r$, then the lines P_1P_2 and P_3P_4 must intersect; otherwise, the diameter of the polygon $P_1P_2P_3P_4$ would exceed r, contradicting the maximality of r. Connect only those vertices whose distance is r. There are two cases to consider:

1. If each point is connected with at most two other points, then there are at most $2n$ ordered pairs of points connected; hence the number of line segments of length r is $\le n$.
2. If a point P_1 is connected with three points P_2, P_3, P_4, with P_1P_3 between P_1P_2 and P_1P_4 (note that angle $P_2P_1P_4 \le \pi/3$; otherwise, $P_2P_4 > r$, contradicting the maximality of r), then P_3 cannot be connected to any other P_i since P_3P_i must intersect both P_1P_2 and P_1P_4. By omitting P_3, the number of points and the number of maximum distances are each reduced by one, and we can apply induction to complete the proof.

Consider now all points whose distances apart are r'. Connect only these points. None of the connecting segments intersect at a point that is not one of the n points; otherwise, a pair of the four points determining these segments would be nearer together than r'. The resulting graph is planar, and since for such a graph $E \leq 3V - 6$ (it is clear that Euler's formula also holds for a planar map and thus the same relations given for polyhedra also hold), we have $3n - 6$ for the desired result.

Theorem 2-15 *In three-dimensional space, the maximum distance between n points cannot occur more than $2n - 2$ times.*

For proof see Ref. 33.

In k-dimensional space, the frequency of occurrence of the maximum distance between n points has the form [22]

$$\frac{n^2}{2} \left(1 - \frac{1}{[k/2]} \right) + O(n^{2-\epsilon})$$

for some $\epsilon > 0$.

The foregoing are a special case of Borsuk's problem (see [32], p. 418).

Is every bounded set A in n-dimensional Euclidean space representable as $A = \cup_{i=0}^{n} A_i$, where diam $A_i <$ diam A, $i = 0, \ldots, n$? The diameter of a set is the greatest distance (or supremum) between any two points in the set.

Remark Let $f(n)$ be the least number of different distances between n arbitrary points in the plane. For example, if $n = 3$, then an equilateral triangle gives $f(3) = 1$. The square and regular pentagon, respectively, give $f(4) = f(5) = 2$. In general,

$$f(n) > \frac{n^{\frac{3}{4}}}{2 \sqrt[3]{9}} - 1$$

Moser [59] has shown that if the points are vertices of a convex polygon, then

$$f(n) \geq \left[\frac{n + 2}{3} \right]$$

SHORTEST PATHS AND RELATED PROBLEMS IN GRAPH THEORY

A common problem which occurs in the theory of graphs is that of finding a path, consisting of the smallest number of arcs between any two points, called a *shortest path*. Sometimes the problem may require finding the shortest simple cycle between two points so that none of the arcs or the vertices are duplicated on the return path with those of the forward path.

A more difficult and related problem is that of finding the shortest path between two points which passes through every one of a given number of points. Sometimes it is desirable to find the shortest cycle passing through a given number of points.

A still more difficult problem is the traveling-salesman problem which arises when in either of the preceding problems the edges are distances.

Exercise 2-25   Formulate the traveling-salesman problem between n cities in matrix form, and show that there are $n!$ possible paths, each of which passes through the n cities. The global optimum (i.e., shortest path) is one of these.

We now give two algorithms for finding shortest paths.

A SHORTEST-PATH ALGORITHM

Let v and w be two vertices of a graph G, and let us seek a shortest path between them. We use the following algorithm: *In a step-by-step fashion we assign to each vertex x of G a number m equal to the shortest distance from v to x as follows. At the 0th step, we assign v, the distance zero. If all vertices assigned the distance m form a known set $E(m)$ at the $(m+1)th$ step, we assign the distance $m+1$ to the vertices of the set $E(m+1) = \{x|x \notin E(k), k \leq m, \text{ and } x \text{ is the terminal vertex of an arc whose initial vertex is } y \in E(m)\}$. The process terminates when w is reached. If $w \in E(m)$, we can trace a shortest path from v to w, backward from w, as follows. For the penultimate vertex, choose any predecessor of w (i.e., any vertex which is immediately before w on any path leading to w) labeled $m-1$. For the ante-penultimate, choose any predecessor of these labeled $m-2$, and so on.*

We have applied the algorithm to an example illustrated in Fig. 2-11. Note that the vertex with distance 1 does not receive another distance

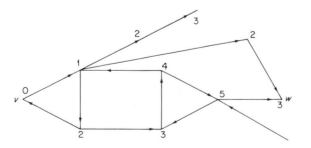

Fig. 2-11

5, nor does w, which received the earlier distance 3, receive another distance 6. The length of the shortest path is 3. It is obvious which one it is.

Exercise 2-26 Apply the foregoing algorithm to find the shortest path from v to w after eliminating the last arc leading to w in the solution path given above.

The algorithm given above is inadequate for treating the problem in which the actual lengths (sometimes called *capacities*) of the arcs are given. In this case one seeks a path of minimum total length, regardless of how many arcs it may include. However, a solution to the previous problem would be obtained if every arc is assigned unit length.

The following algorithm is due to R. W. Floyd [24a]. *Find the shortest distances between all ordered pairs of vertices simultaneously.* It applies to the case of a directed graph. If there is no arc joining a pair of points, infinite length is assigned to a fictitious arc joining them. The algorithm applied to a graph with n vertices utilizes just under n^3 additions and comparisons. It uses the idea that as far as distances via it are concerned, a vertex may be eliminated from further consideration by forming the length of, and employing where necessary, every two-arc path, consisting of an arc from a predecessor to the vertex, and an arc from the vertex to a successor. During the calculation, every ordered pair of vertices is considered joined by an arc of length equal to the current entry in the matrix, so the elimination takes $(n - 1)^2$ operations. Note that it is still necessary to find distances from and to an eliminated vertex.

FLOYD'S ALGORITHM WHEN ARCS HAVE LENGTHS

Let m_{ij} be the current length of a shortest path from i to j. $m_{ik} + m_{kj}$ is the current length of a path from i to j via k; this should replace m_{ij} if it is smaller. These operations must be done in a suitable order if a minimal number of them are to be done. Formally the steps of the Floyd algorithm are as follows.

1. *Set $i = 1$.*
2. *($\forall j \neq i \ni m_{ji} + m_{ik} < m_{jk}$) ($\forall k \neq i$), replace m_{jk} by $m_{ji} + m_{ik}$.*
3. *Increment i by 1.*
4. *If $i \leq n$, go to step 2; otherwise, stop.*

The final matrix gives the length of a shortest path between any two points. By keeping a record of the changes made to obtain the final form, it is possible to retain enough information to enable a shortest path to be traced between any two vertices.

The algorithm will work correctly if some of the arcs have a negative length, provided there is no circuit of negative length in the graph.

Examination of the diagonal elements of the final matrix will reveal this situation, since they give the length of a shortest circuit on the corresponding vertex. If none are negative the results are acceptable.

Consider the example in Fig. 2-12 in which the vertices are labeled numerically and the length of each symmetric pair of arcs is given by its side. Its matrix (m_{ij}) is given by

$$
\begin{array}{c}
\quad\;\; 1 \quad 2 \quad 3 \quad 4 \\
\begin{array}{c} 1 \\ 2 \\ 3 \\ 4 \end{array}
\left[
\begin{array}{cccc}
\infty & 2 & \infty & 6 \\
2 & \infty & 2 & \infty \\
\infty & 2 & \infty & 1 \\
6 & \infty & 1 & \infty
\end{array}
\right]
\end{array}
$$

For example, $m_{13} = \infty$. This is replaced in the 11th step of the algorithm by $m_{12} + m_{23} = 4$. Similarly, $m_{14} = 6$. It is replaced by $m_{13} + m_{34} = 5$ in the 27th step, and so on. Thus, the shortest path from 1 to 3 goes from 1 to 2 and then from 2 to 3. The shortest path from 1 to 4 first follows the shortest path from 1 to 3, and then from 3 to 4. However, the shortest path from 1 to 3 has just been given. Consequently, to go from 1 to 4 one goes from 1 to 2 then to 3 and finally to 4 by $m_{21} + m_{14} = 8$ at step 3. However, this is replaced again by

$$m_{23} + m_{34} = 3$$

at step 25.

Theorem 2-16 *Floyd's algorithm yields the shortest distance matrix if the graph has no circuits of negative length.*

Proof *(Murchland)* [60a] A circuitless path between two vertices repeats no vertices. If it is not circuitless, a path contains one or more circuits or loops but will always have an embedded path without circuits. (This may not be unique.) Since no circuit in the graph has negative length, of all the paths connecting two vertices there is at least one that is both shortest and circuitless.

Let the basic operation—if $m_{ik} + m_{kj} < m_{ij}$, then replace m_{ij} by $m_{ik} + m_{kj}$—be called the *triple* (i,k,j). Call k the *intermediate vertex*.

The algorithm, as stated previously, contains every possible triple precisely once, except that triples with the intermediate vertex the same as the initial or terminal vertex are omitted since they serve no purpose.

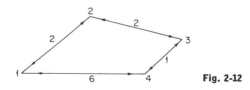

Fig. 2-12

What is important for the proof is that these $n(n-1)^2$ triples are arranged in n groups, with the kth group consisting of every useful triple with intermediate vertex k.

The calculation begins by setting the arc lengths into the matrix. It is easy to see that every entry in the final matrix corresponds to a real path. The proof must show that no distance is too great.

Each shortest distance arising from a single arc persists to the end of the calculation. The first group of triples with intermediate vertex 1 ensures that shortest distances produced by a two-arc path with intermediate vertex 1 are obtained correctly.

Assume as an inductive hypothesis that the algorithm finds the shortest distance between every pair of vertices which have a shortest path, whose highest-numbered intermediate vertex is $k-1$. Because of the chosen arrangement of the triples, these final distances must be obtained before group k is reached.

Let k be the highest vertex on the shortest circuitless path from a vertex v to a vertex w, or, if there are several such paths, let k be the least of the highest intermediate vertices on any of them. Triple (v,k,w) occurs in the kth group of triples. The subpaths from v to k and from k to w of the path containing k have lower intermediate vertices than k. By the inductive assumption, these distances will be obtained correctly and, as noted above, before group k is reached. Hence, executing the triple (v,k,w) will find the shortest distance from v to w since the shortest distances from v to k and k to w will be available to it.

Hence, if the inductive assumption is true for $k-1$, it is true for k. Since we know it is true for 1, we can conclude that the algorithm finds shortest distances correctly whatever the highest intermediate vertex on a shortest path may be.

CONSTRUCTION OF TREES OF MINIMUM TOTAL LENGTH

It is easy to visualize problems in which it is desired to build roads between several centers where there is one and only one path connecting any two centers. Of all such possible road systems between the centers, we seek one with minimum total length. This is the problem of finding a spanning tree of a connected graph with minimum total length. Note that a necessary condition for a tree to have minimum total length is that the length of every chord be greater than or equal to the maximum of the lengths of branches in the fundamental circuit which it determines. Otherwise, a single replacement using this chord could be made. It turns out that this is also a sufficient condition, but the proof is not immediate.

To choose a tree of minimum total length, we first index the edges according to increasing lengths so that the length of e_i is less than or equal to the length of e_j whenever $i < j$. We then start by selecting e_1 and add e_2 if e_2 does not form a circuit with e_1. In general, we continue to consider edges of successively higher indices, selecting an edge whenever it does not form a circuit with the set previously selected and rejecting it otherwise. This process always yields a tree of minimum total length. (See Ref. 50a for proof.)

Examples of other optimization problems in graph theory are the following:

1. Find the shortest simple circuit (called a *hamiltonian circuit*) passing through each vertex of a given connected graph on n vertices. This problem is related to the traveling-salesman problem; however, it does not involve the lengths of the edges, but only their number. In considering this problem, Hamilton took a dodecahedron, partially drove nails into its vertices, and wound a string around the nails as he moved from one nail to another to generate a hamiltonian circuit.

2. *Steiner's problem:* Given n points in the plane, find the shortest way of connecting them so that from any given point one can reach any other point by passing through some of the points if necessary. This may be a minimum spanning tree if a graph is actually given.

3. *The Chinese postman's problem (first studied by Kwan):* Find a closed-edge progression which includes every edge of a connected graph at least once, and which has minimal total weight where a numerical weight is associated with each edge. (Thus, the problem is to duplicate enough edges to obtain a unicursal graph, adding minimal weight in the process.) A graph is unicursal if it is possible to travel along all its edges without repeating any edge [9].

COMPLETE GRAPHS WITHOUT TRIANGLES

Definition A complete graph in the plane is a set of n vertices in the plane, connected by edges two at a time such that two edges intersect in at most one point and two edges with a vertex in common have no intersection.

Theorem 2-17 *The minimum number of edges which can be removed from a complete graph in the plane in order that the remaining graph have no circuits of three edges is given by*

$$\binom{n}{2} - \text{the greatest integer in} \begin{cases} \dfrac{n^2}{4} & n \text{ even} \\[2ex] \dfrac{n+1}{2}\dfrac{n-1}{2} = \dfrac{n^2-1}{4} & n \text{ odd} \end{cases}$$

Proof Dividing the vertices into two sets of equal size (in the odd case, one set has one more vertex) and connecting every vertex of one set with every vertex of the other gives a *bipartite* graph. The number of edges of this graph is the greatest integer part of the above expression. Thus, for both cases the number of edges e_n left behind is not less than this number. To prove that these values are the best possible, we proceed by induction. The result holds for $n = 2$. For any simple graph (one with no more than one edge between a pair of vertices) with $e_n \geq 1$ edges, n vertices (n even), and no triangles, we have $e_n \leq n^2/4$. To see this we divide the vertices into two sets, as above, and consider a pair of vertices one from each set. We connect this pair by an edge. We also connect one of them to every vertex of its corresponding set and the other to all vertices of the other set. No vertex of one set is connected to a vertex of the other, for then we would have a triangle. Thus, from the connections of these two vertices, we have $(n - 2) + 1$ edges to the remaining $n - 2$ vertices.

Thus,

$$(n - 2) + 1 + e_{n-2} \geq e_n$$

But by induction the left side is

$$(n - 1) + \frac{(n - 2)^2}{4} = \frac{n^2}{4}$$

A similar argument applies for the odd case. This completes the proof since $\binom{n}{2}$ is the number of edges of a complete graph.

THE MAXIMUM NUMBER OF THREE-ARC CYCLES IN A DIRECTED GRAPH [3,9]

Again consider a complete graph on n vertices in the plane. Each edge may now be assigned a direction by means of an arrow. An edge with direction is called an *arc*. For each assignment of directions to all edges, one counts the number of simple cycles which have these arcs. Such a cycle is traced by starting with a vertex and following the directions of an outgoing arc to another vertex, then similarly following an outgoing arc to a third vertex, and so on, until finally an arc is followed to the original vertex. Before assigning direction, cycles are known as *circuits*. Obviously at least one method of assigning directions gives a maximum number of such cycles. What is this number? Here we examine the case of cycles consisting of three arcs each.

There is a way of representing such a configuration (which is known as a *directed graph*) by means of a *vertex* matrix. To construct such a matrix, we label the vertices $v_1, \ldots, v_n$ and list them vertically, each to the left of a row of the matrix; then, in the same order, we list each vertex above a column. An entry in the i, j position of the matrix is unity if there is an arc directed from vertex i on the left to the vertex j above. Otherwise, the entry is zero. The main diagonal entries are all zero.

Theorem 2-18 *The maximum number of cycles, each of which consists of three arcs in a complete graph on n vertices, is*

$$\binom{n}{3} + \frac{1}{2}\binom{n}{2} - \frac{n}{2}\left(\frac{n-1}{2}\right)^2 \qquad n \text{ odd}$$

Proof Consider the vertex matrix associated with this graph. The ith row of the matrix gives the incidence relation for arcs positively incident with the ith vertex, i.e., they go out of the vertex, whereas the ith column gives the incidence for arcs negatively incident with this vertex, i.e., they go into the vertex. An entry of this matrix is unity if there is an arc directed from the vertex corresponding to the row of the entry to the vertex corresponding to the column of the entry. Otherwise, the entry is zero. If r_i denotes the sum of elements in the ith row and c_i denotes the corresponding sum in the ith column, then $r_i + c_i = n - 1$, since the ith vertex is connected by $n - 1$ edges to the remaining $n - 1$ vertices.

The total number of circuits with three edges is $\binom{n}{3}$. However, this is not the number of cycles. A cycle must have all edges cyclically directed. Thus, if two arcs are positively incident with a vertex, they cannot be two sides of a cycle because their orientations are opposite for that cycle. Conversely, every three-arc circuit that is not a cycle has precisely two edges positively (negatively) incident with the same vertex.

Since the sum r_i of the elements of the ith row gives the number of arcs directed from the ith vertex, we must exclude from the total number of circuits the quantity $\Sigma_{i=1}^{n} \binom{r_i}{2}$, that is, the sum of the ith row taken two at a time and summed over all rows. This gives, for the number of cycles,

$$\binom{n}{3} - \sum_{i=1}^{n}\binom{r_i}{2} = \binom{n}{3} - \frac{1}{2}\sum_{i=1}^{n}(r_i^2 - r_i)$$

Since our graph is complete, the number of its edges is $\binom{n}{2}$, and we must have $\Sigma_{i=1}^{n} r_i = \binom{n}{2}$ because the total sum of all rows must account for all the edges of the graph.

We now have, for the number of cycles,

$$\binom{n}{3} + \frac{1}{2}\binom{n}{2} - \frac{1}{2}\sum_{i=1}^{n} r_i^2$$

and the problem is to determine r_i so that this quantity is maximum. The choice of r_i corresponds to a complete graph with special orientation that maximizes the number of cycles. It is sufficient to determine r_i so that $\Sigma_{i=1}^{n}r_i^2$ is minimum because this quantity is subtracted from a constant amount in the above expression which is to be maximized. The foregoing argument would also be valid if we used the sum c_i of the column elements and the fact that two arcs having the same orientation toward a vertex with which they are incident cannot be two sides of a cycle. We would then have to find c_i which maximizes

$$\binom{n}{3} + \frac{1}{2}\binom{n}{2} - \frac{1}{2}\sum_{i=1}^{n} c_i^2$$

Thus, we would have the maximum number of cycles if c_i which minimizes

$$\sum_{i=1}^{n} c_i^2$$

is found.

Thus the maximum number of cycles is symmetric in r_i and c_i; that is, they must be equal. Since $r_i + c_i = n - 1$, we have, when n is odd, $r_i = (n - 1)/2$.

MINIMUM COLLISION ACCIDENTS BETWEEN ORIGINS AND DESTINATION [9,93]

In a brick factory there are m ovens in which bricks are baked. The bricks are then loaded on a small, special rail car at each oven and pushed to any one of n platforms, where a loading truck may be available. Since each oven must be connected by rail to each loading platform, the rail lines have a great number of intersections. As the cars go over the intersections, they are often derailed, causing spillage of bricks and a traffic jam within the factory. The problem is to construct the rails from the ovens to the destinations with a minimum number of crossings, thus minimizing the hazards of derailment.

This problem may be solved within the framework of graph theory, where the rail lines correspond to edges of a graph connecting vertices (corresponding to the ovens) to other vertices (corresponding to the loading platforms). One condition is imposed—that no three edges may intersect at the same point unless it is a vertex. Two edges, however, may intersect at an intermediate point. For example, in the case of

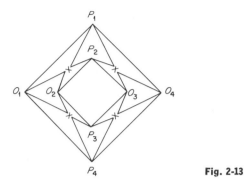

Fig. 2-13

four ovens $O_1, \ldots, O_4$ and four platforms $P_1, \ldots, P_4$ we have four intersections marked with x in Fig. 2-13.

Conjecture (Zarankiewicz) *The minimum number of interior intersections of edges joining every one of p vertices to every one of q vertices of a bipartite graph $C_{p,q}$ in the plane (two edges are assumed to intersect at no more than a single point) is not less than*

$$
I(C_{p,q}) = \begin{cases} (r^2 - r)(s^2 - s) & \text{if } p = 2r,\ q = 2s \\ (r^2 - r)s^2 & \text{if } p = 2r,\ q = 2s + 1 \\ r^2(s^2 - s) & \text{if } p = 2r + 1,\ q = 2s \\ r^2 s^2 & \text{if } p = 2r + 1,\ q = 2s + 1 \end{cases}
$$

or simply

$$
I(C_{p,q}) = \left[\frac{p}{2}\right]\left[\frac{p-1}{2}\right]\left[\frac{q}{2}\right]\left[\frac{q-1}{2}\right]
$$

where $[x]$ denotes the greatest integer not exceeding x.

Remark The bipartite graph $C_{p,q}$ is said to be complete when all p vertices are connected to all q vertices.

In 1954 Zarankiewicz [93] had supplied a proof of the above (also given in Ref. 9) in which Paul Kainen discovered an error in 1964. Zarankiewicz also gave the following general realization scheme for the number of intersections conjectured.

The construction of the connections with the least number of intersections may be obtained as follows: Consider rectangular coordinates in the plane. If $m = 2r$, take on the x axis the points with abscissas

$$-r, -(r-1), \ldots, -2, -1, 1, 2, \ldots, r$$

and if $m = 2r + 1$, take on this axis the points with abscissas

$$-r, -(r-1), \ldots, -2, -1, 1, 2, \ldots, r, (r+1)$$

If $n = 2s$, take on the y axis the points with ordinates

$$-s, \ -(s-1), \ \ldots, \ -2, \ -1, \ 1, \ 2, \ \ldots, \ s$$

and for $n = 2s + 1$ take the points with ordinates

$$-s, \ -(s-1), \ \ldots, \ -2, \ -1, \ 1, \ 2, \ \ldots, \ s, \ (s+1)$$

and then join with a straight-line segment all the points from the x axis to all the points of the y axis. In this case one can easily count all the intersections.

MINIMUM ACCIDENTS AT INTERSECTIONS

Related to the foregoing is the following long-standing conjecture.

Conjecture *The minimum number of intersections I_n of the edges of a complete graph on n vertices drawn in the plane (denoted by C_n) is given by*

$$
I_n = \begin{cases}
\dfrac{n(n-2)^2(n-4)}{64} & n \ even \\[2ex]
\dfrac{(n-1)^2(n-3)^2}{64} & n \ odd
\end{cases}
$$

or simply by

$$I_n = \frac{1}{4}\left[\frac{n}{2}\right]\left[\frac{n-1}{2}\right]\left[\frac{n-2}{2}\right]\left[\frac{n-3}{2}\right]$$

We shall first prove this conjecture for the cases $n = 1, \ldots, 10$. We then state a general symmetry principle, generalizing on the representation of small cases from which (if proved) the conjecture would follow [70].

Consider each vertex of the graph C_n and its $n - 1$ connecting edges (its star) to the remaining vertices. The removal of this vertex and its star eliminates all intersections falling on these edges. The result is a complete graph on $n - 1$ vertices. Any other vertex of the complete graph on n vertices has the same or a different number of intersections on its star. In general, if x_i, $i = 1, \ldots, n$, is the number of intersections on the edges connecting the ith vertex, then the total number of intersections of C_n is $\frac{1}{4}\Sigma_{i=1}^{n}x_i$ since each intersection is counted exactly four times, once for each of the four vertices of the two edges defining the intersection. Thus, we have the following theorem.

Theorem 2-19 *If x_i, $i = 1, \ldots, n$, is the number of intersections falling on the star of the ith vertex of a complete graph C_n, then the total number of intersections in the graph is given by $\frac{1}{4}\Sigma_{i=1}^{n}x_i$.*

Theorem 2-20 *A necessary condition on the minimum number of intersections I_n of a complete graph C_n is that it satisfy the relation*

$$I_n \geq \frac{n}{n-4} I_{n-1} \qquad n \geq 5$$
$$I_n = 0 \qquad\qquad n < 5$$

Proof The average number of intersections per vertex in I_n is given by

$$\frac{4I_n}{n}$$

The removal of a vertex with at least an average number of intersections must leave a C_{n-1} whose intersection number is not less than I_{n-1}. Thus,

$$I_n - \frac{4I_n}{n} \geq I_{n-1}$$

from which the relation follows.

Repetition of the above relation gives

$$I_n \geq \frac{n(n-1)(n-2) \cdots (n-k+1)}{(n-4)(n-5)(n-6) \cdots (n-k-3)} I_{n-k}$$

from which lower bounds on I_n can be obtained if the minimal value of I_{n-k} is known. One may write the above relation as [34]

$$I_n \geq I_t \frac{\binom{n}{t}}{\binom{n-4}{t-4}} \qquad 4 < t \leq n$$

An inductive argument may be used to show that the conjectured formula for I_n holds for even n, given that it holds for the immediately preceding odd case. This follows from

$$I_k \geq \frac{k}{k-4} I_{k-1} = \frac{k}{k-4} \frac{(k-2)^2(k-4)^2}{64}$$
$$= \frac{k(k-2)^2(k-4)}{64}$$

However, if k is odd we have

$$I_k \geq \frac{k}{k-4} \frac{(k-1)(k-3)^2(k-5)}{64}$$
$$= \frac{(k-1)(k-3)^2}{64} \frac{k(k-5)}{k-4}$$
$$= \frac{(k-1)(k-3)^2}{64} \left[(k-1) - \frac{4}{k-4} \right]$$
$$= \frac{(k-1)^2(k-3)^2}{64} - 4\frac{k-1}{k-4} \frac{(k-3)^2}{64}$$

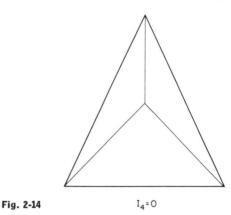

Fig. 2-14 $I_4 = 0$

and induction does not work from the even to the odd case.   Figure 2-14 shows that $I_4 = 0$.

Theorem 2-21 $I_5 = 1$.

Proof   See Ref. 51 or Ref. 9 and Fig. 2-15.

Theorem 2-22 $I_6 = 3$.

Proof   Theorems 2-20 and 2-21 give $I_6 \geq 3$.   However, Fig. 2-16 shows that $I_6 = 3$ is realizable.

An *isomorphism* between two graphs is a 1 to 1 correspondence between their vertices and between their edges which preserves the incidences of corresponding edges with corresponding vertices.

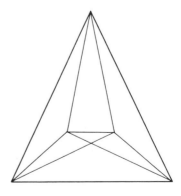

Fig. 2-15 $I_5 = 1$

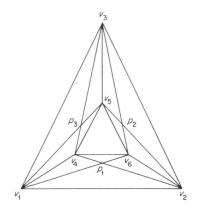

Fig. 2-16 $I_6 = 3$.

Theorem 2-23 *Every complete graph on six vertices with a minimum number of intersections, when its intersections are regarded as vertices, is iso-morphic to the graph of Fig.* 2-16.

Proof See Ref. 69.

In a *stereographic projection*, a graph is first mapped on a sphere whose south pole rests on an interior region and whose north pole is the starting point of line rays which pierce the sphere to the plane below, making correspond to each point of the plane a unique point of the sphere. The sphere with its graph image is now turned upside down, and the graph is mapped from the sphere on the plane using the south pole as the starting point of line rays. In this manner a specific inside region can be changed to an outside region.

Theorem 2-24 $I_7 = 9$, *with unique representation for the corresponding* C_7 *to within stereographic projection.*

Proof Theorem 2-19 may be applied repeatedly to $I_7 = 3$, 4, 5, 6, each time obtaining a vertex with such a number of intersections defined by its star that its removal, together with its star, leaves a C_6 behind, with less than three intersections, contradicting Theorem 2-22.

   We now prove $I_7 \neq 8$ (the case of $I_7 = 7$ is analogous). By Theorem 2-19 we have $(8 \times 4)/7 > 4$. Thus, there is at least one vertex with five intersections. Note that a vertex with six or more intersections would contradict Theorem 2-22. The only possibility here is to take, for example, $x_i = 5, i = 1, \ldots, 4,$ and $x_i = 4, i = 5, \ldots, 7$. In any case, the removal of a vertex which defines five intersections leaves a subgraph C_6, which is minimal. Using Fig. 2-16, we find that the seventh vertex may fall in any one of three different regions, con-

nected to the rest of the graph.   The other regions are symmetric
with these.   The three regions are (1) inside the interior triangle
$v_4v_5v_6$ (outside the exterior triangle $v_1v_2v_3$ is symmetric with this region
by stereographic projection); (2) in a triangle such as $v_2v_6p_2$; and
finally (3) in a triangle such as $v_5v_6p_2$.   In all three cases the edges
connecting the seventh vertex to any of the remaining vertices must
introduce at least six additional intersections, contradicting the fact
that the vertex was assumed to introduce exactly five intersections.
Thus, $I_7 \geq 9$.   However, Fig. 2-17 shows that $I_7 = 9$ is realizable.
Because C_7 with $I_7 = 9$ contains a C_6 with $I_6 = 3$, and this has
a unique representation, our construction of C_7 is unique, using symmetry arguments.

Theorem 2-25 $I_8 = 18$.

Proof   From Theorems 2-20 and 2-24 we have $I_8 \geq 18$.   However,
Fig. 2-18 shows that $I_8 = 18$, is realizable.   There is more than one
representation.

Theorem 2-26 $I_9 = 36$.

Proof   By Theorem 2-20, $I_9 \geq 33$.   Let $I_9 = x$.   Since $(18 \times 4)/8 =$
$72/8 = 9$ and $(19 \times 4)/8 = 76/8 > 9$, for all three cases $x = 33, 34$, and
35, the corresponding C_9 contains a minimal intersection C_7.   Because
a minimal intersection C_7 contains a minimal intersection C_5 and a

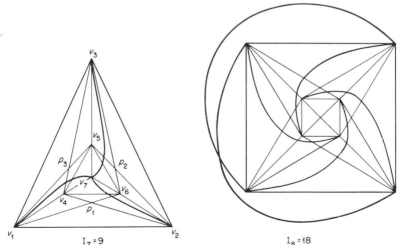

Fig. 2-17   Fig. 2-18

minimal intersection C_3, we have a contradiction to Theorem 2-25 [71]. Since Fig. 2-19 shows that $x = 36$ is realizable, $I_9 = 36$. There is more than one representation.

Theorem 2-27 $I_{10} = 60$.

Proof By Theorems 2-20 and 2-26, $I_{10} \geq 60$. However, Fig. 2-20 shows that $I_{10} = 60$ is realizable. There is more than one representation.

The intersection problem for C_n may be algebraically formulated as follows: Find nonnegative integers x_i, $i = 1, \ldots, n$, such that (1) there is a geometric realization (drawing in the plane) of C_n with x_i

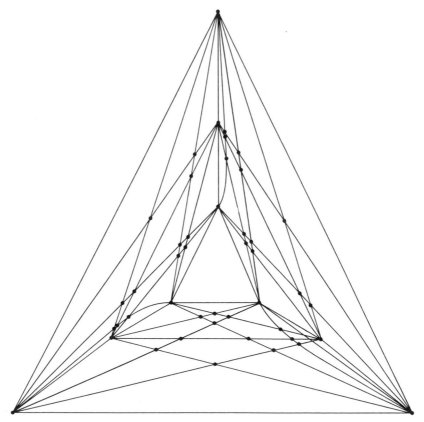

$I_9 = 36$

Fig. 2-19

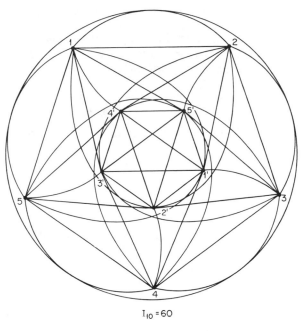

$$I_{10} = 60$$

Fig. 2-20

intersections associated with the ith vertex, and (2) these x_i yield a minimum (integer) value to

$$\frac{1}{4} \sum_{i=1}^{n} x_i$$

Note that this realizable minimum I_n satisfies the condition

$$I_n \geq \frac{n}{n-4} I_{n-1}$$

given in Theorem 2-20.

Theorem 2-28   *The maximum number of intersections of C_n is obtained by taking all its vertices on a polygon and joining them with edges in the interior of the polygon.*

Proof   Since each intersection is determined by four vertices, $\binom{n}{4}$ is the maximum, and the edges interior to the polygon give exactly this number of intersections since the diagonals of every quadrilateral intersect in the interior.

One can prove the following theorems.

Theorem 2-29 *A necessary condition for a minimum (maximum) of $\frac{1}{4}\Sigma_{i=1}^{n}x_i$ is that $x_i = x_j$ (or x_i and x_j are as equal as possible in the sense of integer values) for all i and j.*

Theorem 2-30 *A complete graph with a maximum number of intersections has a realization with $x_i = x_j$ for all i and j.*

Proof We have from the polygonal representation that

$$x_i = \frac{1}{4}\binom{n}{4} \qquad i = 1, \ldots, n$$

COMBINATORIAL SYMMETRY

In geometry, symmetry is defined by means of isometries, called *symmetry operations* (and their groups of automorphisms), which leave a figure unchanged or invariant while permuting its parts. The dimensions, translations, and rotations of the figure and its parts play an important role in characterizing its symmetry.

Here we discuss some methods in problem solving that suggest the existence of a more general concept of symmetry as their underlying common principle. The ideas are still far from explicit formulation and are introduced here to stimulate conceptual development in this area.

This general symmetry depends on rules of construction applied to elements of a set appropriately partitioned into disjoint subsets, together with a semigroup of maps between the members of the partition. A particular combinatorial property is preserved under the semigroup. Thus, the symmetry operations leave the combinatorial property unchanged, while the members of the partition of the set are interchanged elementwise. Recall that a semigroup is a set of elements that is closed under an operation, is associative, and here is required to contain an identity element. (Thus it is called a *monoid*.)

An example is given by the representation of the maximum number of intersections of C_n. Here the set is partitioned into its singletons (the trivial partition), each member being a vertex. The representation is invariant to a transformation which carries a vertex and its star to another vertex and its star, maintaining the order of the edges as they appear in the star. In general, we can consider any partition.

We note in Fig. 2-21, which is a representation of C_k, $k = 4, 5, 6$, with a maximum number of intersections, that the removal of any vertex and its star from C_n leaves a C_{n-1} with a maximum number of intersections. Here each C_n contains all lower-order C_k's, $k = 1, 2, \ldots, n$, each of which occurs $\binom{n}{k}$ times.

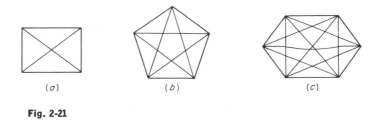

(a)   (b)   (c)

Fig. 2-21

A REGENERATION PRINCIPLE OF COMBINATORIAL SYMMETRY

We find the following observation useful: Maximality is preserved when additional vertices are inserted in the figure, having smaller numbers of vertices. Thus, when symmetry is retained in the construction of a figure which is an extension of a combinatorially symmetric figure on a smaller number of elements, having a special character of the combinatorial property (e.g., maximality of intersections), then that special property is also preserved for the larger set. The process of extension may be regarded also as a superposition of a figure for a larger set of elements over the corresponding figure for a smaller set. In terms of the partition and the semigroup of maps, the insertion of vertices is an extension of the original figure, its partition, and the semigroup of maps.

Thus, the larger figure is an extension of a smaller figure with preservation of symmetry. The smaller figure can then be obtained from the larger one by the removal of appropriate elements, and still smaller figures may be derived from the latter, and so on. In this manner, we obtain a descending sequence of figures, each of which retains the relative combinatorial property. The process of extension with symmetry and preservation of relative properties is referred to as *regeneration*.

The possibility of symmetric regeneration suggests the following conjecture.

Conjecture *If a given combinatorial property is known to hold for the smallest-order symmetric construction applied to a partition of a set and also for an appropriate subset of the family of its immediate ascendants (to ensure that the rules of symmetric construction permit continued ascendance with preservation of the property), then the property holds for an arbitrary ascendant.*

Possibly the most essential criterion for developing symmetrization rules for minimal or maximal C_n is based on the following definition.

Definition A symmetric realization of a complete graph is a symmetric drawing in the plane for which $\Sigma_{i,j=1}^{n}(x_i - x_j)^2 = \min$.

Returning to the problem of minimal C_n, suppose that n is even. Symmetrization from C_{n-2} to C_n by introducing a pair of vertices must conform to the symmetry criteria already used to construct a symmetric C_{n-2}. Geometrically, C_n is said to have the symmetric properties of C_{n-2} if its vertices can be divided into disjoint pairs, with preservation of mutual relationship between pairs.

The pairs are interchangeable according to: (1) the number of intersections sustained on their edges, and (2) the rule or scheme according to which these edges are drawn. Thus, a pair with its connecting edges (a double star) to the remaining C_{n-2} forms a configuration which is identical with that of any of the other $n/2 - 1$ pairs. An edge in the double star of a pair has the same number of intersections following the rules of the symmetric construction as the corresponding edge in the double star of any other pair.

The removal of one vertex of any pair, together with its star, from C_n (n even) must yield the desired C_{n-1} with the conjectured number of intersections. To obtain C_{n-2}, the other vertex of the pair must be removed.

The construction of a symmetric C_n for the conjectured value of I_n which satisfies the pairing requirement has been described in detail in the proof of theorem 1 of Ref. 71. For example, the pairs are identified as in Fig. 2-20 for I_{10}. One vertex belongs to the outer polygon, and its companion is the farthest vertex (or one of the farthest if there is a tie) on the inner polygon.

The removal of any one of the pairs of C_n naturally leaves a symmetric C_{n-2}. The addition of pairs to a lower-order C_n must follow the rules of symmetry used to construct that C_n from its antecedent. The regeneration principle implies the following conjecture.

Conjecture   *If C_n is minimal, then one may choose $r = [n/2]$ pairs of vertices, $P_1, \ldots, P_r$, of C_n such that if C_{2s} is the full subgraph of C_n determined by $P_1, \ldots, P_s$, $1 \leq s \leq r - 1$, then C_{2s} is minimal. Moreover, if n is odd, with vertices $V, P_1, \ldots, P_r$, any C_7 determined by V, P_i, P_j, P_k is minimal.*

The minimum intersection problem for C_n is a special case of the following general problem. Consider a connected graph G with n vertices joined by edges in the plane as follows: each vertex is joined to k other vertices ($2 \leq k \leq n - 1$) in such a way that a maximum number of vertices has degree k. If any two edges can cross at most once at a point other than a vertex, determine the minimum number of intersections $I_n(k)$ of the edges of G.

The solution of this problem should follow from our previous discussion of symmetric realization. Our existing realization may be used to remove the necessary number of edges. It is clear, for example, that the removal of the edges joining the prescribed pairs in the even case deletes the largest number of intersections. In the odd case, one vertex must have no edge removed; otherwise, another vertex would have $(n - 2)$ edges removed. The operation of removing an edge per vertex is continued. This gives

$$I_n(n - 2) = \begin{cases} \dfrac{n(n - 2)(n - 4)(n - 6)}{64} & n \text{ even} \\[2ex] \dfrac{(n - 1)(n - 3)^2(n - 5)}{64} & n \text{ odd} \end{cases}$$

$$I_n(n - 3) = \begin{cases} \dfrac{n(n - 4)(n - 6)^2}{64} & n \text{ even} \\[2ex] \dfrac{(n - 3)^2(n - 5)^2}{64} & n \text{ odd} \end{cases}$$

$$\cdots$$

$$I_n(3) = 0$$
$$I_n(2) = 0$$
$$I_n(1) = 0$$
$$I_n(0) = 0$$

Induction on k may be useful to go from the lower cases to higher ones.

Remark If the regeneration principle holds, then the proof of Zarankiewicz' problem would follow from his symmetric construction. Kainen has proved the following [46]:

Theorem 2-30a *If the conjecture of Zarankiewicz is valid, then*

$$I_n \sim \frac{n^4}{64} \qquad as \ n \to \infty$$

Proof We write $S_n = n^{-4}I_n$ and show that $\lim\limits_{n \to \infty} S_n = \frac{1}{64}$. Note that for fixed p, the complete graph C_n may be decomposed into a complete bipartite graph $C_{p,n-p}$ with the leftover edges discarded. We denote the vertex sets of $C_{p,n-p}$ by V_p and V_{n-p}. Let x be a crossing in a drawing D of C_n. If it belongs to a decomposition $D_{p,n-p}$ of D corresponding to a decomposition $C_{p,n-p}$ of C_n, then exactly two of the four vertices associated with x (i.e., the four end points of the two edges which cross at x) belong to V_p, and this can happen in exactly four distinct ways. (Remember that if the two end points of an edge in D both belong to V_p or to V_{n-p}, then the edge does not belong to $D_{p,n-p}$.) We can select a maximal system m of p-element vertex sets in D with the property that no two sets in m have a two-element subset in common. Let us denote by $\bar{m} = \bar{m}(n,p)$ the number of elements in m. Thus we can find a system $D_1, \ldots, D_{\bar{m}}$ of subsets of D such that each D_j is a drawing of $C_{p,n-p}$ and such that every crossing x in D belongs to at most four of the D_j. Therefore the number of crossings in D is at least one-fourth $d_1 + \cdots + d_{\bar{m}}$, where d_j is the number of crossings in D_j.

By Zarankiewicz' hypothesis, we have

$$I(C_{p,n-p}) = \left[\frac{p}{2}\right]\left[\frac{p-1}{2}\right]\left[\frac{n-p}{2}\right]\left[\frac{n-p-1}{2}\right]$$

Since each D_j contains at least $I(C_{p,n-p})$ crossings, we see that D contains at least

$$\tfrac{1}{4}\bar{m}I(C_{p,n-p})$$

edge crossings. But D and p were arbitrary, so we have

$$I_n \geq \tfrac{1}{4}\bar{m}I(C_{p,n-p})$$

whenever $1 < p < n$.

Erdös and Hanani [22a] have shown that

$$\lim_{n\to\infty} \bar{m}(n,p)\binom{n}{2}^{-1}\binom{p}{2} = 1$$

whenever $2 \leq p \leq n$. Combining these facts, we have for any fixed integer $p > 1$

$$\lim_{n\to\infty} S_n \geq \lim_{n\to\infty} \frac{1}{4}\frac{n(n-1)}{2}\frac{2}{p(p-1)}\left[\frac{p}{2}\right]\left[\frac{p-1}{2}\right]\left[\frac{n-p}{2}\right]$$
$$\left[\frac{n-p-1}{2}\right]n^{-4}$$

$$= \lim_{n\to\infty} \frac{1}{16}\left(\frac{2}{p}\right)\left[\frac{p}{2}\right]\left(\frac{2}{p-1}\right)\left[\frac{p-1}{2}\right]\left(\frac{1}{n}\right)\left[\frac{n-p}{2}\right]$$
$$\left(\frac{1}{n}\right)\left[\frac{n-p-1}{2}\right]$$

$$= \frac{1}{64}q(p)$$

where

$$q(p) = \left(\frac{2}{p}\right)\left[\frac{p}{2}\right]\left(\frac{2}{p-1}\right)\left[\frac{p-1}{2}\right]$$

Clearly $q(p) \leq 1$ and it is easy to see that, given $\epsilon > 0$, we may choose p sufficiently large so that $q(p) > 1 - \epsilon$. Therefore

$$\lim_{n\to\infty} S_n \geq \frac{1}{64}$$

and this, together with the readily established fact that the conjectured value of I_n is realizable and can be used as an upper bound giving $\lim_{n \to \infty} S_n \leq \frac{1}{64}$, yields the proof of the theorem.

2-7 CHESSBOARD COVERING [62,72,91]

Problem What is the maximum number of rooks that can be placed on an 8×8 chessboard so that no two rooks challenge each other? Do the same for queens, knights, and bishops. Generalize to an $n \times n$ chessboard.

Solution for the 8×8 *case* Note that in the case of more than eight rooks or eight queens, two or more would share a row or a column and hence challenge each other. The maximum is eight in each case. The rooks may be placed on the eight squares of a central diagonal, of which there are two. In all, there are 8! possible arrangements of the rooks which satisfy the above requirement. To place eight queens on the board is left as an elementary exercise.

For the knights, note that since a knight moves from a white square to a black square, if 32 knights were placed on all the white squares, none of them would challenge any other one. On the other hand, each black square would be covered by at least two knights. To show that 32 is the maximum, consider a 2×4 chessboard. On it, a knight on any square attacks exactly one other square, and hence a maximum of four knights can coexist peacefully. Covering the chessboard with eight such 2×4 boards gives a maximum of 32 knights. Since no more than four knights can be crowded in the smaller board, considering the 8×8 board, one cannot do better by some in-the-large distribution of the knights because this constraint on the 2×4 board must always be satisfied.

A MAXIMUM PRINCIPLE

If you know a maximum property for a building block, of which you can use replicas to completely cover a larger block without overlap, use it to get an upper bound to the same maximum property for the larger block.

We now turn to covering the chessboard with bishops. We observe that the board has 15 (black and white) parallel diagonals, but only 14 bishops can be placed on the board since bishops placed on two opposite corner squares threaten each other. The 14 bishops can be placed on the bottom row and on the noncorner squares of the top row.

Exercise 2-27 Show that 14 is maximum for bishops.

Exercise 2-28 By similar arguments, show that for an $n \times n$ board, the maximum number of knights is given by

$$\frac{n^2}{2} \qquad n \text{ even}$$

$$\frac{n^2 + 1}{2} \qquad n \text{ odd}$$

Show also that the maximum number of rooks is given by n and the maximum number of bishops is given by $2n - 2$. For queens, a complicated argument shows that the maximum is n. One argument given in Ref. 42a utilizes maximum internally stable sets from graph theory.

Exercise 2-29 Show that for the maximum number of kings, the formula is $[(n + 1)/2]^2$ for n odd and $(n/2)^2$ for n even.

Exercise 2-30 Show that the minimum number of kings which can be placed on an $n \times n$ chessboard so that each square is under the control of at least one king is given by

$$\frac{n^2}{9} \qquad \text{if } n \equiv 0 \bmod 3$$

$$\frac{(n + 2)^2}{9} \qquad \text{if } n \equiv 1 \bmod 3$$

$$\frac{(n + 1)^2}{9} \qquad \text{if } n \equiv 2 \bmod 3$$

Show that the answer of the same problem posed for rooks is n (there are $2n^n - n!$ such arrangements), and that for bishops it is also n.

An algebraic setting The foregoing maximum problems are a special case of the following [72]: Find

$$\max \sum_{i=1}^{n} x_i \qquad x_i = 0 \text{ or } 1 \qquad i = 1, \ldots, n$$

subject to the constraints

$$x_i \sum_{j=1}^{n} a_{ij} x_j = 0 \qquad i = 1, \ldots, n$$

where $a_{ij} = 0$ or 1, $i, j = 1, \ldots, n$, are elements of a symmetric matrix called the *challenge* matrix, each of its rows indicating with 1s the positions challenged from a particular square.

Remark The following unsolved problem is due to H. Heilbron. Can $2n$ queens be placed on an $n \times n$ chessboard so that no three are collinear? Considerable work has failed to crack this problem. According to a theorem of P. Erdös, if p is a prime, p squares can be chosen from a $p \times p$ board so that no three are collinear.

The chessboard–domino-covering problem—an algebraic formulation [47a] We now give an algebraic solution to the chess problem mentioned and solved earlier (see preface): What is the maximum number of dominoes required to cover, without overlap, as many squares as possible of a chessboard from which the bottom left and top right squares are removed? Each domino covers two adjacent squares.

Table 2-3

	0	1	2	3	4	5	6	7
7	y^7	xy^7	·	·	·	·	·	x^7y^7
6	·							·
5	·							·
4	·							·
3	·							·
2	y^2	xy^2	·	·	·	·	·	x^7y^2
1	y	xy	x^2y	x^3y	x^4y	x^5y	x^6y	x^7y
0	1	x	x^2	x^3	x^4	x^5	x^6	x^7
	0	1	2	3	4	5	6	7

We first show that it cannot be done with 31 dominoes. We associate with each square of the chessboard a monomial, as indicated in Table 2-3. Thus with the square i, j we associate $x^i y^j$.

If we multiply $(1 + x + x^2 + \cdots + x^7)(1 + y + y^2 + \cdots + y^7)$, we obtain all positions for the chessboard. Algebraically, deleting the lower left-hand square and the upper right-hand square yields $(1 + x + \cdots + x^7)(1 + y + \cdots + y^7) - 1 - x^7y^7$.

A domino can be placed horizontally or vertically. For example, if we put a domino horizontally on the lower left corner, we obtain a covering of $1 + x$, or if we put it vertically on this corner we cover $1 + y$. In general, a domino occupies horizontal positions $x^a y^b$ and $x^{a+1} y^b$. Thus,

$$x^a y^b + x^{a+1} y^b = x^a y^b (1 + x)$$

Another domino placed horizontally elsewhere gives $x^c y^d (1 + x)$. The covering obtained by the two horizontal dominoes is $x^a y^b (1 + x) + x^c y^d (1 + x)$. In general, horizontally placed dominoes yield an expression of the form $(1 + x) f(x,y)$. For vertical dominoes, the corresponding patterns give $(1 + y) g(x,y)$. To take both expressions, we add $(1 + x) f(x,y) + (1 + y) g(x,y)$. If the dominoes overlap, the coefficients can be more than one; and if a square is not covered, the coefficient is zero. Thus it is desired to find $f(x,y)$ and $g(x,y)$ whose coefficients are 0s and 1s so that

$$(1 + x + \cdots + x^7)(1 + y + \cdots + y^7) - 1 - x^7y^7$$
$$= (1 + x) f(xy) + (1 + y) g(x,y)$$

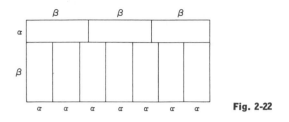

Fig. 2-22

This identity should be true for any values of x and y. In particular, it should hold for $x = -1$ and $y = -1$. These values make the right side equal to zero. On the left, the expression $(1 + \cdots + x^7)$ is zero, and $(1 + \cdots + y^7)$ is also zero and $(-1) - (-1)^7(-1)^7 = -2$. Thus we have $-2 = 0$, a contradiction. It is easy to verify that a maximum of 30 dominoes can be laid over the board.

Remark If the coefficients of f and g are arbitrary instead of 0 or 1, this means that we are using dominoes of different thicknesses, where the thickness is indicated by the coefficient, such as $\frac{1}{2}$ in $\frac{1}{2}x^a y^b(1 + x)$. The problem would be to cover the board with dominoes of uniform thickness.

The following theorem is an interesting and useful generalization of the chessboard-covering problem with dominoes [10].

Theorem 2-31   (N. G. de Bruijn) [15a]   *Given a rectangular case in n-space of dimensions p_i, $i = 1, \ldots, n$, if it can be filled with bricks of dimensions a_j, $j = 1, \ldots, n$, where a_j divides a_{j+1}, $j = 1, \ldots, n$ (such a brick is called harmonic), then it can be filled with bricks all facing the same direction; that is, a_1 divides p_1, a_2 divides p_2, \ldots, a_n divides p_n after a possible reordering of the p's.*

Remark We need the condition that a_j divides a_{j+1}. Otherwise, as shown in Fig. 2-22, the case cannot be filled with bricks parallel to one of its dimensions. If a brick has size $\alpha\beta$, where α does not divide β, neither α nor β divides the case's width $\alpha + \beta$ (its length is $\alpha\beta$).

Proof of Theorem 2-31 We first prove that the theorem is true if the bricks have dimensions $1, 1, \ldots, 1, c$. Such a brick is called a *stick*.

Assume that the given rectangular case is filled with unit cubes, and assign rectangular coordinates $k_1, k_2, \ldots, k_n$ to each cube.

Note that the expression

$$\sum_{\substack{\text{all} \\ \text{sticks}}} \left(\sum_{\substack{\text{all} \\ \text{cubes} \\ \text{in each} \\ \text{stick}}} e^{2\pi i(k_1+k_2+\cdots+k_n)/c} \right)$$

gives a covering of the case. Each stick lies completely parallel to some side p_j of the case. When the first sum is taken over the cubes in a stick, $e^{2\pi i k_j/c}$ runs through those (consecutive) values of k_j pertaining to these cubes. Since there are c such cubes, k_j/c will generate all the residues mod c, giving all c roots of unity. The sum of these terms is zero. Since the entire box is covered with sticks, this double sum must vanish because every cube is accounted for in some stick. However, the double sum is a rearrangement of $\sum_{k_n=1}^{p_n}\sum_{k_{n-1}=1}^{p_{n-1}} \cdots$ $\sum_{k_1=1}^{p_1} e^{2\pi i(k_1+\cdots+k_n)/c}$, which is a covering of the case; and this expression is equal to $\sum_{k_n} e^{2\pi i k_n/c} \sum_{k_{n-1}} e^{2\pi i k_{n-1}/c} \cdots \sum_{k_1} e^{2\pi i k_1/c}$. Thus, one of the terms of this product must vanish. Such a term, which is a sum, can vanish only if its index runs over an integral multiple of c, with the c roots of unity adding to zero; that is, some p_i, $i = 1, \ldots, n$, is a multiple of c. Thus c must divide one of the dimensions of the case, and the whole case can be filled with sticks parallel to that dimension.

In general, if we assume that the case can be filled with bricks of size $a_1 \times a_2 \times \cdots \times a_n$, then clearly it can be filled with sticks of size $1 \times 1 \times \cdots \times 1 \times a_n$, where a_n divides p_i for some i, but without loss of generality we assume that a_n divides p_n. If we consider any face of size $p_1 \cdots p_{n-1}$ of the case, then it is filled with $n-1$ dimensional bricks of size

$$a_1 \times a_2 \times \cdots \times a_{n-2} \times a_{n-1}$$
$$a_1 \times a_2 \times \cdots \times a_{n-1} \times a_n$$
$$a_1 \times a_2 \times \cdots \times a_{n-3} \times a_{n-1} \times a_n$$
$$\cdots \cdots \cdots \cdots$$
$$a_2 \times \cdots \times a_{n-2} \times a_{n-1} \times a_n$$

each time omitting one factor. Since each a_i divides a_{i+1}, the face can be filled with bricks of size $a_1 \times a_2 \times \cdots \times a_{n-1}$. The a_nth dimensions of the bricks must all face in the direction of the dimension p_n. Thus, the bricks completely fill a part of the case between one of its faces and a parallel section, both of size $p_1 \times p_2 \times \cdots \times p_{n-1}$. But the same argument can now be inductively applied to this section parallel to the face, and so on, until the case is filled with bricks all facing the same direction.

In Ref. 15a it is proved that if a brick is not harmonic, then there is a box which can be filled without being a multiple of the brick. A box is a multiple of the brick if its dimensions are all multiples of the dimensions of the brick after rearrangement.

2-8 DISCRETE GEOMETRY: PACKING, COVERING, AND FILLING [11,13,41,56,68,80]

The idea of packing as many objects as possible (without overlap) inside a container of specified form and size has a wide number of applications. These applications range from storing cans of food in a small cupboard to packing cables (cylinders) in a larger cylindrical pipe. It is known that a mathematician was once hired as a consultant by a citrus-fruit shipping company to find the best ways of packing oranges in crates to maximize the use of crates and minimize the squashing of oranges. In this manner, he helped reduce the number of crates used and hence the cost of shipping and, of course, the amount of spoiled oranges.

The density or efficiency of a packing is defined as the ratio of the total measure (e.g., area or volume) of the packed objects to the measure of the space in which the objects are packed. Obviously the efficiency is ≤ 1. A problem related to the problem of packing is that of covering an object with a set of smaller objects, which may or may not overlap, so that every point of the object is contained in at least one of the covering objects. The efficiency here is defined as before, except that in this case it should be ≥ 1.

For the density of packing in the infinite plane, we consider an arbitrary circle of radius R. The set of points it has in common with packed objects constitutes a certain area. We take the ratio of this area with the total area of the circle, and let $R \to \infty$. This limit is independent of the center of the circle.

Exercise 2-31 Consider another circle of radius R whose center is at distance d from the center of the first circle. Show that the density of packing using this circle is bounded below by the density of packing using a circle of radius $R - d$ and is bounded above by that of a circle of radius $R + d$.

Eating food and parking cars are examples of packing. Neat bed covering is an example of covering in which people are trained early in life. Dressing-up is another example; the object to be covered is a part of a larger object—the human body. When the covering objects just fill the space without overlap, it is as if they are also packed in the space. We refer to this borderline case as *filling*.

Often packing and covering problems have been studied in the more easily treated special setting which uses regular configurations. By a *lattice* we shall mean all linear combinations with integer coefficients of

n linearly independent vectors in n-space. The vectors of a lattice may be used to translate any Lebesgue measurable set K. The resulting sets form a lattice packing of K. Translates of K form a covering, if each point of the space lies in at least one of these sets. If a is a vector, a *translate* of K by a is $K + a$.

PACKING IN THE PLANE

Congruent regular hexagons may be used to fill the plane such that three hexagons meet at each vertex. There are two other possibilities for covering the plane with regular polygons. One of these uses regular congruent triangles, six of them meeting at a corner; the other one uses congruent squares, with four squares meeting at each corner. Of the three methods for covering the plane, the hexagonal covering is the best for packing inscribed unit circles inside such polygons. We shall compute the efficiency of this packing, which we denote by E_h, and that of unit circles packed in squares, which we denote by E_s, and leave the efficiency of the third type as an exercise. Let us consider the problem of packing equal circles of radius $r = \frac{1}{2}$ in the plane so that each circle touches six other circles as in Fig. 2-23. Each such circle may be considered as the inscribed circle of a concentric regular hexagon such that the hexagonal covering fills the plane.

The efficiency E_h is obtained by comparing the area of the regular triangle whose vertices are the centers of three adjacent circles, as in Fig. 2-23 (note that due to symmetry this triangle recurs over the entire plane), with the areas of the sectors of the three circles contained inside the triangle.

The area of the triangle is $\sqrt{3}/4$. The area of each sector is $\pi r^2/6$. Thus, the area of the three sectors is given by $3\pi(\frac{1}{2})^2/6 = \pi/8$. The efficiency of this packing is given by

$$E_h = \frac{\pi/8}{\sqrt{3}/4} = \frac{\pi}{\sqrt{12}} \approx 0.9069$$

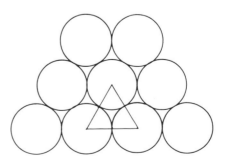

Fig. 2-23

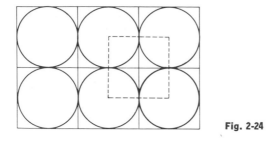

Fig. 2-24

Remark A consequence of work by Thue [79] done in 1910 is that circles cannot be packed in a general way in the plane to yield an efficiency greater than E_h. (We give different proofs of that fact later.)

Again consider circles of radius $r = \frac{1}{2}$ at the lattice of points with integral coordinates of the plane, and suppose that each circle is inscribed in a concentric unit square from a square lattice covering of the plane. We have Fig. 2-24. To measure the efficiency of this packing, and because of the symmetry of the pattern over the entire plane, we compare the area of a unit square whose corners are the centers of four adjacent circles (as shown in Fig. 2-24) with the area of the quarter-circles covering portions of the square. We have

$$E_s \equiv r\,\frac{\pi(\frac{1}{2})^2/4}{1} \approx \frac{3.142}{4} \approx 0.786$$

Therefore, hexagonal circle packing, which has higher efficiency, is a denser packing than circle packing by squares.

Exercise 2-32 Determine the efficiency of a covering of the plane with circles inscribed in congruent regular triangles covering the plane.

Exercise 2-33 Note that the radius of a circle inscribed in a regular polygon of n sides each of length L is given by $r = L \cot (\pi/n)$. Show that the density of packing a circle in such a polygon is given by $(\pi/n) \tan (\pi/n)$. Apply this result to determine the efficiency of packing circles in the three lattice coverings of the plane discussed above.

Problem Determine the number of circles of radius r packed so that each is tangent to six others and contained partly or entirely in a circle of radius $R > r$ that is concentric with one of the circles [17].

Solution For simplicity, we assume first that the distance between the centers of two adjacent circles is unity. Because of the triangular nature of the array of centers, we shall compute the number of centers in one of six similar sectors of the large circle. Let C be the center of this circle. Then C belongs to no sector (Fig. 2-25). What we need to do is to determine the number of centers along an arbitrary vertical line in the sector and scan over this number from zero to n, where n is the number of centers along the radius R.

Let k be the number of centers up to an arbitrarily chosen vertical line, whose number of centers x will now be computed. We have

$$\left(x + k \sin \frac{\pi}{6}\right)^2 + \left(k \cos \frac{\pi}{6}\right)^2 = n^2$$

Thus,

$$x = \left[\sqrt{n^2 - \tfrac{3}{4}k^2} - \frac{k}{2}\right]$$

and the total number of centers N is obtained by summing over k, multiplying by six (sectors), and adding one for C; that is

$$N = \left[1 + 6 \sum_{k=0}^{[n]} \sqrt{n^2 - \tfrac{3}{4}k^2} - \frac{k}{2}\right]$$

Brackets indicate the largest integer function. If the centers are $2r$ units apart, then $R = 2rn$ will contain N centers, and $R = 2rn + r$ will contain N circles. Thus, $n = \{\tfrac{1}{2}[(R/r) - 1]\}$, the braces indicating the largest integer function.

Exercise 2-34 [50] Consider two circles of unit radius. Let (ρ_1, θ_1) and (ρ_2, θ_2) be the polar coordinates of their centers. Then the distance d between their centers is

$$d = [\rho_1{}^2 + \rho_2{}^2 - 2\rho_1\rho_2 \cos(\theta_1 - \theta_2)]^{\frac{1}{2}}$$

Prove that the two circles can be packed in a circle of radius 2 if $d \leq 4$. Note that equality holds when the two circles are tangent.

Exercise 2-35 If N circles, each of radius r, are packed inside the circumference of a circle of radius R so that each circle is tangent to the larger circle and there are no gaps left between the circles, show that

$$\frac{R}{r} = \frac{2}{1 - \tan^2[(\pi/4) - (\pi/2N)]}$$

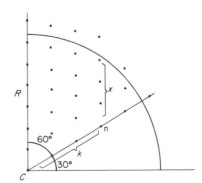

Fig. 2-25

PACKING CIRCLES IN THE PLANE

Here we prove the following theorem.

Theorem 2-32   *The density of the closest packing of equal circles in the plane is $\pi/\sqrt{12}$.*

Proof 1   This proof is given in stages below.

Suppose we have a system of circles of radius 1 with centers at P_1, P_2, . . . , which constitute a packing in the plane. We associate with each point P_i the Voronoi polygon $\Pi(P_i)$, which consists of all points of the plane which are nearer to P_i than to any other center. These polygons are convex and fit together to cover the plane exactly, without overlapping. We prove that

$$\text{area } [\Pi(P_i)] \geq \sqrt{12} \tag{2-1}$$

Lemma 2-3   *Let P_i, P_j, P_k be any three centers, and let X be any point. Then, either $|X - P_i| \geq \sqrt{\frac{4}{3}}$, or $|X - P_j| \geq \sqrt{\frac{4}{3}}$, or $|X - P_k| \geq \sqrt{\frac{4}{3}}$.*

Proof   Without loss of generality we may take X to be the origin. We suppose that $|P_i| < \sqrt{\frac{4}{3}}$, $|P_j| < \sqrt{\frac{4}{3}}$, $|P_k| < \sqrt{\frac{4}{3}}$ and obtain a contradiction.

Since P_i, P_j, P_k are centers of circles with radius 1, which are part of a packing, we have $|P_i - P_j| \geq 2, |P_i - P_k| \geq 2$, and $|P_j - P_k| \geq 2$. Thus,

$$4 \leq |P_i - P_j|^2 = |P_i|^2 + |P_j|^2 - 2|P_i|\,|P_j| \cos \theta_{ij}$$

where θ_{ij} is the angle subtended at O by P_iP_j.   Hence

$$4 < \tfrac{4}{3} + \tfrac{4}{3} - 2|P_i|\,|P_j| \cos \theta_{ij}$$
$$\cos \theta_{ij} < -\tfrac{2}{3}(|P_i|\,|P_j|)^{-1} < -\tfrac{1}{2}$$

This implies that $2\pi/3 < \theta_{ij} \leq \pi$ and similarly for θ_{ik} and θ_{jk}.   This is impossible, and the lemma is proved.

Let $\Pi(P_i) = A_1A_2$, . . . , A_k, where A_1, A_2, . . . , A_k are the vertices of the polygon $\Pi(P_i)$. Then each vertex is equidistant from at least three points P, one of which is P_i; call the others P_j, P_k.

It follows from the lemma that if A is any vertex of $\Pi(P_i)$, then at least one of $|A - P_i|$, $|A - P_j|$, $|A - P_k|$ is $\geq \sqrt{\frac{4}{3}}$.   Since

$$|A - P_i| = |A - P_j| = |A - P_k|$$

we have

$$|A - P_i| \geq \sqrt{\tfrac{4}{3}} \tag{2-2}$$

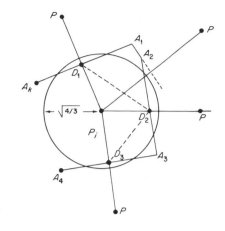

Fig. 2-26

Suppose now that the circle with center P_i and radius 1 is replaced by a circle with center P_i and radius $\sqrt{\frac{4}{3}}$ (Fig. 2-26). Then, by inequality (2-2), the vertices of $\Pi(P_i)$ are not inner points of this circle. Let S denote the region common to this enlarged circle and $\Pi(P_i)$. Clearly, area $\Pi(P_i) \geq$ area S; thus, to prove inequality (2-1) it suffices to prove that

area $S \geq \sqrt{12}$ $\hspace{4cm}$ (2-3)

Let m be the number of straight-line segments bounding S.

Case 1 (L. Fejes Tóth) $m \leq 6$.

Let T_1 be the area of the region inside the enlarged circle, but on that side of one of the straight-line segments bounding S remote from P_i (Fig. 2-27). Then,

area $S = \frac{4}{3}\pi - (T_1 + T_2 + \cdots + T_m)$

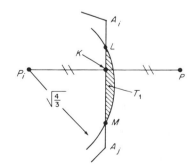

Fig. 2-27

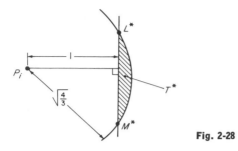

Fig. 2-28

If A_iA_j is that side of $\Pi(P_i)$ which is part of the boundary of T_1, then A_iA_j is the perpendicular bisector of P_iP for one of the P's, and thus $P_iP \geq 2$ so that $P_iK \geq 1$(without any assumption on m). Thus

$$T_1 \leq T^*$$

where T^* is the area of the segment of a circle of radius $\sqrt{\tfrac{4}{3}}$ cut off by a chord of distance 1 from P_i. This is indicated in Fig. 2-28. A simple calculation gives $L^*P_iM^* = \pi/6$ so that

$$T_1 \leq T^* = \frac{1}{2}\frac{4}{3}\left(\frac{\pi}{3} - \sin\frac{\pi}{3}\right) = \frac{2}{3}\left(\frac{\pi}{3} - \frac{\sqrt{3}}{2}\right)$$

Similarly for $T_2, \ldots, T_m$. Hence

$$\text{area } S \geq \frac{4}{3}\pi - m\frac{2}{3}\left(\frac{\pi}{3} - \frac{\sqrt{3}}{2}\right)$$

$$\geq \frac{4}{3}\pi - 4\left(\frac{\pi}{3} - \frac{\sqrt{3}}{2}\right) = \sqrt{12}$$

since $m \leq 6$.

(We get equality only if S is the regular hexagon circumscribed about the circle of radius 1, center P_i and thus inscribed in a circle of radius $\sqrt{\tfrac{4}{3}}$.)

Case 2 (L. Few) $m \geq 7$.

Here S consists of m triangles, together with sectors of a circle with radius $\sqrt{\tfrac{4}{3}}$. The area of a sector is

$$\tfrac{1}{2}\sqrt{\tfrac{4}{3}}\sqrt{\tfrac{4}{3}}\,\theta = \tfrac{1}{2}\sqrt{\tfrac{4}{3}} \times \text{curved length of the sector}$$
$$> \tfrac{1}{2} \times \text{curved length of the sector}$$

The area of each triangle is

$$\tfrac{1}{2} \times \text{base} \times \text{height} \geq \tfrac{1}{2} \times \text{base}$$

since, as remarked above, the height of each triangle is ≥ 1.

Thus,

area of $S \geq \frac{1}{2} \times$ perimeter of S (2-4)

Let $D_1 D_2 \cdots D_k$ be a convex polygon, where each D is the midpoint of one of the straight-line segments bounding S. Then $D_i D_{i+1} \geq 1$ (since the distance between any two P's is ≥ 2, and each D is the midpoint of a $P_i P$). Thus, the perimeter of $S \geq T_1 T_2 + \cdots + T_m T_1 \geq 7$, and, by inequality (2-4), the area of $S \geq 3.5 > \sqrt{12}$. Hence inequalities (2-3) and (2-1) are proven.

It now follows easily that since the original circles have area π, the density of any packing of circles is $\leq \pi / \sqrt{12}$.

We obtain equality in this method if and only if the packing is the hexagonal packing.

This completes the proof.

Proof 2 [55]

1. We assume that we have a packing of nonoverlapping circles in the plane, and that this packing is saturated; i.e., no more circles can be added to it without overlap.

2. The centers of adjacent circles can be joined by straight lines to form a triangular net covering the plane where no triangle has an angle exceeding 120°. To see this, consider a circle with center C_1 and another circle closest to it with center C_2. Consider the strip between the two parallel lines perpendicular to the segment $C_1 C_2$ (Fig. 2-29). Let C_3 be the center of a circle, closest to C_1 or C_2 and to one of the parallel lines (at distance Δ from it). There must be such a circle because of saturation.

If C_3 is inside the strip, the angle $C_1 C_2 C_3$ must be less than 120°. If C_3 is outside the strip, then the diagram and calculation show that each angle of the triangle $C_1 C_2 C_3$ must also be less than 120°.

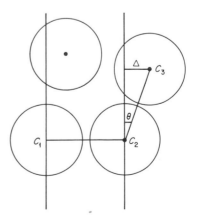

Fig. 2-29

Note that

$$\sin \theta = \frac{\Delta}{C_2 C_3} < \tfrac{1}{2}$$

In this manner the entire net is constructed.

3. If A is the area of a triangle then

$$\sqrt{3} \le \tfrac{1}{2} \times 2 \times 2 \times \sin \alpha \le A < 8$$

The right inequality follows from saturation, which implies that the base and height of each triangle is less than 4. The left inequality holds because every side is of length at least 2 and there is an angle α such that $60° \le \alpha < 120°$. Recall that the area of a triangle is one half the product of the lengths of two sides and the sine of the angle between them.

4. Let us take a circle C of large radius R and center O. Consider the triangular net of centers of circles which partly or completely lie in C. Some edges will cross C to centers lying outside C (within a circle of radius $R + 1$). Euler's formula gives $V - E + F = 1$ for a planar net. (Prove that fact by reducing to a triangle for which, as we have seen earlier in the chapter, $V - E + F = 1$ where V, E, and F are all the vertices, edges, and regions of the net.) If E' is the number of edges included in E and lying on the boundary of the net in C, then each of these edges bounds only one region of the net. We have $3F = 2E - E'$ because each face is bounded by three edges and each edge is counted twice; the E' edges bound only once. Thus $F = 2V - E' - 2$.

5. If we denote the area of the network by $n(C)$ which is equal to AF, then because of (3) and (4)

$$\sqrt{3}\, F \le n(C) < 8F \qquad \text{or} \qquad 1 \le \frac{n(C)}{\sqrt{3}\, F} = \frac{n(C)}{\sqrt{3}\,(2V - E' - 2)}$$

Obviously, by considering two concentric circles, one interior and one exterior to C, we also have

$$\pi(R - 3)^2 < n(C) < \pi(R + 1)^2$$

and hence

$$\lim_{R \to \infty} \frac{n(C)}{\pi R^2} = 1$$

a fact to be used in (6).

6. Let δ_R denote the packing density. Then by definition

$$\delta_R = \lim_{R \to \infty} \frac{\pi V}{\pi R^2}$$

However from (5),

$$\frac{\pi V}{\pi R^2} \leq \frac{\pi V}{\sqrt{3}\,(2V - E' - 2)} \cdot \frac{n(C)}{\pi R^2} \tag{*}$$

Our object is to show that

$$\delta_R = \lim_{R \to \infty} \frac{\pi V}{\pi R^2} \leq \lim_{R \to \infty} \frac{\pi V}{\sqrt{3}\,(2V - E' - 2)} \lim_{R \to \infty} \frac{n(C)}{\pi R^2} = \frac{\pi}{\sqrt{12}}$$

7. Dividing numerator and denominator on the right of (*) by V and noting that $R \to \infty$ implies $V \to \infty$, we would obtain $\pi/\sqrt{12}$ as $R \to \infty$ on the right if we can prove that

$$\lim_{R \to \infty} \frac{E'}{V} = 0$$

Now E' is also the number of vertices (also centers of circles) on the boundary polygon of the network. The area of these circles is $\pi E'$ and is contained in the annulus between circles of radii $R + 2$ and $R - 4$. Thus $\pi E' < 12\pi(R - 1)$. From (4) we have $F = 2V - E' - 2$ or $2V > F$ and from (5) we have $n(C) < 8F$. Hence

$$\frac{\pi E'}{V} < \frac{24\pi(R - 1)}{F} < \frac{192\pi(R - 1)}{n(C)} < \frac{192(R - 1)}{(R - 3)^2} \to 0 \text{ as } R \to \infty$$

This completes the proof. As we have seen earlier, the bound $\pi/\sqrt{12}$ is attained for the hexagonal packing of circles.

Theorem 2-33　*If every point of the plane is covered by (belongs to) a finite number of circles of a unit-circle covering of the plane, then the density of this covering is at least* 1.209.

Proof　We construct a triangular network, as in the packing problem, but start with two circles which intersect in a lune. One of the two intersection points of the lune must be covered by a third circle (if there are several, we choose one) and use its center for the third vertex of the triangle. Every triangle has a circumcircle of, at most, unit radius. But an equilateral triangle would have a larger area which is $\frac{3}{4}\sqrt{3}$. Thus, $n(C) \leq \frac{3}{4}\sqrt{3}\,F$. We have

$$\frac{\pi V}{\pi R^2} = \frac{\pi V}{n(C)}\frac{n(C)}{\pi R^2} \geq \frac{4\pi V}{3\sqrt{3}\,2V}\frac{n(C)}{\pi R^2}$$

and, as $R \to \infty$, we have the proof to the theorem. (A covering which realizes this density is illustrated in Fig. 2-30 [55].)

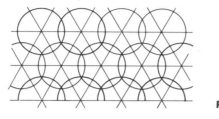

Fig. 2-30

APPLICATIONS

The parking problem [40]   There are many real-life problems which involve some geometric regularities and some irregularities.   One sometimes wonders what is a good basis for approaching a solution to such problems.   The problem of parking cars is an example.   Even though the turning angle of cars necessitates modification of the consideration given below, the answer is sufficiently close to merit one's attention.

Statement   Given a large rectangular area, what is the maximum number of congruent (relatively small) circles which can be packed in it so that any circle can be moved without disturbing any of the others? What is the arrangement?

The answer is to use double rows of circles whereby a circle of one row touches two circles in the neighboring row and the isles between double rows are a diameter wide to slide a circle out.   Around the boundary a single row of circles is used, but one assumes a very large area and does not worry about the boundary.   The density of this packing is $\frac{1}{2}(\sqrt{5} - 1)\pi/\sqrt{12}$.

The real estate problem [81]   Given a large area of land and n congruent rectangular houses placed in it (each of sides a and b), how does one arrange the houses so that the distance between any two houses is maximized?   Conversely, given an optimum desired distance d between houses, what is the maximum number of houses which can be packed in the area?   It turns out that the solution falls into three classes, according to the ratio of the sides of the rectangle.   We assume that the longer side of each house has length $b = 1$.

Let S be the parallel domain at unit distance of a rectangle whose shorter side has the length a.   For convenience, we assume that $d = 2$. Then the centrosymmetric hexagon of least area containing S is of type 1, 2, or 3, according as $2 - \sqrt{2} \le a$ (Fig. 2-31)

$$a \le 4 - \sqrt{12} = 0.536$$
$$4 - \sqrt{12} < a < 2 - \sqrt{2} = 0.586$$

respectively.

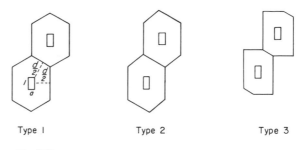

Type 1   Type 2   Type 3

Fig. 2-31

The distance from each house indicated by a rectangle to the bounding hexagon is half the distance of separation. Roughly speaking, this kind of solution is to be expected on intuitive grounds because hexagons give a filling of the plane.

PACKING IN 3–SPACE AND n–SPACE

Let us now examine the packing of spheres in 3-space. One way is to divide (or tesselate) the entire space into unit cubes and inscribe a sphere inside each cube. Since a cube has six neighbors which share a face with it, each inscribed sphere will touch six other spheres.

Exercise 2-36 Show that the efficiency of this packing is approximately 0.524.

Consider again the above tesselation of 3-space and imagine that all the faces of the cubes are removed but that their vertices and edges remain behind. Place a sphere inside a cube so that it touches all the edges and bulges out into neighboring cubes through the gaps left by the removed faces.

Naturally the neighboring cubes have spherical caps partly occupying them, and hence a sphere cannot be put in them (Fig. 2-32a). However, a sphere may be put in their neighboring cubes so that again spherical caps will bulge into these cubes. Continue the packing in this fashion. It is clear that each sphere now touches twelve other spheres at the edges of the cube.

Note that the six bulging caps may be imagined to be cut out and made to bulge inward from the six faces of one cube; thus, with each sphere we may associate two cubes. Assuming that the side of a square has length a, then the volume of the two cubes is $2a^3$ and that of the sphere is $V = \frac{4}{3}\pi(a\sqrt{2}/2)^3$. The efficiency or density of this packing for $a = 1$ is $V/2a^3 = \pi/3\sqrt{2} \sim 0.74048$, which is the densest known packing

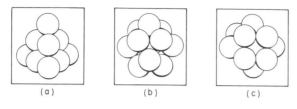

(a)   (b)   (c)

Fig. 2-32

of spheres. Steinhaus [50b], drawing upon this value of packing density, has pointed out that if gasoline is suspended in a soap emulsion whose proportion is more than 75 percent, then presumably the gasoline will not burn entirely as its spheres (or globules) cannot all touch.

Two other ways of packing spheres (Fig. 2-32b and c) in space to obtain this density are known. One is to pack spheres in a planar layer so that each touches six others as in the densest packing of circles. The next layer of spheres is placed on top so that each sphere rests in the hollow between three spheres. The third layer is placed so that its spheres rest over the hollow of the first layer left free by the second layer. Each sphere of the second layer is in contact with 12 spheres. The vertices of contact form a figure known as a cubeoctahedron, obtained by cutting off the vertices of a regular octahedron by a cube whose faces halve the octahedron's edges. It has six squares and eight equilateral triangles. For the third packing, one proceeds as above except that here the spheres of the third layer lie over the spheres of the first layer. Their vertices of contact give a polyhedron of 14 faces, obtained from the cubeoctahedron by halving the latter by passing a plane through the edges forming a hexagon, turning one half against the other 60°, and joining the halves again [50a].

It has been shown [68] that the efficiency of the densest packing of equal spheres in 3-space, without regard to the arrangement of their centers as the case is with lattice packings, cannot exceed 0.7797. Lower bounds on the number of spheres in densest lattice packings are known for $2 \leq n \leq 12$, but not for larger n [68].

We now consider bounds for the densities of packing and covering of n-space with equal spheres.

Consider $n + 1$ unit spheres of radius 1 packed in n-space, whose centers coincide with the vertices of a regular $(n + 1)$-simplex whose edges have length 2. Let σ_n denote the ratio of the volume of that part of the simplex covered by the spheres to the volume of the entire simplex. Rogers [68] has shown that the efficiency of the densest packing of n-space with unit spheres does not exceed σ_n. Daniels (see also Ref. 68, page 90) has given the following asymptotic formula for σ_n:

$$\sigma_n \sim \frac{n}{2^{n/2}e}$$

In general, if $\delta_n{}^L$ denotes the densest lattice packing and δ_n is the densest packing, it is known that for a certain constant C,

$$\frac{nC}{2^n} \leq \delta_n{}^L \leq \delta_n \leq \sigma_n$$

where σ_n can be evaluated in theory for all n and has been for $n = 2, 3, 4$. The upper bound $\delta_n \leq \sigma_n$ is the best known for *every* n. Bounds better than $\delta_n{}^L \geq nC/2^n$ are known for $9 \leq n \leq 12$ (see Ref. 68 for reference to Chaundy, Barnes, Coxeter, and Todd) and for some larger values of n [2a].

The following lower bound on the density of *covering* n-space with $n + 1$ equal spheres is given in Ref. 12. Again we have unit spheres whose centers lie on the vertices of a regular $(n + 1)$-simplex of edge $[2(n + 1)/n]^{\frac{1}{2}}$. The spheres just cover the entire simplex (with overlap).

If τ_n is the sum of the volume of the portions ("sectors") of the spheres lying in the simplex to the volume of the simplex, then a lower bound to the density of covering the space with unit spheres is given by

$$\tau_n = \left(\frac{2n}{n + 1}\right)^{n/2} \sigma_n$$

Problem (unsolved) Given a sphere in 3-space, what is the minimum number of spheres of the same size which can be piled around the given sphere to completely cover it so that all radial lines are blocked? Naturally some spheres may have to be piled on top of the surrounding spheres and perhaps some more on top of these. In [40a] it is shown that this number is ≥ 24. Other work mentioned in Ref. 40a proves that it is ≤ 42.

We now show how bounds may be calculated in n-space.

PACKING EQUAL SPHERES IN n-DIMENSIONS: BLICHFELDT'S METHOD

Lemma 2-4 (Very useful in various modifications of Blichfeldt's [6] method to other packing problems) *Let $X_1, X_2, \ldots, X_m$ be m points in n-dimensional Euclidean space, with each distance $|X_i - X_j| \geq 2$; that is, if $X_i = (x_{1i}, \ldots, x_{ni})$, $X_j = (x_{1j}, \ldots, x_{nj})$, then $[\Sigma_{k=1}^n (x_{ki} - x_{kj})^2]^{\frac{1}{2}} \geq 2$ (for $i \neq j$). Let X be any point of the space. Then*

$$\sum_{i=1}^m |X - X_i|^2 \geq \sum_{i=1}^m |\bar{X} - X_i|^2 = \frac{1}{m} \sum_{1 \leq i < j \leq m} |X_i - X_j|^2 \geq 2(m - 1)$$

where $\bar{X}$ is the centroid of the m points, that is, $\bar{X} = (1/m)\Sigma_{i=1}^m X_i$.

Proof

$$\sum_{i=1}^{m} |X - X_i|^2 = \sum_{i=1}^{m} |(X - \bar{X}) + (\bar{X} - X_i)|^2$$

$$= \sum_{i=1}^{m} |X - \bar{X}|^2 + 2(X - \bar{X}) \sum_{i=1}^{m} (\bar{X} - X_i)$$

$$+ \sum_{i=1}^{m} |\bar{X} - X_i|^2$$

$$= m|X - \bar{X}|^2 + \sum_{i=1}^{m} |\bar{X} - X_i|^2$$

[since $\Sigma_{i=1}^{m}(\bar{X} - X_i) = 0$ by the definition of $\bar{X}$]

$$\geq \sum_{i=1}^{m} |\bar{X} - X_i|^2$$

$$= m|\bar{X}|^2 - 2\bar{X} \sum_{i=1}^{m} X_i + \sum_{i=1}^{m} |X_i|^2$$

$$= -m|\bar{X}|^2 + \sum_{i=1}^{m} |X_i|^2$$

$$= -\frac{1}{m} \left(\sum_{i=1}^{m} X_i \right)^2 + \sum_{i=1}^{m} |X_i|^2$$

$$= \left(1 - \frac{1}{m} \right) \sum_{i=1}^{m} |X_i|^2 - \frac{2}{m} \sum_{1 \leq i < j \leq m} X_i X_j$$

$$= \frac{1}{m} \sum_{1 \leq i < j \leq m} |X_i - X_j|^2$$

$$\geq \frac{4}{m} \sum_{1 \leq i < j \leq m} 1 = \frac{4}{m} \frac{m(m-1)}{2} = 2(m-1)$$

This proves the lemma.

Let the spheres of a packing of unit spheres be replaced by spheres with the same centers, with radii $\sqrt{2}$ and with a density $2 - \rho^2$ at distance ρ from the center. Let X be any point of the space. We prove that

density at $X \leq 2$ \hfill (2-5)

The only spheres contributing to the density at X are those whose centers are within a distance $\sqrt{2}$ from X. Denote these centers by X_1, X_2,

. . . , X_m. Then, by our density law,

$$\text{density at } X = \sum_{i=1}^{m} (2 - |X - X_i|^2) = 2m - \sum_{i=1}^{m} |X - X_i|^2$$
$$\leq 2m - 2(m - 1) = 2$$

by the lemma.

Now let M be the "mass" of an enlarged sphere. Then

$$M = \int_0^{\sqrt{2}} (2 - \rho^2) d(J_n \rho^n)$$

where J_n is the volume of the unit n-dimensional sphere. Integration by parts gives

$$M = (2 - \rho^2) J_n \rho^n \Big|_0^{\sqrt{2}} + \int_0^{\sqrt{2}} 2 J_n \rho^{n+1} \, d\rho = \frac{2(\sqrt{2})^{n+2}}{n+2} J_n \qquad (2\text{-}6)$$

Let N be the number of centers in a large cube of side $2t$, centered at the origin O, and with sides parallel to the axes. The density of the packing is defined as [6]

$$\delta = \sup_{t \to \infty} \frac{N J_n}{(2t)^n} \equiv \frac{\text{volume of spheres}}{\text{volume of cube}} \qquad (2\text{-}7)$$

Now the enlarged spheres are contained in a cube of side $2(t + \sqrt{2})$. The mass of the enlarged spheres is NM and by (2-5)

$$NM \leq 2\{2(t + \sqrt{2})\}^n \qquad (2\text{-}8)$$

Hence, by Eqs. (2-6), (2-7), and inequality (2-8)

$$\delta \leq \sup_{t \to \infty} 2 \left(\frac{t + \sqrt{2}}{t} \right)^n \frac{n+2}{2(\sqrt{2})^{n+2}} = \frac{n+2}{2(\sqrt{2})^n}$$

ALTERNATIVE METHOD GIVING A SLIGHTLY WEAKER RESULT [80]

If $U = (u_1, \ldots, u_n)$ and $V = (v_1, \ldots, v_n)$, then $UV = u_1 v_1 + \cdots + u_n v_n$.

Lemma 2-5 *There are at most $n + 1$ points $X_1, X_2, \ldots,$ in n-dimensional space such that $X_i X_j < 0$ whenever $i \neq j$.*

Proof Suppose there are at least $n + 2$ such points. Since

$$2 X_i X_j = X_i^2 + X_j^2 - (X_i - X_j)^2$$

it follows that $X_i - X_j$ depends on the origin O but not on the choice of (mutually orthogonal) axes. Choose the axes so that

$$X_1 = (a, 0, 0, \ldots, 0) \qquad a \geq 0$$

Let $X_2 = (x_1, x_2, \ldots, x_n)$. If $X_1 X_2 < 0$, then $ax_1 < 0$ so that $x_1 < 0$. If $X_3 = (y_1, y_2, \ldots, y_n)$, then $y_1 < 0$. If $X_2 X_3 < 0$, then $x_1 y_1 + x_2 y_2 + \cdots + x_n y_n < 0$. But $x_1 < 0$, $y_1 < 0$, so that

$$x_2 y_2 + \cdots + x_n y_n < 0$$

Thus, we have at least $n + 1$ points $X_2^*, \ldots$, in $(n-1)$-dimensional space $[X_2^* = (x_2, \ldots, x_n), X_3^* = (y_2, \ldots, y_n),$ etc.], with $X_i^* X_j^* < 0$ [in $(n-1)$-dimensional space]. Proceeding, we obtain at least four points in two-dimensional space, with $X_i X_j < 0$, that is, the angle at $O > \pi/2$. This is a contradiction, and Lemma 2-5 is proved.

Now take the spheres of a packing of unit spheres and replace each sphere by a concentric sphere of radius $\sqrt{2}$. Let X be any point of the space. We prove that X is inside at most $n + 1$ of the enlarged spheres. Denote these centers by $X_1, X_2, \ldots$. Since $X_i X_j \geq 2$ (packing of unit spheres),

$$\begin{aligned}
4 \leq |X_i - X_j|^2 &= |(X_i - X) + (X - X_j)|^2 \\
&= |X_i - X|^2 + |X - X_j|^2 + 2(X_i - X)(X_j - X) \\
&< 4 + 2(X_i - X)(X_j - X)
\end{aligned}$$

since $|X_i - X| < \sqrt{2}$ as X is inside the enlarged sphere of center X_i. Thus,

$$(X_i - X)(X_j - X) < 0$$

Put $Y_i = X_i - X$. Then,

$$Y_j Y_j < 0$$

Hence, by the lemma, there are at most $n + 1$ such points Y_i and hence at most $n + 1$ points X_i.

If δ is the density of the original packing, the density of the "packing" of enlarged spheres is $\delta(\sqrt{2})^n$. Since no point is covered more than $n + 1$ times, we have for the density of the packing

$$\delta(\sqrt{2})^n \leq n + 1 \qquad \text{or} \qquad \delta \leq \frac{n+1}{(\sqrt{2})^n}$$

FILLING

Problem   Divide n-space into congruent convex polytopes. Alternatively, find a convex polytope which by translation and rotation can be used as the basic building block to fill the space. This problem is so far completely solved only for the plane (see below).

Many, but not all, fillings are known for 3-space. For example, if we take any of the fillings of the plane and build a prism over them, we obtain a filling of 3-space with congruent prisms. In some cases the prisms can be divided into congruent pieces, and any of these pieces can be considered as the building block. For example, each prism in a prismatic filling built over a square filling of the plane may be divided into cubes. Figure 2-33 gives a 3-space filling with cubes. Similarly, congruent triangular prisms (an infinite variety) may be obtained from each prism built over a triangular filling of the plane. Four kinds of tetrahedra are known which can be used to fill 3-space.

The following lemma will be useful in our discussion of filling the plane with congruent polygonal regions.

Lemma 2-6 *The average number of boundary edges of a region in a finite planar map is less than six.*

Proof If we use Euler's formula without counting the outside region, we have $V - E + F = 1$. From $3V \leq 2E$ we obtain $E \leq 3F - 3$. If the regions are labeled $i = 1, \ldots, F$, and if the number of edges of the ith region is E_i, we have $\Sigma_{i=1}^{F} E_i \leq 2E \leq 6F - 6$ since some but not all edges are on two faces. Dividing by F we have

$$\frac{1}{F} \sum_{i=1}^{F} E_i \leq 6 - \frac{6}{F} < 6$$

which proves Lemma 2-6

Corollary *In a finite planar map there is at least one region bounded by not more than five edges. Now as $F \to \infty$, the average attains but does not exceed 6.*

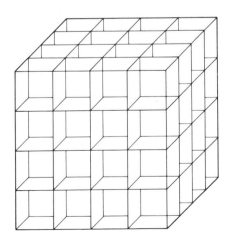

Fig. 2-33 Cubic filling of space.

It follows that if a filling of the plane with congruent convex polygons without gaps and without overlap is desired, then one need not consider polygons the number of whose sides exceeds six. Such a problem is referred to as a *paving, tiling,* or *tesselation* problem. It is clear that the plane may be tiled with equilateral triangles, squares, or regular hexagons.

Exercise 2-37 Show that the plane can be paved with triangles that are congruent repetitions of any triangle and with quadrilaterals that are congruent repetitions of any quadrilateral.

   Hint: Distort a tiling of the plane with regular triangles or with squares.

R. B. Kershner [48] has shown that there are three types of hexagonal pavings and eight types of pentagonal pavings; the first three of the latter may be considered as special cases of the former since they can be converted to hexagons by appropriately inserting a vertex along an edge. This gives the complete paving of the plane by convex polygons. Figure 2-34 gives the pavings, stating the conditions on the angles (indicated by capital letters) and the edges (indicated by lowercase letters).

Exercise 2-38 Consider the densest packing of circles in the plane where each circle touches six others. By attaching to each circle two appropriate triangular gores associated with the spaces between the circles, show that one has a tiling of the space with identical figures. Show that three different such tilings are possible.

APPLICATIONS

Crystals [49] A crystal consists of a very large number of replications of a tiny unit with a polyhedral shape. The units are assumed to consist of atoms or ions closely packed by the forces of attraction. Such a representation has been experimentally verified to hold for metals, alloys, and inorganic salts—a majority of solids. For example, in garnet this unit is the rhombic dodecahedron, illustrated in Fig. 2-35. Crystalline copper and mercury reveal a packing in which the unit cell is a cube. In crystal, the replications occur by successive parallel displacements of the unit building block. Argentite (Ag_2S) is a crystal whose unit is a cubeoctahedron.

Honeycombs A honeycomb is a filling of a part of space with congruent cells, each of which is a part of a hexagonal prism. One end consists of a hexagon which is the opening to the cell, and the other end is comprised of three equal rhombi put together as shown in Fig. 2-36. Each rhombic face is shared with another cell whose hexagonal opening is on the opposite side of the given cell.

   Thus, the two layers of cells are not separated by a plane, but by a

bent sheet of rhombi.   For a long time, people have been amazed as to
how the bees have come about this natural talent of constructing a regular scheme for the honeycomb [78,84].   Some have provided a physical
argument that each bee, working in its initially tubular-shaped cell,
attempts to push the wax surface as far out as possible.   However, since
neighboring bees are doing the same thing in their tubular cells, the result
is the hexagonal honeycomb.   However, cells worked on by lonely bees

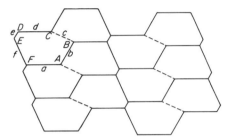

1. Hexagon of type I; $A+B+C=2\pi, a=d$

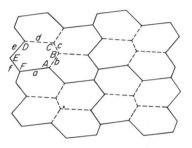

2. Hexagon of type 2; $A+B+D=2\pi, a=d, c=e$

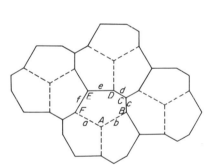

3. Hexagon of type 3; $A=C=E=\frac{2}{3}\pi, a=b, c=d, e=f$

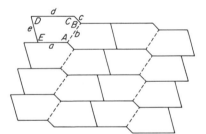

4. Pentagon of type I; $A+B+C=2\pi$

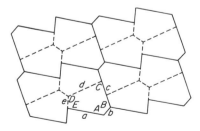

5. Pentagon of type 2; $A+B+D=2\pi, a=d$

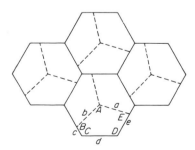

6. Pentagon of type 3; $A=C=D=\frac{2}{3}\pi, a=b, d=c+e$

Fig. 2-34—*(Continued on page 134)*

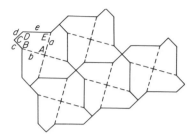

7. Pentagon of type 4; $A = C = \frac{1}{2}\pi, a = b, c = d$

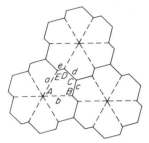

8. Pentagon of type 5; $A = \frac{1}{3}\pi, C = \frac{2}{3}\pi, a = b, c = d$

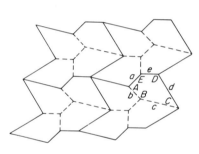

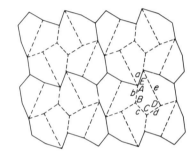

10. Pentagon of type 7; $2B + C = 2\pi, 2D + A = 2\pi, a = b = c = d$

9. Pentagon of type 6; $A + B + D = 2\pi, A = 2C, a = b = e, c = d$

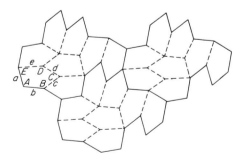

11. Pentagon of type 8; $2A + B = 2\pi, 2D + C = 2\pi, a = b = c = d$

Fig 2-34—(*Continued*)

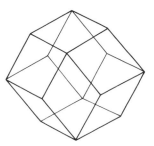

Fig. 2-35   A rhombic dodecahedron.

without neighbors have been observed to have the regular shapes, and to our knowledge the debate is not yet settled.

Fejes Tóth has shown that the bee cell does not supply the answer to the problem: Among all open cells of volume V generating a honeycomb (of any width), find the cell of least area [84].   Note that two cells may be put together with their open (hexagonal) ends touching.   This gives an elongated rhombic dodecahedron.   Fedorov has shown that rhombic dodecahedrons can be used to fill the space.   However, if we take an octahedron and appropriately truncate (cut off) its vertices with planar sections, maintaining regularity and congruence among faces, and then cut the resulting figure in half by a plane orthogonal to one of its hexagonal zones of faces, the result is a cell which generates a honeycomb.   Among the open cells of given volume which generate a honeycomb, this cell has the least area.   The bees, for some reason, construct longer than optimal length walls for their rhombic dodecahedron.   Fejes Tóth's analysis shows that it would be more efficient if the bees replaced the three rhombi at the closed end with two hexagons and two rhombi. This would save the bees per cell 35 percent of the area of an opening. Possibly the bees know the right solution but they don't like it.   Otherwise, why would hard-working creatures like the bees throw economy to the wind!

Coloring [9]   A map is a graph in the plane and the regions enclosed by its simple circuits plus the outside region, such that every vertex is of degree greater than two, and each edge bounds exactly two regions.

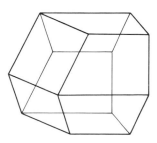

Fig. 2-36

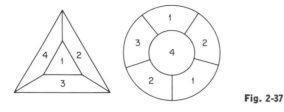

Fig. 2-37

Consider any arbitrary map in the plane. In general, a map may be regarded as an irregular tiling of the plane. Coloring a map so that no two regions with a common boundary curve (called *adjacent regions*) have the same color is equivalent to finding a second tiling congruent with the first tiling, which uses colored tiles so that no adjacent tiles have the same color.

Maps may be drawn on planes, spheres, and a variety of surfaces. The coloring problem remains the same. In all cases, one is concerned with the problem of finding the most economical number of colors for coloring an arbitrary map on the surface. The answer is known for a large variety of surfaces. However, as pointed out in Chap. 1, it is not known in the plane.

The following examples show that four colors are a lower bound for the number of colors needed in the plane (Fig. 2-37).

The problem of four-coloring the regions of a planar map is equivalent to that of four-coloring the vertices of a dual map so that no two vertices which are incident with the same edge (called *adjacent vertices*) have the same color. The dual map is obtained by associating a vertex with each region and connecting a pair of vertices by an edge, if the corresponding regions have a boundary line in common. Multiple edges are used if the corresponding regions have multiple boundary lines in common. Corners of the original map, where only two boundary edges meet, must be smoothed to a single boundary edge.

Theorem 2-34 *Five colors are sufficient for coloring the regions of a planar map.*

Proof We prove the theorem by induction on the dual; i.e., we color the vertices. Assume it is true for $n - 1$ vertices. The graph has at least one vertex v whose degree ≤ 5. If this were not true, then by using the relationship between the faces and edges $3r \leq 2m$ and $6n \leq 2m$ (that is, we assume the contrary that every vertex has at least degree 6) and substituting in Euler's formula, we obtain (an analogous conclusion to that reached in Sec. 2-3 between the edges and faces of a polyhedron)

$$0 = \frac{2m}{6} - m + \frac{2m}{3} \geq 2$$

a contradiction. Now if we remove v from the graph, the resulting graph can be colored with five colors by our induction hypothesis. Let us now consider the worst possibility, i.e., that five vertices v_1, . . . , v_5 are adjacent to v and arranged in clockwise direction. Suppose that the coloring of the graph without v (when v is removed, the edges incident with it are also removed) assigns a different color to each of these vertices (otherwise one of the remaining colors could be assigned to v and the theorem is proved). Let the respective colors be c_1, . . . , c_5. We now show that it is possible to reallocate the colors so that v will receive a color different from the vertices with which it is incident; i.e., at least two of these vertices will be assigned the same color. Consider the subgraph of vertices colored with c_1 and c_3 (the same colors as for v_1 and v_3). If v_1 and v_3 are not connected (i.e., there is no chain between them) in this subgraph, then the vertices colored with c_1 of the component which contains v_1 can be colored with c_3 and those colored with c_3 in that component are now colored with c_1. In this manner, both v_1 and v_3 receive the color c_3, and v can be colored with c_1. If, on the other hand, v_1 and v_3 are connected in the subgraph of vertices colored with c_1 and c_3, then, for example, v_2 and v_4 cannot be connected in the subgraph of vertices colored with c_2 and c_4. Otherwise, the chain connecting them must meet the chain connecting v_1 and v_3, and the vertex where the two chains meet will have assigned to it one color from one subgraph and a second color from the second subgraph. This subgraph which includes v_2 and v_4 can be recolored in the same manner as the disconnected case for v_1 and v_3 above, and hence v_2 and v_4 receive the same color. The other color is then assigned to v. This completes the proof.

The problem of four-coloring the original map is equivalent to that of coloring the regions of a trivalent map. In such a map every vertex (an intersection point of boundary lines) has degree 3. This means that it is the intersection point of exactly three boundary lines.

To show how the problem of coloring the regions of any map can be reduced to that of coloring the regions of a trivalent map, we show how the vertices of the original map, whose degree differs from 3, can be reduced to vertices of degree 3. This reduction is accomplished by replacing any vertex of degree $\neq 3$ with a closed polygonal region with as many vertices as there were edges incident with the original vertex. Each of the new vertices has one of these edges incident with it and is of degree 3. The resulting map is trivalent. When this map has been colored, a coloring of the original map is obtained by shrinking each of the new regions back to its original vertices. Thus, if four colors suffice for coloring a trivalent map, then they also suffice for coloring the original map.

One may now consider the dual of a trivalent map and concentrate on four-coloring its vertices. Note that knowing the economical number of colors does not help one in coloring a particular map. This task could still be a source of frustration.

COVERING COORDINATE LATTICE POINTS

We now examine some elementary packing and covering problems, involving lattice points of the Euclidean plane (points all of whose coordinates are integers).

Theorem 2-35 (Newman) *An $n \times n$ square S in arbitrary position in the plane covers at most $(n + 1)^2$ lattice points* [61].

Proof If C is the smallest convex set containing the lattice points in S, we have without difficulty area$(C) \leq n^2$ and perimeter$(C) \leq 4n$. Pick has proven (see Ref. 13) that the area of a simple polygon (no two edges cross each other) whose vertices are lattice points and which has b lattice points on its boundary and c lattice points in its interior is given by $(b/2) + c - 1$. Thus area$(C) = (b/2) + c - 1 \leq n^2$. Since the distances between any two lattice points ≥ 1, a curve of length b contains b lattice points, and hence $b \leq$ perimeter$(C) \leq 4n$, from which $b/2 \leq 2n$. Thus $b + c \leq n^2 + 2n + 1 = (n + 1)^2$.

Exercise 2-39 Show that the number of squares formed in the Euclidean plane by sets of four points (as corners of the squares) of an array of $m \times n$ lattice points ($m \geq n$) is [52]

$$\frac{(n - 1)n(n + 1)(2m - n)}{12}$$

(For oblique squares use the sides as hypotenuses of triangles of sides a and b.)

Theorem 2-36 (Blickfeldt) *Let S be a set in the plane whose area is > 1. Then S contains two distinct points (x_1, x_2), (y_1, y_2) such that $y_1 - x_1$ and $y_2 - x_2$ are integers.*

Proof Associate with each lattice point of the plane a unit lattice square of which the lattice point is the southeast corner. Consider the intersection of S with these squares. Translate all the unit lattice squares which intersect with S so that they coincide with the square Δ whose southeast corner is the origin and with which all the southeast corners must coincide. Consider the intersections of S with these unit squares. These intersections are now all in Δ. Since the area of S exceeds unity, two of these intersections must overlap in Δ. Let (α, β) be the coordinates of a point in the overlapping region. Clearly, $0 \leq \alpha, \beta \leq 1$. Consider the lattice points which are southeast corners of the two squares whose intersections with S overlap in Δ, and let their coordinates be (a,b) and (c,d). Then $(x_1,x_2) = (\alpha + a, \beta + b)$ are the coordinates of the point belonging to the intersection of S, with one of the squares in the original configuration, and

$$(y_1,y_2) = (\alpha + c, \beta + d)$$

are its coordinates as it belongs to the other intersection. Thus, both points belong to S Obviously $y_1 - x_1$ and $y_2 - x_2$ are integers since $c - a$ and $d - a$ are integers [91].

Theorem 2-37   (Minkowski)   *A convex set S in the plane which is centrally symmetric with respect to the origin O and has an area >4 contains a lattice point other than O.*

Proof   If $X = (x_1,x_2) \in S$ and $X' = (x_1/2,x_2/2)$, then X' lies on OX and $\overline{OX'} = \tfrac{1}{2}\overline{OX}$. If we make a point X' correspond to each point X, then the set S' of all X' is similar to S in the ratio $1:2$, and because the area is proportional to the square of the linear dimension we have

$$|S| = \tfrac{1}{4}|S'| > \tfrac{1}{4} \times 4 = 1$$

where vertical bars indicate area.

By Blickfeldt's theorem, S' contains two points $Y' = (y_1',y_2')$ and $Z' = (z_1',z_2')$ such that $z_1' - y_1'$ and $z_2' - y_2'$ are integers.   Corresponding to these points, we have the points $Y = (2y_1',2y_2')$ and $Z = (2z_1',2z_2')$ in S. Because of the symmetry of S about O, it must also contain $-Y = (-2y_1',-2y_2')$, the mirror image of $(2y_1',2y_2')$ with respect to O. The convexity of S implies that the midpoint of the segment $\overline{(-Y)Z}$ also belongs to S.   The coordinates of this point are

$$\left(\frac{-2y_1' + 2z_1'}{2}, \frac{-2y_2' + 2z_2'}{2}\right) = (z_1' - y_1', z_2' - y_2')$$

The coordinates of the point on the right are integers (not both zero), and hence it is a lattice point in S.   Since S also contains the mirror image of the foregoing point, it contains at least two lattice points. This completes the proof.

Remark   It can be shown that

$$\frac{(x - a/3)^2}{a^2} + \frac{y^2}{b^2} = \frac{5^{2k}}{9} \qquad k = 0, 1, \ldots$$

passes through exactly $2k + 1$ lattice points and the ellipse

$$\frac{(x - a/2)^2}{a^2} + \frac{y^2}{b^2} = \frac{5^{k-1}}{4} \qquad k = 1, 2, \ldots$$

passes through exactly $2k$ lattice points. Here a and b are distinct positive integers. In the first case b must be a prime of the form $4\alpha + 3$ and must not be divisible by 3. In the second case a must not be divisible by 2, and b must be a prime of the form $4(2k) + 3$.

Analogous results for an ellipsoid are known [90].

2-9 MAXIMA AND MINIMA IN SET THEORY

Optimization sometimes occurs in conjunction with problems of set theory. We give here three illustrations and the statements of some well-known theorems. A well-known elementary problem in this category is that of determining the minimum number of socks to be drawn in the dark from a drawer full of white and black socks in order to obtain a matching pair. The examples below are more sophisticated. We first prove (see Chap. 1, Ref. 15a):

Theorem 2-38 *The maximum number of triples formed from n objects such that any two triples overlap in at most one object is asymptotically equal to $n^2/6$.*

Proof The number of triples is at least $n(n - 3)/6$. To see this, number the objects 1, 2, . . . , n, and form all triples whose numbers sum to 0 (mod n). Such triples have at most one object in common, for if they have two, then the third numbers must be congruent modulo n and hence would be equal and the triples would be the same. The number of such triples is estimated from the total number of solutions of $x + y + z \equiv 0$ (mod n), in which $x \neq y \neq z$. Now x has n choices, and y must be chosen so that the following relations are satisfied modulo n: $y \neq x$, $y \neq z \equiv -x - y$, i.e., $2y \neq -x$ and $y \neq -2x$, i.e., y is chosen so that $x \neq z$, since $x \equiv z$ implies that $y \equiv -2x$, which we exclude. Thus y has at least $n - 3$ choices. The value of z is automatically determined. Thus the total number of choices is at least $n(n - 3)$, giving at least $n(n - 3)/6$ triples since x, y, z can be distributed in six ways among the three positions of a triple.

Again the number of triples is at most $n(n - 1)/6$. To see this, note that there are three couples in each triple and that no two couples in the set of all couples are the same, otherwise their triples would overlap in two objects. Since the total number of couples is $\binom{n}{2}$ and since each triple accounts for three couples, the number of triples is at most $\frac{1}{3}\binom{n}{2} = n(n - 1)/6$. The asymptotic result now follows.

Suppose that n points are taken k at a time, which gives $\binom{n}{k}$ subsets. These subsets are then distributed into r classes $C_1, \ldots, C_r$. If m is an integer, $m > k$, can one find m points such that all the subsets, of k elements each, of these m points fall in one of the classes C_i? We have [67] the following theorem.

Theorem 2-39 (Ramsey) *There is a smallest integer $n_0 = n_0(k,m,r)$ such that if $n \geq n_0$, then, for any distribution of the subsets of k points into r classes, there is a set of m points for which all of its subsets of k points fall in one class.*

The function $n_0(k,m,r)$ is known as Ramsey's function and is only known for simple cases. It is known that $n_0(2,3,2) = 6$, $n_0(2,4,2) = 18$, $n_0(2,3,3) = 17$. (These ideas have been generalized by Erdös and Rado [20].)

Theorem 2-40 *If X is a set of n points $n \geq 1$, and if A_i, $i = 1, \ldots, k$, is a collection of subsets of X such that every subset of X can be expressed in terms of the A_i with the set-theoretic operations of union, intersection, and complementation, then the minimum value of k is $-[-\log_2 n]$, where the brackets denote the greatest integer function [19].*

Proof This problem is equivalent to that of expressing every subset of a single element in the prescribed way. A_i is called a *carrier* of $x \in X$ if and only if $x \in A_i$. Since all single elements are distinct, it is both necessary and sufficient that each $x \in X$ have a different set of carriers. Now k sets yield 2^k sets of carriers (that is, each $x \in X$ must satisfy: given $y \in X$, x has a carrier which is not a carrier of y), and we must have $2^k \geq n$, from which the result follows.

Remark We have $\{x\} = \bigcap_{x \in A_i} A_i \cap (\sim \bigcup_{x \notin A_i} A_i)$

Exercise 2-40 Prove that if $A_i \subset S$, $i = 1, \ldots, m$, are subsets of a set S of N elements and if each A_i contains at least n elements then some element of S must belong to at least mn/N of the subsets A_i.

Frank Harary has made the following extremely useful observation regarding variations on a theorem by Menger. One of these variations (Whitney's) has already been given earlier in the chapter. Paths here sometimes also mean chains.
In 1927 Karl Menger [9] published this remarkable theorem: (*i*) For any two non-adjacent vertices of a graph, the maximum number of vertex-disjoint paths joining them equals the minimum number of vertices which separate them. Not until 1956 was the corresponding result (*ii*) derived (by Ford and Fulkerson) for edge-disjoint paths joining a pair of vertices and edges which separate them. Another theorem,

equivalent to that of Menger, appeared in 1932 (Whitney): (*iii*) A graph is n-connected if and only if every pair of vertices is joined by at least n vertex-disjoint paths. Theorems (*i*), (*ii*), and (*iii*) are corollaries of the max-flow–min-cut theorem of Ford and Fulkerson. Harary points out that several other theorems sound different from Menger's theorem but are in fact equivalent to it. These include the following.

(*iv*) (P. Hall, 1935): Let $I = \{1, 2, \ldots, n\}$ be a finite set of indices. Let S_i, $i = 1, \ldots, n$, be subsets of a set S. There exist distinct representatives x_i, $i = 1, \ldots, n$, $x_i \in S_i$, $x_i \neq x_j$ for $i \neq j$, if and only if for every $k = 1, \ldots, n$ and choice of k distinct indices $i_1, \ldots, i_k$ the subsets $S_{i_1}, \ldots, S_{i_k}$ contain between them at least k distinct elements.

(*v*) (König, 1931): In a matrix of 0s and 1s, the minimum number of rows which contain a unit element is equal to the maximum number of 1s which can be chosen with no two in the same row.

(*vi*) (Dilworth, 1948): In a partially ordered set E, the minimal number of disjoint chains which together contain all the elements of E is equal to the maximal number of elements in a subset of E whose elements are pairwise incomparable, if this number is finite.

(*vii*) (Minty, 1960): If the edges of a nonseparable graph (which has no vertex whose removal with its edges disconnects the graph) are oriented arbitrarily and are then colored red, white, and blue, and if one of the white edges is further distinguished from the others by calling it George, then there exists either a cycle containing George and not having any red edges, or a cocycle containing George and not having any blue edges, such that all the white edges in either cycle or cocycle take their directions from George.

(*viii*) (Beineke and Harary, 1967): If (m,n) is a connectivity pair (number of edges incident with each) of two vertices of a graph, then there are $m + n$ edge-disjoint paths joining them, of which m are vertex-disjoint.

Harary also points out that other variations of Menger's theorem occur in the literature of linear programming and its duality theorems. Review articles have been written giving a number of variations on the theorem (*iv*) of Hall.

REFERENCES

1. Adler, Claire Fisher: An Isoperimetric Problem with an Inequality, *Am. Math. Monthly*, vol. 52, pp. 59–69, 1945.
2. Balinski, M. L.: On the Graph Structure of Convex Polyhedra in n-Space, *Pacific J. Math.*, vol. 11, no. 2, 1961.
2a. Barnes, E. S., and G. E. Wall: Some Extreme Forms Defined in Terms of Abelian Groups, *J. Aust. Math. Soc.*, vol. 1, pp. 47–63, 1959.
3. Berge, C.: "The Theory of Graphs," John Wiley & Sons, Inc., New York, 1962.
4. Blachman, Nelson M.: The Closest Packing of Equal Spheres in a Larger Sphere, *Am. Math. Monthly*, vol. 70, no. 5, pp. 526–529, May, 1963.
5. Blažek, J., and M. Koman: A Minimal Problem Concerning Complete Plane Graphs, in "Theory of Graphs and Its Applicatons," *Proc. Symp. Smolenice* (June, 1963), Academic Press, Inc., New York, 1964.
6. Blichfeldt, H. F.: The Minimum Value of Quadratic Forms, and the Closest Packing of Spheres, *Math. Ann.*, vol. 101, pp. 605–608, 1929.
7. Boltyanskii, V. G.: "Equivalent and Equidecomposable Figures," D. C. Heath and Company, Boston, 1963.
8. Bricard, R.: Sur un Question de Géométrie Relative aux Polyèdres, *Nouvelles Ann. Math.*, vol. 55, pp. 331–334, 1896.

8a. Brown, T. A.: Simple Paths on Convex Polyhedra, *Pac. J. Math.*, vol. 11, pp. 1211–1214, 1961.

9. Busacker, Robert G., and Thomas L. Saaty: "Finite Graphs and Networks: An Introduction with Applications," McGraw-Hill Book Company, New York, 1965.

10. Chang, Theodore: Much Ado About Nothing, *Eng. News*, pp. 27–28, October, 1966.

11. Courant, Richard, and Herbert Robbins: "What is Mathematics?" Oxford University Press, London, 1961.

12. Coxeter, H. S. M., L. Few, and C. A. Rogers: Covering Space with Equal Spheres, *Mathematika*, vol. 6, pp. 147–157, 1959.

13. Coxeter, H. S. M.: "Introduction to Geometry," John Wiley & Sons, Inc., New York, 1962.

14. Coxeter, H. S. M., M. G. Greening, and Ron Graham: Sets of Points with Given Minimum Separation, *Am. Math. Monthly*, vol. 75, no. 2, February, 1968.

15. Croft, H. T., and D. C. B. Marsh: A Max-min Problem, *Am. Math. Monthly*, pp. 86–87, January, 1967.

15a. de Bruijn, N. G.: Filling Boxes with Bricks, *Am. Math. Monthly*, vol. 76, no. 1, January, 1969.

16. Demir, Huseyin: Maximum Area of a Region Bounded by a Closed Polygon with Given Sides, *Math. Mag.*, vol. 39, no. 4, pp. 228–231, September, 1966.

17. Demir, Huseyin, and Alan Sutcliffe: Circle Packing, *Math. Mag.*, pp. 427–428, November–December, 1961.

18. Dirac, G. A.: Some Theorems of Abstract Graphs, *Proc. London Math. Soc.*, ser. 3, vol. 2, pp. 69–81, 1952.

19. Dwinger, Philip, and Daniel A. Marcus: A Minimum Number of Subsets, *Am. Math. Monthly*, vol. 75, no. 4, pp. 410–411, April, 1968.

20. Erdös, P., and R. Rado: A Partition Calculus in Set Theory, *Bull. Am. Math. Soc.*, vol. 62, pp. 427–488, 1956.

21. Erdös, P.: On Sets of Distances of n Points, *Am. Math. Monthly*, pp. 248–250, 1946.

22. Erdös, P.: On Sets of Distances of n Points in Euclidean Space, *Magy. Tud. Akad. Mat. Kut. Int. Koŝl*, vol. 5, pp. 165–169, 1960.

22a. Erdös, P., and H. Hanani: On a Limit Theorem in Combinatorial Analysis, *Publ. Math. Debrecen*, vol. 10, pp. 10–13, 1963.

23. Few, L.: The Shortest Path and the Shortest Road Through n Points, *Mathematika*, vol. 2, pp. 141–144, 1955.

24. Few, L.: Covering Space by Spheres, *Mathematika*, vol. 3, pp. 136–139, 1956.

24a. Floyd, R. W.: Algorithm 97, Shortest Path, *Commun. ACM*, vol. 5, no. 6, p. 345, 1962.

25. Ford, L. R., and D. R. Fulkerson: Maximal Flow Through a Network, *Can. Math. J.*, vol. 8, pp. 399–404, 1956.

25a. Frank, H., and I. T. Frisch: "Communication, Transmission and Transportation Networks," Addison Wesley Publishing Company, Inc., Reading, Mass. (in press).

26. Goldberg, Michael: Covering by Dissected Squares, *Am. Math. Monthly*, vol. 59, pp. 699–700, December, 1952.

27. Goldberg, Michael: The Isoperimetric Problem for Polyhedra, *Tôhoku Math. J.*, vol. 40, pt. I, pp. 226–236, December, 1934.

28. Goldberg, M., and B. M. Stewart: A Dissection Problem for Sets of Polygons, *Am. Math. Monthly*, vol. 71, no. 10, pp. 1077–1095, 1964.

29. Goldberg, Michael: On the Original Malfatti Problem, *Math. Mag.*, vol. 40, no. 5, pp. 241–247, November, 1967.

30. Golomb, S. W.: "Polyominoes," Charles Scribner's Sons, New York, 1965.
31. Goodman, A. W.: On Sets of Acquaintances and Strangers at any Party, *Am. Math. Monthly*, pp. 778–783, November, 1959.
32. Grünbaum, Branko: "Convex Polytopes," Interscience Publishers, New York, 1967.
33. Grünbaum, B.: A Proof of Vazsonyi's Conjecture, *Bull. Res. Council Israel*, vol. 6A, no. 1, pp. 77–78, October, 1956.
34. Guy, R. K.: A Combinatorial Problem, *Bull. Malay. Math. Soc.* 7, no. 2, pp. 68–72, July, 1960.
35. Guy, Richard K., Tom Jenkyns, and Jonathan Schaer: The Toroidal Crossing Number of the Complete Graph, University of Calgary (Canada), Dept. of Mathematics, Res. Paper No. 18, May, 1967.
36. Hall, Jr., Marshall: "Combinatorial Theory," Blaisdell Publishing Company, 1967.
37. Hancock, Harris: "Development of the Minkowski Geometry of Numbers," vols. 1 and 2, Dover Publications, Inc., New York, 1939.
38. Harary, Frank: "A Seminar on Graph Theory," Holt, Rinehart and Winston, Inc., New York, 1967.
39. Heesch, Heinrich, and Otto Kienzle: "Flächenschluss," Springer-Verlag OHG, Berlin-Göttingen-Heidelberg, 1963.
40. Heppes, A.: On the Densest Packing of Circles not Blocking Each Other, *Stud. Sci. Math. Hung.*, vol. 2, no. 1–2, pp. 257–263, 1967.
40a. Heffer, A.: On the Number of Spheres Which Can Hide a Given Sphere, *Can. J. Math.*, vol. 19, pp. 413–418, 1967.
41. Hilbert, D., and S. Cohn-Vossen: "Geometry and the Imagination," Chelsea Publishing Company, New York, 1952.
42. Hildebrand, F. B.: "Methods of Applied Mathematics," Prentice-Hall, Inc., Englewood Cliffs, N.J., 1961.
42a. Hoffman, E. J., J. C. Loessi, and R. C. Moore: Constructions for the Solution of the m Queens Problem, *Math. Mag.*, pp. 66–72, March, 1969.
43. Jacobson, R. A., and K. L. Yocom: Paths of Minimal Length within a Cube, *Am. Math. Monthly*, pp. 634–639, June–July, 1966.
44. Jacobson, R. A., and K. L. Yocom: Shortest Paths within Polygons, *Math. Mag.*, pp. 290–293, November–December, 1966.
45. Jucovič, E., and J. W. Moon: The Maximum Diameter of a Convex Polyhedron, *Math. Mag.*, vol. 38, no. 1, January, 1965.
46. Kainen, Paul: On a Problem of Erdös, *J. Comb. Theory*, vol. 5, pp. 374–377, 1968.
47. Kazarinoff, Nicholas D.: "Geometric Inequalities," Random House, Inc., New York, 1961.
47a. Kelley, J. B.: Polynomials and Polyominoes, *Am. Math. Monthly*, vol. 73, pp. 464–471, May, 1966.
48. Kershner, R. B.: On Paving the Plane, *Am. Math. Monthly*, vol. 75, no. 8, pp. 839–844, October, 1968.
49. Kitaigorodskiy, A. I.: "Order and Disorder in the World of Atoms," Springer-Verlag New York Inc., 1967.
50. Kravitz, Sidney: Packing Cylinders into Cylindrical Containers, *Math. Mag.*, vol. 40, no. 2, pp. 65–71, 1967.
50a. Kruskal, J. B., Jr.: On the Shortest Spanning Subtree of a Graph and the Traveling Salesman Problem, *Proc. Am. Math. Soc.*, pp. 48–50, 1956.
51. Kuratowski, Kasimir: Sur le problème des courbes gauches en topologie, *Fund. Math.*, vol. 15, pp. 271–283, 1930.

52. Langman, Harry: "Play Mathematics," Hafner Publishing Company, Inc., New York, 1962.
53. Lietzmann, W.: "Visual Topology," American Elsevier Publishing Company, Inc., New York, 1965.
54. Lindsey II, John H.: Assignment of Numbers to Vertices, *Am. Math. Monthly*, pp. 508–516, May, 1964.
54a. Lyusternik, L. A.: "Shortest Paths, Variational Problems," The Macmillan Company, New York, 1964.
55. Meschkowski, Herbert: "Unsolved and Unsolvable Problems In Geometry," Oliver & Boyd Ltd., London, 1966.
56. Minkowski, Hermann: "Geometrie der Zahlen," Chelsea Publishing Company, New York, 1953.
57. Moon, J. W.: On the Distribution of Crossings in Random Complete Graphs, *J. Soc. Ind. Appl. Math.*, vol. 13, pp. 506–510, 1965.
58. Moon, J. W., and L. Moser: Simple Paths on Polyhedra, *Pacific J. Math.*, vol. 13, no. 2, pp. 629–631, 1963.
59. Moser, Leo: On The Different Distances Determined by n Points, *Am. Math. Monthly*, vol. 59, pp. 85–91, 1952.
60. Mott-Smith, J.: "Mathematical Puzzles for Beginners and Enthusiasts," McGraw-Hill Book Company, New York, 1946.
60a. Murchland, J. D.: Shortest Distances by a Fixed Matrix Method, Transport Network Theory Unit Publication, London, 1968.
61. Newman, D. J.: A Maximum Covering of Lattice Points by a Square, *Am. Math. Monthly*, vol. 75, no. 5, May, 1968.
62. Newman, Irving, and Robert Patenaude: Nonattacking Knights on a Chessboard, *Am. Math. Monthly*, p. 210, February, 1964.
63. Oler, Norman: The Slackness of Finite Packings in E_2, *Am. Math. Monthly*, vol. 69, no. 6, pp. 511–514, June–July, 1962.
64. Ore, Oystein: The Four Color Problem, Academic Press, Inc., New York, 1967.
65. Page, Yonder, and J. L. Selfridge: Another Square-covering Problem, *Am. Math. Monthly*, p. 185, February, 1960.
66. Pinzka, C. F., J. F. Leetch, and D. A. Moran: The Soap Contest, *Am. Math. Monthly*, vol. 68, no. 3, pp. 295–296, March, 1961.
67. Ramsey, F. P.: On a Problem of Formal Logic, *Proc. London Math. Soc. (2)*, vol. 30, pp. 264–286, 1930.
68. Rogers, C. A.: "Packing and Covering," Cambridge University Press, New York, 1964.
69. Saaty, T. L.: Remarks on the Four Color Problem, The Kempe Catastrophe, *Math. Mag.*, January, 1967.
70. Saaty, T. L.: Symmetry and the Crossing Number for Complete Graphs, *J. Nat. Bur. Standards*, April–May, 1969.
71. Saaty, T. L.: Two Theorems on the Minimum Number of Intersections for Complete Graphs, *J. Comb. Theory*, vol. 2, no. 4, pp. 571–584, June, 1967.
72. Scheid, Francis: Some Packing Problems, *Am. Math. Monthly*, pp. 231–235, March, 1960.
73. Segre, B., and K. Mahler: On the Densest Packing of Circles, *Am. Math. Monthly*, pp. 261–270, May, 1944.
74. Smalley, Ian: Simple Regular Sphere Packings in Three Dimensions, *Math. Mag.*, vol. 36, no. 5, pp. 295–299, November, 1963.
75. Steinhaus, H.: "Mathematical Snapshots," Oxford University Press, Fairlawn, N.J., 1950.

76. Stover, Donald W.: "Mosaics," Houghton Mifflin Company, Boston, 1966.
77. Sominskii, I. S.: "The Method of Mathematical Inductions," D. C. Heath and Company, Boston trans. from 5th Russian ed., 1959.
78. Thompson, D'Arcy Wentworth: "On Growth and Form," Cambridge University Press, New York, 1966.
79. Thue, A.: Über die dichteste Zusammenstellung von kongruenten Kreisen in einer Ebene, *Christiania Vid. Sel'sk. Skr.*, vol. 1, pp. 3–9, 1910.
80. Tóth, L. Fejes: "Lagerungen in Der Ebene Auf Der Kugel Und Im Raum," Springer-Verlag OHG, Berlin, 1953.
81. Tóth, L. Fejes: On the Arrangement of Houses in a Housing Estate, *Stud. Sci. Math. Hung.*, vol. 2, no. 1–2, pp. 37–42, 1967.
82. Tóth, L. Fejes: "Regular Figures," Pergamon Press, New York, 1964.
83. Tóth, L. Fejes: New Proof of a Minimum Property of the Regular n-Gon, *Am. Math. Monthly*, p. 589, 1947.
84. Tóth, L. Fejes: What the Bees Know and What They Do Not Know, *Bull. Am. Math. Soc.*, vol. 70, no. 4, pp. 468–481, July, 1964.
85. Trigg, Charles W.: "Mathematical Quickies," McGraw-Hill Book Company, New York, 1967.
86. Ungar, P.: Minimal Path Connecting n Points, *Am. Math. Monthly*, vol. 57, p. 261, 1950.
87. Weyl, Hermann: "Symmetry," Princeton University Press, Princeton, N.J., 1952.
88. Whitney, Hassler: Congruent Graphs and the Connectivity of Graphs, *Am. J. Math.*, vol. 54, pp. 150–168, 1932.
89. Witgen, G.: Découpage du Cube, *Rev. Franç. Rech. Opération.*, vol. 7, no. 26, pp. 92–93, 1963.
90. Wulczyn, Gregory: Ellipses Passing through a Prescribed Number of Lattice Points, *Am. Math. Monthly*, vol. 75, p. 671, June–July, 1968.
91. Yaglom, A. M., and I. M. Yaglom: "Challenging Mathematical Problems with Elementary Solutions," Holden-Day, Inc., San Francisco, 1964.
92. Yaglom, I. M., and V. G. Boltyanskii: "Convex Figures," Holt, Rinehart and Winston, Inc., New York, 1961.
93. Zarankiewicz, K.: On a Problem of P. Turán Concerning Graphs, *Fund. Math.*, vol. 41, pp. 137–145, 1954.
94. Zassenhaus, Hans: Modern Developments in the Geometry of Numbers, *Bull. Am. Math. Soc.*, vol. 67, no. 5, 1961.

3
Some Elementary Applications

3-1 INTRODUCTION

Some optimization problems which are real-life problems requiring integer
solutions may be formulated directly without recourse to the underlying
set-theoretic and corresponding geometric formulation.   In this chapter,
we give some examples and their solutions.

3-2 INFORMATION THEORY

From the standpoint of information or knowledge, the presence of a
problem is a state of uncertainty.   Solving the problem totally or partially is removing or reducing this uncertainty.   Thus, a problem may
be first regarded in terms of the amount of uncertainty in it.   Its solution
may be generated by logical operations and experimental tests to gather
information which decreases the uncertainty (to zero if possible).   Uncertainty or entropy content (the negative of this quantity is defined as the

information content) of a set of n mutually exclusive events is given by

$$H(p_1, \ldots, p_n) = - \sum_{i=1}^{n} p_i \log p_i \qquad \sum_{i=1}^{n} p_i = 1$$

Thus, there are n distinct factors in the problem, and the probability that the ith factor presents itself in defining the problem is p_i. In the continuous case entropy is given by [11]

$$H[f(x)] = -E[\log f(x)] = - \int_{-\infty}^{\infty} f(x) \log f(x) \, dx$$

$$\int_{-\infty}^{\infty} f(x) \, dx \equiv 1 \qquad \int_{-\infty}^{\infty} x f(x) \, dx = 1 \qquad \int_{-\infty}^{\infty} x^2 f(x) \, dx = \sigma^2$$

Similar expressions may be given for the case of several variables.

The logarithm in the definition of entropy arises from requiring additivity in the sense that the sum of the entropies obtained from two events is equal to the entropy from the events taken together. Symbolically, this yields the functional equation

$$f(x) + f(y) = f(xy)$$

for which one has $f(x) = \log x$ as a solution.

Theorem 3-1 *In the discrete case, the uncertainty is maximum when $p_i = p_j$ for all i and j.*

Proof For any continuous convex function $F(x)$, we have

$$F\left(\frac{1}{n} \sum_{i=1}^{n} a_i\right) \leq \frac{1}{n} \sum_{i=1}^{n} F(a_i)$$

where a_i, $i = 1, \ldots, n$, are positive numbers. If we let $a_i = p_i$, $F(x) = x \log x$, we have

$$F\left(\frac{1}{n}\right) = \frac{1}{n} \log \frac{1}{n} \leq \frac{1}{n} \sum_{i=1}^{n} p_i \log p_i = - \frac{1}{n} H(p_1, \ldots, p_n)$$

from which we have

$$H(p_1, \ldots, p_n) \leq \log n \leq H\left(\frac{1}{n}, \ldots, \frac{1}{n}\right)$$

and the proof is complete [8].

Remark By assuming continuity for H in all the p_i, it is possible to apply the Lagrange-multiplier method to prove this theorem. However, one must first show that the maximum is not attained on the boundary of the simplex $\Sigma_{i=1}^{n} p_i = 1$. This would follow by putting one or more $p_i = 0$ and using $\lim_{p_i = 0} p_i \log p_i = 0$ and the fact that

$- \log 1/k < \log 1/n$ for $k < n$.   One concludes that the optimum is in the interior where $0 < p_i < 1$, $i = 1, \ldots, n$, and hence is obtained by differentiation.

Exercise 3-1   Carry out the foregoing proof.   Also prove the following theorem.

Theorem 3-2   *In the continuous case the normal distribution gives the maximum entropy.*

The characterization of a function should help increase information about its regularity and decrease the amount of work needed to generate sufficient information to remove the uncertainty.   Obviously, then, the maximum of a function is hardest to find when the function is completely irregular.   If limited experimentation is available, all one could hope for is to remove some uncertainty and obtain an estimate of the maximum from among the values being examined in the limited effort.

3-3 COUNTERFEIT COINS AND COUNTERFEITERS [1,4,10,11]

The definition of entropy will now be used to find an a priori upper bound on N, where N is the number of coins from among which a single counterfeit may be isolated on an equal-arm balance in a given number of weighings n; we also determine whether the counterfeit is heavier or lighter than a good coin.

It may be assumed that it is equally probable that any of the coins is the counterfeit and hence is heavier or lighter than any other coin. Since there are N coins, this gives, in all, $2N$ possibilities.   Since any of these possibilities is equally probable, one has

$$p_i = \frac{1}{2N} \qquad \text{for } i = 1, \ldots, 2N$$

The total entropy is then easily calculated as $\log 2N$.   Note that the entropy would be less if it were not true that all coins are equally probable.   In order to isolate the counterfeit coin in n weighings, it is necessary that the weighings have at least total entropy equal to $\log 2N$.   If the entropy of the weighings is less than $\log 2N$, generally the counterfeit coin cannot be identified.

If an equal number of coins is placed on each side of the balance, then, if we assume that the counterfeit can be present in any such weighing, we obtain a bound on the value of the entropy.   We then proceed to improve on this bound.

Now, from a single weighing, one has three possible outcomes: the left arm of the balance is lighter, heavier, or equal to the right arm.

Each of the three outcomes has a certain probability w_i, and the information gain obtained by the weighing is a maximum when the w_i are all equal. Hence we assume each weighing so designed as to (approximately) satisfy this condition, so that the entropy of a weighing is given by

$$- \sum_{i=1}^{3} w_i \log w_i = \log 3 \qquad \text{where } w_i = \tfrac{1}{3}$$

Note that i ranges over the number of possible outcomes. The entropy in n weighings is given as the sum of the entropies of each weighing and is

$$\log 3 + \cdots + \log 3 = \log 3^n$$

Thus, to identify the counterfeit coin, the entropy from the weighings cannot be less than $\log 2N$, or, putting it differently, $\log 2N$ must be less than $\log 3^n$. Suppose that the two are equal. Then

$$\log 3^n = \log 2N$$

or $\qquad N = \dfrac{3^n}{2}$

Since this is not an integer, one takes the greatest integer smaller than this number, which gives

$$N = \frac{3^n - 1}{2}$$

It will now be shown that the entropy of the weighings is insufficient to identify a counterfeit coin from among $(3^n - 1)/2$ coins. Note, first, that N is of the form $3M + 1$, where M is an integer. It is not difficult to see that the maximum gain of entropy is obtained if the first move is to divide the coins into three equal collections. A collection of M coins is placed in each pan, leaving aside $M + 1$ coins. If the pans balance, the entropy to be obtained in the remaining $n - 1$ weighings must at least equal to

$$\log 2(M + 1) = \log (3^{n-1} + 1)$$

having used the fact that $M = (N - 1)/3$ and that $N = (3^n - 1)/2$. Since $\log (3^{n-1} + 1)$ is greater than the maximum entropy obtained in $n - 1$ weighings, that is, $\log 3^{n-1}$, it is clear that the problem is not solvable for

$$N = \frac{3^n - 1}{2}$$

Thus, the number of coins cannot exceed

$$N = \frac{3^n - 3}{2}$$

It can be shown that the problem is actually solvable for this number of coins. This simple example effectively demonstrates how, by proceeding from abstract considerations, one obtains quantitative formulas as the solution of a problem.

We devise a strategy for solving the problem for the case $N = 9$, utilizing information theory. The strategy is to generate the maximum possible amount of information at each weighing.

If p_l, p_r, and p_b are the respective probabilities that the balance tips to the left, to the right, and not at all, then the information generated in one weighing is

$$H = -p_l \log p_l - p_b \log p_b - p_r \log p_r$$

which, by the previous theorem, is maximum if the probabilities are all equal. Thus, our best strategy is to conduct the weighing so that all three alternatives are equally likely.

If k coins are placed in the left pan, k coins are placed in the right pan, and $9 - 2k$ are left aside, then

$$p_b = \frac{9 - 2k}{9} \qquad p_l = p_r = \frac{k}{9}$$

which are equal for $k = 3$. Therefore, we put three coins in each pan, leaving three aside. If the balance does not tip, then the counterfeit coin is one of those left aside. The same argument can now be applied to these three coins, discarding the first six coins.

If the balance tips in the first weighing, then, in order that it balance with probability $\frac{1}{3}$ in the second weighing, one coin must be removed from each pan. On the other hand, to have equal probabilities for tipping the balance to the left or to the right, the counterfeit must be interchanged with a coin from the other pan. Now if the result is a balance, the counterfeit is one of the two coins removed, etc. In any case, the third weighing will suffice to isolate the counterfeit and determine whether it is heavier or lighter.

Exercise 3-2 Apply a similar strategy to the case $N = 27$, using $n = 3$ weighings, to isolate a counterfeit coin known to be lighter.

THE COUNTERFEIT COINERS [6]

There are N coiners engaged in making the same denomination coin; however, some may be counterfeiters. Any two counterfeit coins have the same weight, which is slightly different from that of a good coin. Each coiner produces either all good or all counterfeit coins. With one guaranteed good coin, a set of infinitely refinable weights, a beam balance, and as many coins from each coiner as may be needed, determine in three weighings whether any coiner is a counterfeiter and which ones.

Solution   In the first weighing determine W_g, the weight of a good coin. In the second weighing take one coin from each coiner and determine the weight T of the total. The discrepancy is $D = T - NW_g$. If $D = 0$, all coiners are honest. If $D \neq 0$, take 2^{i-1} coins from the ith coiner, $i = 1, \ldots, N$, and determine the total weight T'. The discrepancy here is $D' = T' - (2^N - 1)W_g$. Find the integer S such that $D'/D = S/\beta(S)$, where $\beta(S)$ is the number of ones in the binary representation of S. Let $S = \Sigma_{i=1}^{N} B_i 2^{i-1}$, where $B_i = 0$ or 1. Then $\beta(S)$ is the number of dishonest coiners, and the ith coiner is honest or dishonest according as $B_i = 0$ or 1.

3-4 THE FAIR-DIVISION PROBLEM (HOW TO CUT A CAKE FAIRLY) [2,5]

This problem is familiar in the case of two people who are faced with dividing the cake into two parts, such that each of them receives a part with which he (within his own measure) is treated fairly. The problem is solved by having one person divide the cake and the other make the first choice.

In the case of $n > 2$ people, Banach and Knaster have solved the problem. A knife is moved in a parallel direction, scanning the entire cake. Each time it is over a position which yields a portion satisfactory to one of the participants, that portion is cut and given to him, and the process is repeated with the others. If more than one person wants the piece, it is given to any one of the contestants. It can be shown that this is a fair method. Another method is given below.

A related problem is the "problem of the Nile." Each year, the Nile floods, devastating the land of predynastic Egypt. The value of different portions of the land depends on the height of the flood (it is assumed that there are n possible heights). How should the land be divided among k residents so that each obtains $1/k$ of the land value for any height of the flood?

A third problem is the "ham-sandwich problem." A ham sandwich, containing butter, is to be divided with a knife into two parts such that each ingredient (i.e., bread, butter, and ham) is halved. By means of measure theory, existence theorems are given for the solution of such problems.

In the cake-division problem, it is desired to divide the cake among n people so that each, according to his own judgment, receives a portion equal to at least $1/n$ of the total. Label the individuals $1, 2, \ldots, n$. Let $m_j(p)$ be the measure of individual j assigned to a piece p. No relation is assumed between the measures. If j receives a portion p_j, then $m_j(p_j) \geq 1/n$. Each measure is assumed to be additive, with unit value for the total measure of the cake. (Technically one may require the measure to be nonatomic; i.e., it does not happen that there are parts of a piece of cake which have the same value as the piece itself or have no value at all.)

Consider the problem in which [5] it is desired to divide a cake into k pieces between two individuals, 1 and 2, so that player 1 takes 1 part and player 2 takes $k - 1$ parts. Their respective pieces p_1 and p_2 must satisfy their criteria of fairness; i.e.,

$$m_1(p_1) \geq \frac{1}{k}$$

$$m_2(p_2) \geq \frac{k-1}{k}$$

Lemma   *The scheme in which player 2 divides the cake into k pieces and player 1 chooses one of them is a fair one.*

Proof   To prove that this scheme is fair, note that player 2 can divide the cake into k pieces, $p_1, \ldots, p_k$, with $m_2(p_i) \geq 1/k$, $i = 1, \ldots, k$. Since $\Sigma_{i=1}^{k} m_1(p_i) = 1$, there must be a piece p_j such that $m_1(p_j) \geq 1/k$.

We now turn to the general problem in which it is desired to divide a cake fairly between n individuals so that if player j receives piece p_j, then $m_j(p_j) \geq 1/n$, $j = 1, \ldots, n$.

Theorem 3-3   *The following division scheme is a fair one:*
At the first stage the cake is given to player 1.
At the second stage player 2 divides the cake into two pieces with player 1, according to the lemma with $k = 2$. If the pieces are p_1 and p_2, considered fair to 1 and 2, respectively, then

$$m_1(p_1) \geq \tfrac{1}{2}$$
$$m_2(p_2) \geq \tfrac{1}{2}$$

At the third stage, player 3 divides p_1 with 1 into three pieces of which he chooses q_1 such that $m_3(q_1) \geq \tfrac{1}{3}m_1(p_1)$. He also divides p_2 with 2 into three parts of which he chooses q_2 with $m_3(q_2) \geq \tfrac{1}{3}m_2(p_2)$. If r_1 and r_2 are the remaining pieces to 1 and 2, respectively, then

$$m_1(r_1) \geq \tfrac{2}{3}m_1(p_1)$$
$$m_2(r_2) \geq \tfrac{2}{3}m_2(p_2)$$

At the kth stage, k divides the pieces remaining to each of the individuals, 1, 2, $\ldots$, $k - 1$. He does this with each of them separately. Each of 1, 2, $\ldots$, $k - 1$ divides his pieces into k parts, and then the kth individual chooses one part from each portion.
At the nth stage, the process terminates.

Proof The scheme is fair to j. Note that since j does not participate until the jth stage, it suffices to show that the kth stage with $j \le k \le n$ is fair to j; that is, at the kth stage j can get a piece q, with $m_j(q) \ge 1/k$. The proof is inductive. The jth stage is fair to j for $j = 1$. If p_1, . . . , p_{j-1} are the pieces given to 1, . . . , $j - 1$ at the jth stage, then j can obtain from each of them by the scheme of the lemma a piece q_i, $i = 1$, . . . , $j - 1$, such that

$$m_j(q_i) \ge \frac{1}{j} m_j(p_i)$$

But

$$\sum_{i=1}^{j-1} m_j(p_i) = 1$$

therefore

$$\sum_{i=1}^{j-1} m_j(q_i) \ge \frac{1}{j}$$

and the $(j - 1)$th stage is fair. We show that if the $(k - 1)$th stage is fair to j, $j \le k \le n$, then so is the kth stage. If j receives a piece p at the end of the $(k - 1)$th stage, then the induction assumption is that $m_j(p) \ge 1/(k - 1)$. The scheme of the lemma, with j making the division with each of the others, assures j a piece q, with $m_j(q) \ge [(k - 1)/k]m_j(p) \ge 1/k$. Thus, the scheme is fair for any stage k and, in particular, for $k = n$ whereby $m_j(p) \ge 1/n$.

3-5 THE NUMBER OF TESTS—BY EXHAUSTION

Problem [7] What is the maximum number of tests which may be constructed such that each has $n \ge 10$ multiple-choice questions, each of which has $k > 1$ choices such that the score given by $[(r - w)/(k - 1)]100/n$ (in which r is the number of right choices and w is the number of wrong ones) is an integer?

Solution

1. $r + w < n$; that is, not all questions are answered. Here $|r - w| \le n$, and $|r - w|$ assumes integral values, starting with zero but not exceeding n. Also $|100(r - w)|$ assumes the values 0, 100, 200, . . . , etc., not exceeding $100n$ subject to $100n \ge 1,000$. Consequently $(k - 1)n$ must be a divisor of all these values at the same time. In particular, it must be a divisor of 100; that is, since $n \ge 10$, it must assume the values 10, 20, 25, 50, or 100. Thus, from

$$(k - 1)n = 10 \qquad (k - 1)n = 20 \qquad (k - 1)n = 25 \qquad (k - 1)n = 50$$
$$(k - 1)n = 100$$

we have the following possible tests:

(n,k): (10,2), (10,3), (10,6), (10,11), (20,2), (20,6), (25,2), (25,3), (25,5), (50,2), (50,3), (100,2)

2. If all questions are answered, then $r + w = n$, and we may replace w by $n - r$ in the expression giving the score. If it is known that n is even, then $2r - n$ is also even, and hence $(k - 1)n$ must divide 200. In that case, we have the following additional tests:

(n,k): (10,5), (10,21), (20,3), (20,11), (40,2), (40,6), (50,5), (100,3), (200,2)

3-6 THE JEEP PROBLEM [3,11]

We shall illustrate a problem in which it is desired to minimize a function subject to constraints given as difference equations.

Problem   It is desired to advance a vehicle 1,000 miles from an original position with a minimum expenditure of fuel. The vehicle has maximum fuel capacity of 500 units, which it uses at the uniform rate of one unit per mile. The vehicle must stock its own storage points from its one tank by making round trips between storage points. Determine the storage points along the route which minimize the fuel consumption for the entire trip. Determine the number of round trips required between each pair of storage points. Determine the minimum amount of fuel required at the start.

Formulation and solution   If s_i is the amount of fuel stored at the ith storage point $(i = 0, 1, \ldots, n)$, d_i is the distance between the $(i - 1)$st and the ith storage points, and k_i is the number of round trips the vehicle makes between these two points, then

$$s_{i-1} = s_i + 2k_i d_i + d_i \qquad i = 1, \ldots, n \tag{3-1}$$

Thus, the amount of fuel stored at the $(i - 1)$st point is equal to the amount stored at the ith point plus the amount consumed along the route in making k_i round trips and a single forward trip.

It is not difficult to see that a minimum use of fuel is made if for each trip the vehicle proceeds loaded at full capacity. For in that case, a smaller number of trips would be made, and hence less fuel is consumed in travel. Also, in order to have no fuel left at the end, it is necessary that the vehicle be loaded with 500 units of fuel at the 500-mile point. From these two facts, it follows that the ith storage point should be located so that the vehicle makes k_{i+1} round trips between this point and the $(i + 1)$st storage point and one last forward trip, always fully loaded and ultimately leaving no fuel behind at the ith storage point. Working backward, the last statement is valid back to the first storage point but is not possible for the starting point since the position of that point is predetermined.   Hence, the vehicle will make its last forward trip between the starting point and the first storage point with a load $c \leq 500$.   Thus we have

$$s_i = k_i(500 - 2d_i) + 500 - d_i \qquad i = 2, \ldots , n$$
$$s_1 = k_1(500 - 2d_1) + c - d_1 \tag{3-2}$$

It is desired to minimize s_0, given by

$$s_0 = s_1 + 2k_1d_1 + d_1$$

Now, using for s_1 the value previously given, one has

$$s_0 = 500k_1 + c \tag{3-3}$$

Since the vehicle can travel the last 500 miles without need for stored fuel, in order to minimize s_0, it suffices to put $s_n = 500$ and to place the storage points along the first 500 miles of the route.   Thus,

$$\sum_{i=1}^{n} d_i = 500$$

Now, from the second equation of the problem, one has

$$d_i = \frac{500k_i + 500 - s_i}{2k_i + 1} \qquad i = 2, \ldots , n$$

Replacing i by $i + 1$ in the first equation, and substituting for s_i in the expression for d_i, one has

$$d_i = \frac{500k_i + 500 - s_{i+1} - 2k_{i+1}d_{i+1} - d_{i+1}}{2k_i + 1} \qquad \begin{array}{l} i = 2, \ldots , n \\ k_{n+1} \equiv 0 \end{array}$$

Finally, replacing s_{i+1} by its equal from the second equation and simplifying yields

$$d_i = \frac{500(k_i - k_{i+1})}{2k_i + 1} \qquad \begin{array}{l} i = 2, \ldots , n \\ k_{n+1} \equiv 0 \end{array}$$

Similarly, one has

$$d_1 = \frac{500(k_1 - k_2) + c - 500}{2k_1 + 1}$$

Since $d_i > 0$, it follows that $k_i > k_{i+1}$.   Thus, we wish to minimize

$$s_0 = 500k_1 + c$$

subject to the constraint

$$\sum_{i=1}^{n} d_i = 500 \sum_{i=1}^{n} \frac{k_i - k_{i+1}}{2k_i + 1} + \frac{c - 500}{2k_1 + 1} = 500$$

This can be written as

$$\sum_{i=1}^{n} \frac{k_i - k_{i+1}}{2k_i + 1} - \frac{1 - c/500}{2k_1 + 1} = 1 \qquad k_{n+1} \equiv 0$$

Since $k_1 > k_2 > \cdots > k_i > \cdots > k_n$, the second term on the left is less than the least value which any term in the sum can assume; that is,

$$\frac{k_i - k_{i+1}}{2k_i + 1} > \frac{1}{2k_1 + 1} \qquad i = 2, \ldots, n$$

Simply stated, this relation requires a choice of the k_i for which

$$\sum_{i=1}^{n} \frac{k_i - k_{i+1}}{2k_i + 1}$$

exceeds unity with a minimum k_1.

It will now be shown that the minimum value of k_1 is obtained by taking $k_i - k_{i+1} = 1$ $(i = 1, \ldots, n)$ and $k_n = 1$. Suppose that for $i = i_0$, $k_{i_0} - k_{i_0+1} = m$, an integer > 1. Then for the i_0th term, one has

$$\frac{k_{i_0} - k_{i_0+1}}{2k_{i_0} + 1} = \frac{m}{2(k_{i_0+1} + m) + 1}$$

where the denominator jumps from $2k_{i_0+1} + 1$ to $2(k_{i_0+1} + m) + 1$ when i decreases from $i_0 + 1$ to i_0.

Now, by taking $k_{i_0} - k_{i_0+1} = 1$, this jump can be replaced by a gradually increasing sum of terms

$$\frac{1}{2(k_{i_0+1} + 1) + 1} + \frac{1}{2(k_{i_0+1} + 2) + 1} + \cdots + \frac{1}{2(k_{i_0+1} + m) + 1}$$

This sum is greater than the previous expression, which is m times the smallest term in the sum. It follows that a minimum k_1 is attained by taking $k_i - k_{i+1} = 1$, that is, by using unit differences and $k_n = 1$. Because of the monotone property of the k_i, one chooses n such that $k_n = 1$, $k_{n-1} = 2$, $\ldots$, in such a manner as to produce k_2 with

$$\sum_{i=2}^{n} \frac{k_i - k_{i+1}}{2k_i + 1} < 1 < \sum_{i=1}^{n} \frac{k_i - k_{i+1}}{2k_i + 1}$$

In this case, $k_2 = 6$. The corresponding d_i are then calculated, working backward from the 500-mile point. The distance which remains is taken as d_1, with a corresponding $k_1 = 7$ round trips. This choice of k_1 minimizes s_0, and the corresponding choice of d_i satisfies the distance constraint.

Note that if the original total difference is chosen appropriately, the d_{n-i} go as the harmonic series with odd denominators. A consideration of the slowness of divergence of this series casts some light on the economic difficulty of importing into and improving underdeveloped countries.

Exercise 3-3 Show that $k_i = 8 - i$, $d_i = 500/(17 - 2i)$, $i = 1, \ldots, 7$, and $S_0 = 3,8336.45$.

3-7 THE COCONUT PROBLEM OF CHAP. 1 [9]

If we denote the initial amount of coconuts by X and if the ith sailor takes the amount x_i (after the mth division everyone takes the amount x_m), we have

$$x_1 = \frac{X - d_1}{n} \tag{3-4}$$

$$x_i = \frac{(n - 1)x_{i-1} - d_i}{n} \qquad i = 2, \ldots, m \tag{3-5}$$

Note that d_i for $i > m$ do not affect the solution. It will be convenient to take their kth differences to be zero; that is, $\Delta^k d_i = 0$, $k > m$. Note also, that $d_i \geq 0$, $i = 1, \ldots, m$, and hence $x_i \leq x_{i-1}$. Thus, if x_m is positive, then also x_i for $i < m$ and X are positive.

If we define

$$\Delta x_i = x_{i+1} - x_i$$

then Eq. (3-5) may be written as

$$n \, \Delta x_i + x_i = -d_{i+1} \qquad i = 1, 2, \ldots, m \tag{3-6}$$

A particular solution of this equation is given by

$$P_i = - \sum_{k=0}^{m-1} (-n)^k \, \Delta^k d_{i+1}$$

Using Newton's formula, we have

$$d_{i+1} = \sum_{j=0}^{m-1} \Delta^j d_1 C_j{}^i$$

where

$$C_j{}^i = \binom{i}{j}$$

Using the facts $\Delta^k C_j{}^i = C_{j-k}^i$ and $C_j{}^i = 0, j < 0$, we have, on substituting and interchanging summation,

$$P_i = - \sum_{j=0}^{m-1} \sum_{k=0}^{j} (-n)^k \, \Delta^j d_1 C_{j-k}^i \tag{3-7}$$

The solution of Eq. (3-6) is then the sum of the general solution of the homogeneous equation plus the particular solution P_i. We have

$$x_i = \frac{X - d_1 - nP_1}{n - 1}\left(\frac{n - 1}{n}\right)^i + P_i \qquad i = 1, \ldots, m$$

Now, to determine X, we note that x_m must be a positive integer r. We put $i = m$, equate to r, and solve for X; we have

$$X = \frac{(r - P_m)n^m}{(n - 1)^{m-1}} + d_1 + nP_1 \tag{3-8}$$

The last two terms are integers. Since n and $n - 1$ are coprime, X is an integer if and only if for some integer s we have

$$r - P_m = s(n - 1)^{m-1} \tag{3-9}$$

In order that X be the smallest positive integer, r must be the smallest, and hence s must be chosen to give the smallest r. Thus, we take

$$s = \left[\frac{-P_m}{(n - 1)^{m-1}}\right] + 1 \tag{3-10}$$

This gives

$$x_m = s(n - 1)^{m-1} + P_m$$

and by means of the original equation we have

$$x_{m-k} = s(n - 1)^{m-1-k}n^k + P_{m-k}$$

Now substituting Eqs. (3-10) and (3-9) into Eq. (3-8), evaluating Eq. (3-7) at $i = 1$ and $i = m$, and also substituting in Eq. (3-8), we have

$$X = \left\{\left[\frac{\sum_{j=0}^{m-1}\sum_{k=0}^{j}(-n)^k \Delta^j d_1 C^m_{j-k}}{(n - 1)^{m-1}}\right] + 1\right\} n^m + (1 - n)\sum_{j=0}^{m-1}(-n)^j \Delta^j d_1$$

To simplify calculations for large n and m, one may compute the smallest integer C for which $X > 0$, $x_i > 0$, $i = 1, \ldots, m$, and write

$$X = Cn^m + (1 - n)\sum_{j=0}^{m-1}(-n)^j \Delta^j d_1$$

This is valid even if $d_i < 0$ for some i.

Exercise 3-4

1. Find X if $d_i = d$, $i = 1, \ldots, m$.
2. Set $n = 5$, $m = 4$, $d_1 = 4$, $d_2 = 3$, $d_3 = 1$, $d_4 = 1$. Show that $X = 314$.

Exercise 3-5 A fish aquarium contains n units of water. Each week one unit evaporates and must be replaced with fresh water. Because fresh water contains uniformly a certain amount of salt, and in order to prevent the concentration of salt in the aquarium from becoming dangerously high for the fish, another unit is removed from the aquarium (leaving $n - 2$ behind) and then two units of fresh water are added. Prove that in the steady state (i.e., ultimately) the maximum concentration of salt per unit in the aquarium reaches twice that in fresh water. (*Hint:* Use a difference equation model.)

3-8 AN UNBOUNDED-MAXIMUM PROBLEM [12]

Given k dominoes, whose shape is that of a parallelpiped, suppose these dominoes are stacked, one on top of another, in a precise fashion in a vertical pile. Assume now that it is possible to slide dominoes in a parallel direction, obtaining a configuration similar to a staircase in order to obtain the maximum span in horizontal coverage and without toppling the dominoes. If the dimension of a domino along the desired direction is equal to unity, determine the maximum span as a function of the number of dominoes.

Solution   Consider the kth domino from the top. The center of gravity of the set of $k - 1$ dominoes above it, with respect to the $(k - 1)$st domino, is computed as follows. The center of gravity of the $k - 2$ dominoes which lies above one edge of the $(k - 1)$st domino exerts a weight which is balanced at the center of gravity of the system of $(k - 1)$ dominoes by the weight of the $(k - 1)$st domino at its center of gravity. Thus, if the distance from the balancing edge to the center of gravity of the system of $(k - 1)$ dominoes is x, as measured from the balancing edge of the $(k - 1)$st domino, then we must have $(k - 2)x = 1 \left(\frac{1}{2} - x \right)$. This gives $x = 1/[2(k - 1)]$, $k > 1$.   The first or top domino protrudes $\frac{1}{2}$ of its length with respect to the second; the second domino protrudes $\frac{1}{4}$ of its length with respect to the third; the third protrudes $\frac{1}{6}$ of its length with respect to the fourth; and so on.   This gives the sum

$$\frac{1}{2} + \frac{1}{4} + \frac{1}{6} + \cdots + \frac{1}{2(k - 1)} = \frac{1}{2}\left(1 + \frac{1}{2} + \frac{1}{3} + \cdots + \frac{1}{k - 1}\right)$$

The quantity on the right gives the maximum span from the supporting edge of the kth domino. Since the sum on the right as $k \to \infty$ is the harmonic series, which diverges, the horizontal distance spanned has no upper bound and hence also has no maximum.

3-9 THE EXISTENCE OF WINNING STRATEGIES [14]

Consider a crisis situation between two nations A and B, and suppose that it is desired to resolve the crisis by negotiations.   Let us also suppose that this particular situation does not permit a draw (standoff or stalemate), that offers or moves are made alternately, and that the number of rounds n is finite (i.e., the bargaining terminates). By a *strategy for a nation* we mean a sequence of moves from beginning to end, each of which may depend on the moves of the other nation. A winning strategy for a nation is a strategy which eventually leads to a win, no matter what strategy the other nation follows. We prove the following theorem.

Theorem 3-4 *There is a strategy ensuring a win for nation A, or there is a strategy ensuring a win for nation B.*

Proof The fact that there is a finite sequence of moves makes it easy to see that one of the negotiators must have a winning strategy, determined at the very first move he makes. The first move is made from a winning position, which is one with the property that with proper subsequent play he can win no matter what the other player does. First note that *no draw* means that one nation must win (regardless of who moves first). If he is to win, somewhere toward the end, he is in a winning strategy position. Consider the very first time that one of them, for example, player A, has a winning strategy; then the move which B makes just before putting A in that position must be a mistake, otherwise A's winning strategy position would have started a move earlier. Thus, if A wins, B must make a mistake. On the other hand, if B does not make a mistake, A cannot win. Alternatively, unless A makes a mistake, B cannot win. Thus, neither of them would win if neither of them made a mistake. This is a contradiction because the game must terminate without a draw in a finite number of moves. Thus, one of them must have a winning strategy from the start. This completes the proof.

3-10 A GAMBLING TABLE [13]

Problem On a certain gambling table there are N squares, marked "2 to 1," "3 to 1," . . . , and "$N + 1$ to 1." A sum of money is placed on each square, and one of the squares is selected as a winner, paying the player at the odds marked on that square. The player loses the amount placed on the other squares. What is the maximum N for which it is possible for a player to place money so that he can never suffer a net loss?

Solution If S_k is the sum placed on the kth square and T is the total bet, then for no net loss it is necessary and sufficient that $(k + 2)S_k \geq T$, or $1/(k + 2) \leq S_k/T$ $(k = 1, 2, \ldots, N)$ hold. Summing both sides over k gives $\Sigma_{k=1}^{n} 1/(k + 2) \leq 1$. The maximum N for which this holds is 4. The player can so bet that the net gain is independent of the square selected.

REFERENCES

1. Eves, Donald, E. D. Schell, and Joseph Rosenbaum: The Extended Coin Problem, *Am. Math. Monthly*, pp. 46–48, January, 1947.

2. Dubins, L. E., and E. H. Spanier: How to Cut a Cake Fairly, *Am. Math. Monthly*, pp. 1–17, January, 1961.
3. Fine, N. J.: The Jeep Problem, *Am. Math. Monthly*, pp. 24–31, January, 1947.
4. Fine, N. J.: The Generalized Coin Problem, *Am. Math. Monthly*, pp. 489–491, October, 1947.   See also *Math. Gazette*, pp. 227–229, 1945, and pp. 231–234, 1946.
5. Fink, A. M.: A Note on the Fair Division Problem, *Math. Mag.*, pp. 341–342, November–December, 1964.
6. Ford, Jr., L. R., and Julian Baun: The Counterfeiters of Lower Slobovia, *Am. Math Monthly*, vol. 61, pp. 472–473, September, 1954.
7. Howell, J. M., and Francis A. C. Sevier: Integral Test Scores, *Math. Mag.*, pp. 224–225, March–April, 1957.
8. Khinchin, A. I.: "Mathematical Foundations of Information Theory," Dover Publications, Inc., New York, 1957.
9. Kirchner, Roger B.: The Generalized Coconut Problem, *Am. Math. Monthly*, pp. 516–518, June–July, 1960.
10. Raisbeck, Gordon: "Information Theory," The M.I.T. Press, Cambridge, Mass., 1963.
11. Saaty, Thomas L.: "Mathematical Methods of Operations Research," McGraw-Hill Book Company, New York, 1959.
12. Sharp, R. T.: Piled Dominos, *Pi Mu Epsilon J.*, p. 322, April, 1953, and p. 411, April, 1954.
13. Van Voohris, W. R., and C. F. Pinzka: A Gambling Table, *Am. Math. Monthly*, vol. 61, pp. 474–475, 1964.
14. Westwick, Roy, W. A. McWorter, and Donald Quiring: Games with a Winning Strategy, *Am. Math. Monthly*, p. 604, May, 1967.

4
Optimization Subject to Diophantine Constraints

4-1 INTRODUCTION

A Diophantine equation (after Diophantus, A.D. 250) is a polynomial equation in several variables whose coefficients are rational (for example, $6x + 4y + z = 40$), and for which a solution in integers (often positive) is desired. Note that an equation whose coefficients are rational is equivalent to an equation with integer coefficients. For instance,

$$\tfrac{6}{5}x^2 + \tfrac{4}{3}y + z = \tfrac{1}{2}$$

can be written as

$$36x^2 + 40y + 30z = 15$$

An equation which requires a rational solution is also sometimes referred to as a Diophantine equation.

The nomenclature is sometimes extended to include more general equations. A system of Diophantine equations consists of a system of polynomial equations, with rational coefficients, whose simultaneous solution in integers (or in rationals) is desired. An integral solution in which the greatest common divisor of the values of the variables is unity is known as a *primitive solution*.

The solution of a linear Diophantine equation is closely related to the problem of finding the number of partitions of a positive integer N into parts from a set S whose elements are positive integers $a_1, a_2, \ldots, a_n$. Thus, the problem is to find the number of solutions in integers of the equation

$$a_1x_1 + a_2x_2 + \cdots + a_nx_n = N \qquad \begin{matrix} x_j \geq 0 \\ j = 1, \ldots, n \end{matrix}$$

Often, a Diophantine equation or a system of such equations

$$g_i(x_1, \ldots, x_n) = 0 \qquad i = 1, \ldots, m$$

may occur as a set of constraints of an optimization problem. The requirement that all the variables be nonnegative, that is, $x_j \geq 0, j = 1, \ldots, n$, is frequently an essential constraint. Maximizing or minimizing a bounded function $f(x_1, \ldots, x_n)$, defined over the discrete solution set of such a system of constraints, is a difficult problem. Naturally such a problem would not be solvable if the constraints have no solution. Occasionally insight may be obtained by embedding the problem in a corresponding continuous problem and applying the theorem for optimizing semicontinuous functions over compact sets. As we have seen in Chap. 2, some optimization problems require that a solution in integers of the constraints yield a maximum (or minimum) value of $f(x_1, \ldots, x_n)$, which is also an integer. The requirement that f have an integer value is an added complication. Obviously it is not, if f is a polynomial with integer coefficients.

In general, the constraint system cannot be solved easily. If the constraints are linear, considerable information can be gained by examining the vertices of the corresponding convex polyhedron.

There are few theorems in Diophantine analysis which are of such generality as to make statements regarding large classes of Diophantine equations possible. It is not certain that a given algebraic equation which requires a solution in integers would actually have one. For example, the question of the existence of solutions in positive integers to Fermat's famous equation, $x^n + y^n = z^n$ for $n > 2$, is still not completely settled.

Among Hilbert's list of 20 unsolved problems presented before the International Mathematical Congress in Paris in 1901, the following problem, which remains unsolved in general, is included.

Hilbert's tenth problem Find an algorithm for determining whether any given Diophantine equation has an integral solution.

Some Diophantine equations have been classified, and their solutions have been investigated. If such equations arise as constraints in an optimization problem, one might use this information as a first step in the optimization process. We now briefly examine some methods of solving elementary Diophantine equations and give examples of optimizing a discretely valued function subject to simple Diophantine constraints. In Chap. 5 general methods are given for the solution of linear-optimization problems that are linear programs. Although some nonlinear examples occur in this chapter, no adequate study of nonlinear problems is available as yet.

4-2 ON THE SOLVABILITY OF DIOPHANTINE EQUATIONS

An algorithm required by Hilbert's problem, as stated in its generality, does not exist but, as will be observed later, may exist for special classes of Diophantine equations.

A Diophantine equation may have no solution. An illustration of this is given by the equation $x^2 - 3y^2 = 17$. Note that any integral x is of the form $3n$, $3n \pm 1$. Substituting in the equation, we have

$$3(3n^2 - y^2) = 17$$
$$3(3n^2 \pm 2n - y^2) = 16$$

respectively. It is not difficult to see that these equations are impossible to solve in integers. For example, in the first equation, for any choice of the integers n and y, the left side is divisible by 3, but the right side is not. Similarly,

$$x^4 + y^4 + z^4 - x^4y^2 - y^4z^2 - z^4x^2 \pm x^2y^2z^2 = 0$$

has no integer solutions. Thus, if we assume that x, y, z have no common factor, then they cannot all be of the form $3n$. But if any or all of x, y, z are of the forms $3n \pm 1$, the left member of the equation is congruent to $\pm 1 \bmod 3$.

Again, a Diophantine equation may have only a finite number of solutions. For example, the quintic equation

$$x^5 + x - 1 = y^2$$

only has the two solutions: $x = 1$, $y = \pm 1$.

Exercise 4-1 Determine all integer solutions of $\Sigma_{i=1}^n x_i{}^2 = 100$, $1 \le n \le 100$.

A Diophantine equation may have infinitely many solutions. A well-known equation with an infinite number of solutions in positive integers is Pell's equation:

$$x^2 - Ay^2 = 1$$

where $A > 0$ and A is not a square. If (x_1, y_1) and (x_2, y_2) are two solutions of this equation then, from the identities

$$(x_1{}^2 - Ay_1{}^2)(x_2{}^2 - Ay_2{}^2) = (x_1x_2 + Ay_1y_2)^2 - A(x_1y_2 + x_2y_1)^2$$
$$= (x_1x_2 - Ay_1y_2)^2 - A(x_1y_2 - x_2y_1)^2$$

we conclude that $(x_1x_2 + Ay_1y_2,\ x_1y_2 + x_2y_1)$ is also a solution and $(x_1x_2 - Ay_1y_2,\ x_1y_2 - x_2y_1)$ is yet another solution. One can continue to compose new solutions in this way.

If we write Pell's equation in the form

$$(x + y\sqrt{A})(x - y\sqrt{A}) = 1$$

then we also have

$$(x + y\sqrt{A})^n(x - y\sqrt{A})^n = 1$$

for any n, in particular when n is a natural number.

We can write

$$(x + y\sqrt{A})^n = X_n + Y_n\sqrt{A}$$

since in the expansion of the left-hand side, we can group together the terms in which $\sqrt{A}$ does not appear, denote these by X_n, and denote the coefficient of $\sqrt{A}$ by Y_n. We also have

$$(x - y\sqrt{A})^n = X_n - Y_n\sqrt{A}$$

It follows that

$$(X_n + Y_n\sqrt{A})(X_n - Y_n\sqrt{A}) = 1$$

Thus, if x and y are solutions, then X_n and Y_n are also solutions.

Exercise 4-2   Write down the expression for X_n in terms of x and y. Do the same for Y_n.

One can show that starting with a fundamental solution (x_1, y_1) in which x_1 and y_1 are nonzero integers for which $x + y\sqrt{A}$ has its smallest value, an infinite number of solutions can be obtained from the recurrence relation

$$x_{n+1} = x_1 x_n + Ay_1 y_n$$
$$y_{n+1} = y_1 x_n + x_1 y_n$$

which may be written in the matrix form

$$\begin{bmatrix} x_{n+1} \\ y_{n+1} \end{bmatrix} = \begin{bmatrix} x_1 & Ay_1 \\ y_1 & x_1 \end{bmatrix} \begin{bmatrix} x_n \\ y_n \end{bmatrix}$$
$$= \begin{bmatrix} x_1 & Ay_1 \\ y_1 & x_1 \end{bmatrix}^{n+1} \begin{bmatrix} 1 \\ 0 \end{bmatrix}$$

A proof which shows that a fundamental solution always exists, and which we do not give here, is available. This proof does not provide fundamental solutions.

Exercise 4-3 Verify the following fundamental solutions for the indicated values of A:

A	(x_1, y_1)
2	(3,2)
3	(2,1)
5	(9,4)
6	(5,2)

It is interesting to note that if $A = 46$, then $(x,y) = (24335,3588)$, which is hard to obtain by guessing.

Not all equations of the form $x^2 - Ay^2 = -1$ can be solved. For example, $x^2 - 3y^2 = -1$ has no solutions.

For an equation in a single unknown and with integral coefficients

$$a_n x^n + a_{n-1}x^{n-1} + \cdots + a_1 x + a_0 = 0$$

we know that if the equation has an integral solution, then this solution must be a factor of a_0. Thus, one way to test for such a solution is to find all factors of a_0 and substitute them to see if they satisfy the equation. If none does, the equation has no integral solution. If any does, it is obviously such a solution.

It is clear that every Diophantine inequality is expressible as a Diophantine equation by the addition of a nonnegative slack variable. On the other hand, every Diophantine equation may be expressed as two Diophantine inequalities, e.g., by writing an equation of the form

$$f = g \qquad \text{as } f \geq g \text{ and } g \geq f$$

Thus, the problems of existence and solution for systems of Diophantine inequalities or equations are closely related.

The following are examples of how Diophantine equations arise in the formulation and solution of a problem.

Problem A wholesale jobber received radios from the manufacturer, packed in two types of cartons. Each type held a different number of radios. The shipping clerk found that by judiciously selecting the right number of one or both kinds, he could fill almost any size order without opening a carton. Indeed, there were exactly six orders possible which would require a carton to be opened and repackaged [21a].

One day the manufacturer discontinued the smaller carton and sent a new size, containing a different number of radios. The shipping clerk calculated that with the new setup, there were 10 different orders which would be impossible to fill without repacking. How many radios were contained in this new carton?

Solution   If $(m,n) = 1$, the number of positive integers which are not of the form $Am + Bn$, when A and B are nonnegative integers, is $(m - 1)(n - 1)/2$. Moreover, the value of each integer which is not of this form is less than $(m - 1)(n - 1)$. Let a be the number of radios packed in each small carton, and let b be the number in each large carton of the two original types. Let c be the number of radios packed in each carton of the type which is substituted for the smaller cartons. We have $(a - 1)(b - 1)/2 = 6$ and $(c - 1)(b - 1)/2 = 10$. Hence $5(a - 1) = 3(c - 1)$, or $5a - 3c = 2$. Only one solution yields a corresponding integer value of b which is a positive integer greater than a. This unique solution is $a = 4$, $c = 6$, $b = 5$. Thus, each of the new cartons contains six radios. When using the original cartons, containing four and five radios, the clerk could not ship 1, 2, 3, 6, 7 or 11 radios without opening a carton. Using cartons containing five and six radios, he could not ship 1, 2, 3, 4, 7, 8, 9, 13, 14, and 19 radios without opening a carton.

Problem   Consider Fig. 4-1, in which three circles of different integer-valued diameters
[18]   just cover the diameter of the larger circle and have their centers located on this diameter. If the diameter of the larger circle is $2r$, and if the area covered by the three circles is half the area of the larger circle, find the diameters of the covering circles.

Solution   Let x, y, z be the desired diameters; then

$$x + y + z = 2r$$
$$x^2 + y^2 + z^2 = \frac{(x + y + z)^2}{2}$$

Simultaneous solution of this system leads to

$$x = \left(\frac{\sqrt{z} \pm \sqrt{z + y(r - z)}}{z} \right)^2$$
$$y = \left(\frac{-\sqrt{z} \pm \sqrt{z + y(r - z)}}{2} \right)^2$$

in which, for any given r, the selection of nonnegative integer values for z must lead to nonnegative integer values for x and y. Thus, for $r = 13$ and $z = 1$, we have $x = 9$ and $y = 16$.

Exercise 4-4   Find positive integers x, y, z which maximize $x^2 + y^2 + z^2$ subject to $x + y + z = a$, where a is a given positive integer.

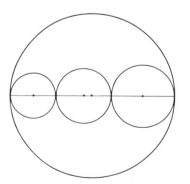

Fig. 4-1

Problem An airline buys Boeing 707 aircraft at 6×10^6 each, Boeing 727 at 4×10^6 each, and Caravelles at 10^6 each. If a total sum of 4×10^7 is paid for 20 aircraft, including at least one of each kind, how many aircraft of each kind does the airline buy?

If x, y, z are the respective numbers bought of each kind of aircraft mentioned in the problem, then one must find nonnegative integers x, y, z which satisfy

$$x + y + z = 20$$
$$6x + 4y + z = 40$$

Exercise 4-5 Formulate the following problem algebraically [35]:

A band of 13 pirates obtained a certain number of gold coins. They tried to distribute them equitably but found that they had 8 left. Two pirates died of smallpox; then, upon trying to distribute the coins equitably among the 11 remaining pirates, they found that there were 3 left. Thereupon they shot 3 pirates, but still there was a remainder of 5 coins when they attempted an equal division among the 8 remaining pirates. How many coins were there?

Hint: Obtain a relation of the form $13x + 8 = 11y + 3 = 8z + 5$ and reduce it to a pair $13x - 11y = -5$, $11y - 8z = 2$.

Exercise 4-6 Find the lengths of the sides of all right triangles of integral sides, with areas equal to the length of the perimeter.

Verify that the above problem has the following algebraic formulation:

$$\frac{xy}{2} = x + y + z$$
$$z^2 = x^2 + y^2$$

4-3 LINEAR DIOPHANTINE EQUATIONS [22]

The following theorems give the conditions, subject to which one equation and then a linear system are solvable in integers, not necessarily positive.

Theorem 4-1 *A necessary and sufficient condition for a solution in integers of the linear equation*

$$\sum_{j=1}^{n} a_j x_j = b$$

where a_j ($j = 1, \ldots, n$) and b are integers, is that the greatest common divisor $(a_1, \ldots, a_n)$ of $a_1, \ldots, a_n$ divides b.

Proof Let d be the greatest common divisor of $a_1, \ldots, a_n$. We assume that $b \geq 0$, for if $b < 0$ we multiply both sides of the equation by (-1).

We first show that the theorem is true if $b = d$. In the process of this proof, we conclude that no integer solutions are possible for $b < d$. Finally we give the proof for $b > d$. Thus, suppose first that $b = d$.

Consider the set S of all integers of the form

$$a_1x_1 + a_2x_2 + \cdots + a_nx_n \tag{4-1}$$

in which $x_1, \ldots, x_n$ take on all integer values: positive, negative, and zero. Sums and differences of such integers are also in S. Also, $a_1, \ldots, a_n$ belong to S. The greatest common divisor of all these numbers is d. To see this, note that d divides all these numbers, and that no other number greater than d does, for then it would also divide $a_1, \ldots, a_n$; therefore it cannot be greater than d. If $\bar{s}$ is the smallest natural number in S, and if s is any other number in S, then we can write $s = \bar{s}q + r$, where q and r are integers with $0 \le r \le \bar{s}$. Thus $r - \bar{s}q$, and hence r also belongs to S. Because $r < \bar{s}$, we must have $r = 0$, and hence every number in S is a multiple of $\bar{s}$. Thus, $\bar{s}$ divides $a_1, \ldots, a_n$. By assumption, d is in S, and hence $\bar{s}$ divides d or $\bar{s} \le d$. But $d < \bar{s}$ cannot hold since d is a multiple of $\bar{s}$. Therefore, $\bar{s} = d$. Since

$$\bar{s} = a_1x_1 + \cdots + a_nx_n$$

the equation has a solution in integers for $b = d$, and there is nothing more to prove for this case.

Suppose now that $b > d$. Since d divides b, we have $b = kd$, where k is an integer. Since $a_1x_1 + \cdots + a_nx_n = d$ has a solution in integers, then so does the equation obtained by multiplying both sides by k. The converse holds since, as shown above, any integer value of $a_1x_1 + \cdots + a_nx_n$ must be a multiple of d.

Exercise 4-7 Show that the equation

$$2x + 6y = 9$$

has no solution in integers.

Theorem 4-2 *A system of independent linear equations*

$$\sum_{j=1}^{n} a_{ij}x_j = b_i \qquad i = 1, \ldots, m$$

with integral coefficients and integral b_i ($i = 1, \ldots, m$) has a solution in integers $x = (x_1, \ldots, x_n)$ if and only if the greatest common divisor of all mth order determinants of the matrix of coefficients (a_{ij}) is equal to the greatest common divisor of all mth order determinants of the augmented matrix.

Exercise 4-8 Show that the system

$$19x + 10y + 7z + 3 = 0$$
$$5x + 2y + 2z + 1 = 0$$

has no solution in integers even though each equation does. Note that the system implies the equation $3x + 6y - 1 = 0$ which has no solution.

For a simple geometric illustration of the idea of a solution in non-negative integers, consider the following problem.

Problem   Find nonnegative integers x_j, $j = 1, \ldots, n$, such that

$$\sum_{j=1}^{n} a_j x_j = \max$$

subject to

$$\sum_{j=1}^{n} b_j x_j = C$$

Note that with $=$ replaced by $\leq$, this problem is called the *knapsack problem* (discussed in Chap. 5). To solve this problem in integers (not necessarily positive), it is necessary and sufficient that C be divisible by the greatest common divisor of $\{b_j\}$, $j = 1, \ldots, n$. For a solution in positive integers, it is necessary, for example, that in addition, $C \geq \Sigma_{j=1}^{n} b_j$ holds. For a nonnegative solution, $C \geq \min_j b_j$ is necessary. However, these conditions are not sufficient.

Geometrically the problem requires finding a vector of nonnegative integral components such that $a \cdot x = \max$ and $b \cdot x = C$. We put the constraint (which defines a hyperplane in n-space) in normal form by dividing by $|b| = (\Sigma_{j=1}^{n} b_j^2)^{\frac{1}{2}}$, the magnitude of b. In that case $b/|b|$ gives the directional cosines, and b itself is orthogonal to the hyperplane. The distance from the origin to this hyperplane is $C/|b|$. All vectors x in the hyperplane give the same projection on b with magnitude $C/|b|$. The problem is to find a vector x from the origin to a lattice point on the constraint hyperplane which also lies on the hyperplane $\dfrac{a}{|a|} \cdot x = \dfrac{M}{|a|}$ (where M is some constant) such that the distance of the latter hyperplane from the origin, that is, $\dfrac{M}{|a|}$, is maximum. Note that, in general, the solution will be on a part of the constraint hyperplane, which, together with the coordinate planes, define an $(n+1)$-simplex. Thus, the solution would be bounded.

THE METHOD OF CONTINUED FRACTIONS [16,26]

Continued fractions provide one way for solving linear and some nonlinear Diophantine equations.

The concept of a continued fraction is easily understood by means of an example:

$$\frac{33}{7} = 4 + \frac{5}{7} = 4 + \frac{1}{7/5} = 4 + \frac{1}{1 + 2/5}$$

$$= 4 + \cfrac{1}{1 + \cfrac{1}{5/2}}$$

$$= 4 + \cfrac{1}{1 + \cfrac{1}{2 + 1/2}} = 4 + \cfrac{1}{1 + \cfrac{1}{2 + \cfrac{1}{1 + 1}}}$$

Such a development is known as a *continued fraction*. In more compact notation, the last expression may be written as $4 + \dfrac{1}{1+} \dfrac{1}{2+} \dfrac{1}{1+1}$. It is clear that a continued fraction may or may not terminate. In the latter case, it is called an *infinite continued fraction*.

In general, if we write a continued fraction in the form

$$a_1 + \frac{1}{a_2+} \frac{1}{a_3+} \frac{1}{a_4+} + \cdots$$

then the fractions obtained by taking the first term, the first two terms, the first three terms, etc., are known as the *convergents* of the continued fract on. Thus they are given by

$$a_1, \quad a_1 + \frac{1}{a_2}, \quad a_1 + \frac{1}{a_2 + 1/a_3}, \quad \cdots$$

or

$$\frac{a_1}{1}, \quad \frac{a_1 a_2 + 1}{a_2}, \quad \frac{a_3(a_1 a_2 + 1) + a_1}{a_3 a_2 + 1}, \quad \cdots$$

which may be simply denoted by $c_1, c_2, c_3, \ldots, c_n$. If we write $c_{n-1} = p_{n-1}/q_{n-1}$ and $c_n = p_n/q_n$, we can show by induction that

$$p_n = a_n p_{n-1} + p_{n-2}, \quad q_n = a_n q_{n-1} + q_{n-2}$$

Also,

$$p_n q_{n-1} - q_n p_{n-1} = (-1)^n$$

A variety of Diophantine equations have been solved by the method of continued fractions. However, we are not in a position to give an exhaustive statement of the use of this method. Here we simply give an illustration. Consider the equation

$$\alpha x - \beta y = 1$$

and suppose that α/β has the continued-fraction expansion $a_1, a_2, \ldots, a_n$, with convergents $c_1 \ c_2, \ldots, c_n$. Now $p_n = \alpha$, $q_n = \beta$, and hence $\alpha q_{n-1} - \beta p_{n-1} = (-1)^n$. If n is even, i.e., if there is an even number of a's, then $(-1)^n = 1$, and a particular solution of our equation is $\bar{x} = q_{n-1}$, $\bar{y} = p_{n-1}$. If n is odd, then $(-1)^n = -1$, and the partial-fraction expansion may be modified by replacing

$$\frac{1}{a_n} \quad \text{by} \quad \frac{1}{(a_n - 1) + \frac{1}{1}} \quad \text{if } a_n > 1$$

or replacing

$$\frac{1}{a_{n-1} + 1/a_n} \quad \text{by} \quad \frac{1}{a_{n-1} + 1} \quad \text{if } a_n = 1$$

Both cases give an even number of partial quotients, and, on recalculating p_{n-1} and q_{n-1}, we still have

$$\alpha q_{n-1} - \beta p_{n-1} = 1$$

To obtain the general solution, we subtract $\alpha \bar{x} - \beta \bar{y} = 1$ from

$$\alpha x - \beta y = 1$$

and obtain

$$\alpha(x - \bar{x}) = \beta(y - \bar{y})$$

Since α and β are relatively prime, β must divide $x - \bar{x}$; that is, $x - \bar{x} = \beta t$ or $x = \bar{x} + \beta t$.   Similarly, $y = \bar{y} + \alpha t$, $t = 0$, ± 1, ± 2, . . . , which gives the general solution.

Exercise 4-9   Show that the general solution of $\alpha x - \beta y = \gamma$ may be written as $x = c\bar{x} + \beta t$, $y = c\bar{y} + \alpha t$, where $\bar{x}$, $\bar{y}$ are particular solutions of $\alpha x - \beta y = 1$.

THE RULE OF VIRGINS FOR SOLVING LINEAR EQUATIONS

Regula virginum, or the "rule of virgins," is the method of eliminating one unknown at a time and was used in the past to obtain nonnegative solutions of systems.   Associated with it are the names of Euler and Sylvester.

To illustrate the method, consider the equation

$$11x + 3y = 23$$

We solve first for y since it has the smaller coefficient, obtaining

$$y = \frac{23 - 11x}{3} = 7 - 3x + \frac{2 - 2x}{3} = 7 - 3x + t$$

where $t = (2 - 2x)/3$ or $3t + 2x = 2$ Because x and y must be integers, t must also be an integer.

In the last equation we solve for x since its coefficient is the smaller one.   We have

$$x = \frac{2 - 3t}{2} = 1 - t - \frac{t}{2} = 1 - t - u$$

where $u = t/2$, or $t = 2u$.   Since x and t must be integers, u must be an integer also.

Now, if u is an integer, then $t = 2u$ gives t as an integer, and also

$$x = 1 - 3u$$
$$y = 4 + 11u$$

are integers.

Thus, by assigning u the integer values 0, ± 1, ± 2, . . . , we obtain all possible integer values of x and y which satisfy the equation. A requirement that x and y be positive leads to finding u, which satisfies $1 - 3u > 0$, $4 + 11u > 0$; that is, $-\frac{4}{11} < u < \frac{1}{3}$. This gives $u = 0$ and hence $x = 1$, $y = 4$ as the only positive integral solution.

The foregoing may be slightly modified. To solve [31]

$$31x_1 + 14x_2 = 7$$

we consider the term with the larger coefficient and then write, using the coefficient of x_2,

$$31x_1 \equiv 7 \bmod 14$$

This gives

$$3x_1 \equiv 7 \bmod 14 \qquad \text{or} \qquad x_1 \equiv 7 \bmod 14$$

Thus,

$$x_1 = 7 + 14$$

and substitution in the equation gives

$$x_2 = -15 - 31t$$

As before, assigning integer values to t yields the required solution.

To solve $a_1x_1 + a_2x_2 + a_3x_3 = b$, we first solve $a_3x_3 \equiv b \bmod d_1$, where $d_1 = (a_1,a_2)$ is the greatest common divisor of a_1 and a_2. This introduces a parameter t_1, with $x_3 = \bar{x}_3 + dt_1$, where $d = (d_1,a_3)$. This is then substituted in the equation, and then a second integral parameter t_2 is introduced, corresponding to t in the previous example. Consider the equation $20x_1 + 34x_2 + 40x_3 + 77x_4 = 127$. Since $(20,34,40,77) = 1$, there are integer solutions. Also, since $(20,34,40) = 2$, we consider the equation $77x_4 \equiv 127 \bmod 2$ or $x_4 \equiv 1 \bmod 2$. Thus, $x_4 = 1 + 2t_1$. Substituting in the equation, we get $10x_1 + 17x_2 + 20x_3 = 25 - 77t_1$. Since $(10,17,20) = 1$, this equation has solutions for all t_1. In particular, since $(10,17) = 1$, we can put $x_3 = t_2$ and obtain

$$10x_1 + 17x_2 = 25 - 77t_1 - 20t_2$$

If we consider this equation mod 10, we obtain $7x_2 \equiv 5 - 7t$, and to solve this equation we multiply by 3 and obtain $x_2 \equiv 5 + 9t_1$, since $-21 \equiv -1 \equiv 9 \bmod 10$. Thus, $x_2 = 9t_1 + 10t_3 + 5$. Substitution in the previous equation gives

$$10x_1 = 25 - 77t_1 - 20t_2 - 17(9t_1 + 10t_3 + 5)$$

from which we have

$$x_1 = -6 - 23t_1 - 2t_2 - 17t_3$$
$$x_2 = 9t_1 + 10t_3 + 5$$
$$x_3 = t_2$$
$$x_4 = 1 + 2t_1$$

To find all nonnegative solutions in integers $x_i \geq 0$, $i = 1, \ldots, 4$, we note from $40x_3 \leq 127$ that $0 \leq x_3 \leq 3$ and hence $0 \leq t_2 \leq 3$. Also $1 + 2t_1 \geq 0$ implies that $t_1 \geq 0$. Note that $-6 - 23t_1 - 17t_3 \geq 2t_2$ implies that $t_3 \leq -1$, otherwise $t_1 = 0$ yields a negative value to the left-hand side. In general, the inequalities $t_1 \geq 0$, $0 \leq t_2 \leq 3$, $-6 - 23t_1 - 17t_3 \geq 2t_2$ determine the feasible region which we now show is empty. By looking at the equation, it is clear that $x_4 = 0$ or 1. If $x_4 = 0$, the equation has no solution. If $x_4 = 1$, the resulting equation obviously has no positive solution. Thus, the equation has no solution in positive integers.

Exercise 4-10 Consider the aircraft-buying problem of Sec. 4.2. Eliminate y, then x, obtaining $x = z - 20 + z/2$, from which obtain $z = 2u$ for some integer u. Thus, obtain

$$x = 3u - 20 > 0$$
$$y = 40 - 5u > 0$$
$$z = 2u > 0$$

from which conclude that $u = 7$, $x = 1$, $y = 5$, $z = 14$ is the desired solution.

Exercise 4-11 Show that the minimum solution of the gold-coin exercise of Sec. 4.2 is 333 coins.

To solve a system of linear Diophantine equations in integers, one finds all solutions of the first and substitutes these (with their parameters) in the second, then solves the second and substitutes in the third, etc. If a solution in positive integers is desired, the condition is imposed at the last stage, and one works backward—a very awkward procedure. The system [32]

$$6x_1 + 3x_2 + 2x_3 + x_4 = 20$$
$$x_1 + x_2 + x_3 + x_4 = 10$$

has the following solutions: (0,0,10,0), (0,1,8,1), (0,2,6,2), (0,3,4,3), (0,4,2,4), (0,5,0,5), (1,0,5,4), (1,1,3,5), (1,2,1,6), (2,0,0,8).

Exercise 4-12 Show that (1,1,3,5) minimizes $\Sigma_{i=1}^{3}|x_i - x_{i+1}|$ subject to the last two equations as constraints.

General solution   If a linear Diophantine equation [2]

$$a_1 x_1 + \cdots + a_n x_n = b$$

with integer coefficients, has a solution in integers, then b must be divisible by the greatest common divisor (g.c.d.) d_n of $a_1, \ldots, a_n$. Thus, we write $b = d_n t_n$, where t_n is an arbitrary integer.

Theorem 4-3   *The general solution of the equation*

$$a_1 x_1 + \cdots + a_n x_n = d_n t_n \qquad n \geq 2$$

may be shown by induction on n to be (see later for derivation)

$$x_1 = t_n x_1^{(n)} + t_{n-1} \frac{a_n}{d_n} x_1^{(n-1)} + t_{n-2} \frac{a_{n-1}}{d_{n-1}} x_1^{(n-2)} + \cdots + t_1 \frac{a_2}{d_2}$$

$$x_2 = t_n x_2^{(n)} + t_{n-1} \frac{a_n}{d_n} x_2^{(n-1)} + t_{n-2} \frac{a_{n-1}}{d_{n-1}} x_2^{(n-2)} + \cdots - t_1 \frac{d_1}{d_2} \quad (4\text{-}2)$$

$$\cdots \cdots \cdots \cdots \cdots \cdots \cdots \cdots \cdots \cdots$$

$$x_{n-1} = t_n x_{n-1}^{(n)} + t_{n-1} \frac{a_n}{d_n} x_{n-1}^{(n-1)} - t_{n-2} \frac{d_{n-2}}{d_{n-1}}$$

$$x_n = t_n x_n^{(n)} - t_{n-1} \frac{d_{n-1}}{d_n}$$

where $t_1, \ldots, t_{n-1}$ are arbitrary integers, $d_1 = a_1$, $d_2 = $ g.c.d. of a_1 and $a_2, \ldots, d_n = $ g.c.d. of $a_1, \ldots, a_n$, and where $x_i^{(j)} i, j = 1, \ldots, n$, are the solutions of

$$d_2 = a_1 x_1^{(2)} + a_2 x_2^{(2)}$$
$$d_3 = a_1 x_1^{(3)} + a_2 x_2^{(3)} + a_3 x_3^{(3)}$$
$$\cdots \cdots \cdots \cdots \cdots \cdots \cdots \cdots$$
$$d_n = a_1 x_1^{(n)} + a_2 x_2^{(n)} + \cdots + a_n x_n^{(n)}$$

The method of solving any of the last set of equations is accomplished by the following theorem [37].

Theorem 4-4   *For any given positive integers $a_1, \ldots, a_n$, the least positive number of the form $a_1 x_1 + \cdots + a_n x_n$ ($x_1, \ldots, x_n$ integers) is $d = $ (g.c.d. of $a_1, \ldots, a_n$).*

Proof   Suppose that $0 < a_1 x_1 + \cdots + a_n x_n = s \neq d$. Since d must divide s, for at least one coefficient a_k we have $a_k = qs + r$, $0 < r < s$. This gives

$$a_k = q(a_1 x_1 + \cdots + a_n x_n) + r$$

or

$$0 < a_1(-qx_1) + a_2(-qx_2) + \cdots + a_k(1 - qx_k) + \cdots + a_n(-qx_n)$$
$$= r < s$$

We now put $x_j{}^1 = -qx_j, j = 1, \ldots, n, j \neq k$, and $x_k{}^1 = 1 - qx_k$, and continue until d is reached.

Partial proof of Theorem 4-3   Bond [2] shows that the essential inductive step for deriving the system (4-2) is as follows: Let the result be true for $n = k, k \geq 2$. If $x_1{}^{(k+1)}, \ldots, x_{k+1}^{(k+1)}$ is a solution of

$$a_1x_1 + \cdots + a_{k+1}x_{k+1} = d_{k+1}$$

and $x_1, \ldots, x_{k+1}$ is a solution of

$$a_1x_1 + \cdots + a_{k+1}x_{k+1} = t_{k+1}d_{k+1}$$

with $a_1, \ldots, a_{k+1}, t_{k+1}$, nonzero integers, then

$$a_1(x_1 - t_{k+1}x_1{}^{(k+1)}) + \cdots + a_{k+1}(x_{k+1} - t_{k+1}x_{k+1}^{(k+1)}) = 0$$

Dividing through by d_{k+1}, transposing the last term on the left to the right side, and noting that $a_1/d_{k+1}, \ldots, a_{k+1}/d_{k+1}$ are relatively prime, the last equation holds if and only if

$$x_{k+1} - t_{k+1}x_{k+1}^{(k+1)} = (-t_k)\frac{d_k}{d_{k+1}}$$

For each choice of an integer value of t_k, we have by induction

$$x_1 - t_{k+1}x_1{}^{(k+1)} = t_k \frac{a_{k+1}}{d_{k+1}} x_1{}^{(k)} + t_{k-1} \frac{a_k/d_{k\,|\,1}}{d_k/d_{k+1}} x_1{}^{(k-1)} + \cdots + t_1 \frac{a_2/d_{k+1}}{d_2/d_{k+1}}$$

$$x_2 - t_{k+1}x_2{}^{(k+1)} = t_k \frac{a_{k+1}}{d_{k+1}} x_2{}^{(k)} + t_{k-1} \frac{a_k/d_{k+1}}{d_k/d_{k+1}} x_2{}^{(k-1)} + \cdots - t_1 \frac{d_1/d_{k+1}}{d_2/d_{k+1}}$$

$$\cdots \cdots \cdots \cdots \cdots \cdots \cdots \cdots \cdots$$

$$x_k - t_{k+1}x_k{}^{(k+1)} = t_k \frac{a_{k+1}}{d_{k+1}} x_k{}^{(k)} - t_{k-1} \frac{d_{k-1}/d_{k+1}}{d_k/d_{k+1}}$$

and where

$$\frac{a_1}{d_{k+1}} x_1{}^{(i)} + \cdots + \frac{a_i}{d_{k+1}} x_i{}^{(i)} = \frac{d_i}{d_{k+1}} \qquad \text{for } i = 2, \ldots, k$$

Transposing the terms involving t_{k+1} to the right side and simplifying, we obtain the desired form for $x_1, \ldots, x_{k+1}$. It is easy to verify that each choice of integers $t_1, \ldots, t_k$ does lead to a solution in integers of $a_1x_1 + \cdots + a_{k+1}x_k = t_{k+1}d_{k+1}$.

Example   One may start by arbitrarily choosing $x_1{}^{(0)}, \ldots, x_n{}^{(0)}$ and successively choose $x_1{}^{(i)}, \ldots, x_n{}^{(i)}$, according to the foregoing procedure, until d is reached and hence one has a solution of the Diophantine equation whose coefficients are

$a_1, \ldots, a_n$ and whose right side is d. Incidentally this is also a useful procedure for finding the g.c.d. of $a_1, \ldots, a_n$.

If we apply the procedure of the general solution to the equation

$$3x_1 + 2x_2 + x_3 = 13$$

we first use it to find the g.c.d. of 3, 2, 1 and would find that $d_3 = 1$, from which $t_3 = 13$. We must also find the g.c.d. of 3, 2 which we know by inspection to be 1. We then solve

$$3x_1^{(2)} + 2x_2^{(2)} = 1$$
$$3x_1^{(3)} + 2x_2^{(3)} + x_3^{(3)} = 1$$

We find by this process the particular solutions

$$(x_1^{(2)}, x_2^{(2)}) = (1, -1)$$
$$(x_1^{(3)}, x_2^{(3)}, x_3^{(3)}) = (1, -1, 0)$$

We then have, for the general solution of our equation,

$$x_1 = 13 + t_2 + 2t_1$$
$$x_2 = -13 - t_2 - 3t_1$$
$$x_3 = -t_2$$

For nonnegative integer solutions, we put

$$13 + t_2 + 2t_1 \geq 0$$
$$13 + t_2 + 3t_1 \leq 0 \qquad t_2 \leq 0$$

From $13 + t_2 \geq -2t_1$ and $13 + t_2 \leq -3t_1$, we have $-3t_1 \geq -2t_1$, which is valid if and only if $t_1 \leq 0$. Thus, all solutions lie in the triangular region of the t_1, t_2 plane whose vertices are $(\frac{13}{3}, 0)$, $(-\frac{13}{2}, 0)$, and $(0, -13)$.

Maximizing $8x_1 + 5x_2 + x_3$ subject to $3x_1 + 2x_2 + x_3 = 13$, x_i, $i = 1, 2, 3$, nonnegative integers leads to the following: Find nonnegative integers u_1 and u_2 which maximize

$$8(13 - u_2 - 2u_1) + 5(-13 + u_2 + 3u_1) + u_2 = -u_1 - 2u_2 + 39$$

subject to $13 - u_2 - 2u_1 \geq 0$, $-13 + u_2 + 3u_1 \geq 0$, $u_2 \geq 0$, which is an integer linear-programming problem. In general, a system of $m \leq n$ Diophantine equations in n variables leads to a system of mn inequalities in $(n - 1)$ variables. A solution in nonnegative integers of the original system would be obtained when one has appropriately solved the inequality system in integers.

4-4 SOME NONLINEAR EQUATIONS

Let us show that the equation [19]

$$x^2 + y^2 = z^2$$

has an infinite number of solutions in integers. We may assume that x, y, z are relatively prime in pairs for if they are not, and if d is their greatest common divisor, then, after dividing by d^2, we arrive at the desired situation. Thus, two of them must be odd. We show first that this pair cannot be x and y. If x is odd, then $x \equiv 1$ or 3 mod 4, and hence $x^2 \equiv 1 \bmod 4$. Similarly if y is odd, $y^2 \equiv 1 \bmod 4$, and hence $x^2 + y^2 \equiv 2 \bmod 4$. But $x^2 + y^2 = z^2$, while, for every integer z, $z^2 \equiv 0$ or $1 \bmod 4$. Thus one of x and y is odd; for example, y is odd, but x is even. Thus,

$$x^2 = 4t^2 = z^2 - y^2 = (z - y)(z + y)$$

Now each of $z - y$ and $z + y$ has 2 as a greatest common divisor. Thus, we must have

$$z - y = 2m^2$$
$$z + y = 2n^2$$

in order that x^2 will come out as a square of a product of integers, from which x would be an integer.

Thus $z = m^2 + n^2$, $y = n^2 - m^2$, and $x = 2mn$. The integers m and n are called *generators of the triangle*. The general solution is given by

$$
\begin{aligned}
x &= 2kmn \\
y &= k(n^2 - m^2) \qquad m - n \equiv 1 \bmod 2 \\
z &= k(m^2 + n^2)
\end{aligned}
$$

where k is an arbitrary integer.

We shall now consider positive-integer solutions of $a^b = b^a$ [34]. We start with the observation that

$$
\sqrt[n]{n+1} = \begin{cases} 2 & n = 1 \\ \sqrt{3} & n = 2 \\ < \sqrt{3} & n > 2 \end{cases}
$$

The last fact follows from the first three-term expansion of $(1 + 2)^n$; that is,

$$
\begin{aligned}
3^n = (1 + 2)^n &> 1 + n2 + \frac{n(n-1)}{2!} 2^2 \\
&= (1 + 2n + n^2) + n(n - 2) > (n + 1)^2
\end{aligned}
$$

Hence $\sqrt[n]{n+1} < \sqrt{3}$. Thus, for $n \geq 1$, the only integer value of $\sqrt[n]{n+1}$ is 2. Suppose that $a > b$; then since $a^b = b^a$,

$$a = b^{a/b} = b \cdot b^{(a/b)-1}$$

Since a and b are integers, $b^{(a/b)-1}$ must be an integer also, which we denote by n and write $a = nb$. Thus, $(nb)^b = (b^n)^b$, from which $nb = b^n$ or $b = \sqrt[n-1]{n}$. Thus, in order that b be an integer, we must have, by the above, $n - 1 = 1$ or $n = 2$, from which $b = 2$ and $a = 4$. Therefore, if $a \neq b$, the positive integer solutions are $a = 4$, $b = 2$ or $a = 2$, $b = 4$.

We now investigate the solvability in positive integers of the quadratic in two variables [16]

$$a_{11}x_1^2 + 2a_{12}x_1x_2 + a_{22}x_2^2 + 2a_1x_1 + 2a_2x_2 + a_3 = 0$$

whose six coefficients are integers.

We solve as a quadratic in x_1, obtaining

$$a_{11}x_1 + a_{12}x_2 + a_1 = \pm[(a_{12}^2 - a_{11}a_{22})x_2^2 + 2(a_{12}a_1 - a_{11}a_2)x_2 \\ + (a_1^2 - a_{11}a_3)]^{\frac{1}{2}}$$

To obtain positive integer values for x_1 and x_2, the discriminant must be a perfect square; i.e., we should be able to write it in the form

$$px_2^2 + 2qx_2 + r = y^2 \qquad \text{where } y \text{ is a variable}$$

Solving for x_2 gives

$$px_2 + q = \pm \sqrt{q^2 - pr + py^2}$$

Again, the condition that the discriminant be a perfect square leads to an equation of the form

$$x^2 - py^2 = q^2 - pr \qquad \text{where } x \text{ is a variable}$$

which must be solvable in integers. This equation may be written in the form $x^2 \pm Ny^2 = \pm a$, where N and a are positive integers. The equation $x^2 - Ny^2 = \pm 1$ is, of course, Pell's equation.

Remark If a_{11}, a_{22}, and a_{12} are all positive, then for large x_1 and x_2 the quadratic part is dominant, and hence the left side cannot vanish. Thus, the number of positive integral solutions is finite.

Exercise 4-13 Show that if $a_{12}^2 - a_{11}a_{22} < 0$, then the number of integral solutions is finite.

Exercise 4-14 Show that $x^2 + Ny^2 = -a$ has no real solutions, and that $x^2 + Ny^2 = a$ has a finite number of solutions.

We shall be interested in the equation

$$x^2 - Ny^2 = \pm a$$

If $N = M^2$ is a perfect square, then the equation $x^2 - M^2y^2 = a$ may be factored into $(x + My)(x - My) = a$. If $a = f_1f_2$, $f_1 > f_2$, then we put $x + My = f_1$, $x - My = f_2$. Thus, the integral solutions, if any, are obtained from the different factorizations of a.

Exercise 4-15 Show that $x^2 - y^2 = 60$ has the solutions

$$(x,y) = (8,2), (16,14)$$

The case where N is not a perfect square is complicated.   The reader is referred to the textbook literature for its treatment.

Example   A set of objects is so arranged as to form a perfect triangle, with one object at a vertex followed by two objects in line behind, three objects in line behind the two objects, etc., up to N objects (see Fig. 4-2).   It is possible to rearrange this triangular arrangement into two perfect triangular arrangements that are identical.   Find the exact number of objects if the number of objects in the first arrangement is between 1,000 and 10,000.

Solution   The first arrangement has $S = N(N + 1)/2$ objects, while each of the others has $M(M + 1)/2$, and we have the following equation [13]

$$\frac{N(N + 1)}{2} = \frac{2M(M + 1)}{2} \tag{4-3}$$

One method of approach to obtain the solution is the following.

On completing the square on both sides and simplifying, we have

$$(2N + 1)^2 - 2(2M + 1)^2 = -2$$

If we substitute $x = 2N + 1$, $y = 2M + 1$, our equation takes the simple form (which we shall not use)

$$x^2 - 2y^2 = -2$$

If we solve for N in the quadratic [Eq. (4-3)], we have

$$2N = -1 \pm \sqrt{1 + 8M(M + 1)}$$

Let $M = N - k$, and our equation becomes

$$2N = 4k - 1 \pm \sqrt{1 + 8k^2} \tag{4-4}$$

Hence $1 + 8k^2$ must be a perfect square.   Note that $k = 1$ gives $N = 0$ or $N = 3$, and the total number of objects is six, which can be divided into two triangles each with three objects.   For arbitrary k we denote by P the smaller of the two values of N, and by Q the larger one.   If we substitute Q for N in Equation (4-4) and simplify, we obtain the quadratic in k:

$$8k^2 - 8k(1 + 2Q) + 4Q(Q + 1) = 0$$

Thus, Q gives rise to two values of k, k_1, and k_2, with $k_1 < k_2$.   Now, for each of these two k values, we have a corresponding P and Q, but one value is the same in both cases because a given value of Q was used to obtain k_1 and k_2.   One of these two equal values corresponds to a Q in the case of k_1 and to a P in the case of k_2. Now the Q value corresponding to k_2 is again used to determine two values of k, one of which is k_2, and a new $k_3 > k_2$, and so on.

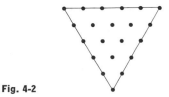

Fig. 4-2

We have the following recursion relations:

$$2Q_i = 4k - 1 - \sqrt{1 + 8k^2}$$
$$2P_{i+1} = 4k - 1 + \sqrt{1 + 8k^2}$$
$$Q_i + P_i = 4k - 1$$

The last relation holds as the sum of the two roots [see Equation (4-4)] and enables one to pass from a P to a Q corresponding to the same k. Note that if one root k_1 is an integer, then so is k_2 since $k_1 + k_2 = 1 + 2Q$ is an integer.

We begin with $k = 1$. Using (4-4), we have $P_1 = 0$, $Q_1 = 3$, and $S_1 = 6$, where S_i denotes the total number of objects computed for k_i, $i = 1, 2, \ldots$. Now $Q_1 = P_2 = 3$ and $S_2 = 6$ since $k_1 + k_2 = 1 + 2Q$. With $k_2 = 6$, we have $Q_2 = 20$ since $P_2 + Q_2 = 4k_2 - 1$, from which $S_2 = 210$. Finally, $k_3 = 35$, $Q_3 = 119$, and $S_3 = 7,140$, which is the desired answer.

A useful formula is obtained from

$$S_i = \frac{Q_i(Q_i + 1)}{2}$$

and is given by

$$S_i = k_i k_{i+1}$$

Also, from

$$k_i + k_{i+1} = 1 + 2Q_i$$
$$Q_{i+1} + Q_i = 4k_{i+1} - 1$$

we have

$$_{i+2} - 6k_{i+1} + k_i = 0 \tag{4-5}$$

with $k_0 = 0$, $k_1 = 1$, which avoids the intermediate passage to P_i and Q_i. In addition, $\alpha_{i+1}/\alpha_i \to 3 + 2\sqrt{2}$ as $i \to \infty$, and hence $S_{i+1}/S_i \to 17 + 12\sqrt{2}$.

The above solution is the only one since any other N gives rise in Equation (4-3) to a solution k, and by means of Equation (4-5) one stops at the smallest positive k_0, which is necessarily $k_0 = 0$.

4-5 OPTIMIZATION SUBJECT TO DIOPHANTINE CONSTRAINTS

Because as yet we have few general methods for solving Diophantine equations, it is natural to use the information that is available in the solution of relevant optimization problems subject to constraints. For example, it is known that the general solution in integers (not necessarily nonnegative) of

$$\alpha x + \beta y = \gamma$$

is

$$x = \bar{x} + \frac{\beta}{(\alpha, \beta)} t \qquad y = \bar{y} - \frac{\alpha}{(\alpha, \beta)} t$$

where $(\bar{x},\bar{y})$ is a particular solution, and where (α,β) is the greatest common divisor of α and β.

It may be desired to find a value of t which minimizes

$$f(x,y) = c_1 x^2 + c_2 y^2 \qquad c_1, c_2 > 0$$

subject to the above equation as a constraint. Substitution for x and y yields a quadratic in t. Calculus methods may be used, followed by finding the nearest integer value of t. Because of the convexity of $f(x,y)$, this is the appropriate minimum sought.

The following are examples of problems of theoretical and applied interest that are simple to state, and for which general solutions are not yet known.

1. Given a positive integer C, find a positive integer partition

$$\sum_{j=1}^{n} x_j = C$$

such that the least common multiple of $x_1, \ldots, x_n$ is maximum.

If all the primes occurring in x_j, $j = 1, \ldots, n$, are $p_1, \ldots, p_s$, and if

$$x_j = p_1^{\alpha_{1j}} \cdots p_s^{\alpha_{sj}} \qquad j = 1, \ldots, n$$

then the least common multiple of $x_1, \ldots, x_n$ is given by

$$L = p_1^{\alpha_1} p_2^{\alpha_2} \cdots p_s^{\alpha_s}$$

where

$$\alpha_i = \max (\alpha_{i1}, \ldots, \alpha_{in}) \qquad i = 1, \ldots, s$$

2. The following example arises in studying the structure of telephone exchanges [32]: Minimize in positive integers the nonlinear expression

$$\sum_{j=2}^{n} |x_j - x_{j-1}|$$

subject to the constraints

$$\sum_{j=1}^{n} x_j = C \qquad \text{and} \qquad \sum_{j=1}^{n} a_j x_j = C_1$$

where the given integers C and C_1 satisfy

$$C \leq C_1 \leq \alpha C$$

for a given even integer α, and where the positive integer coefficients a_j, $j = 1, \ldots, n$, divide α. No explicit solution is known for this problem, but extensive tables have been compiled by the British Government Printing Office; however, R. Syski has pointed out that the tables do not list nonunique solutions.

3. If $x_j = m_{0j}/m_{1j}$ is the ratio of the initial mass to the payload mass of the jth stage of an n-stage rocket, and if $a_j = m_{0j}/m_{2j}$, where m_{2j} is the structural mass of the jth stage, then a problem in rocket design asks that one find nonnegative integers, x_j, $j = 1, \ldots, n$, which minimize $\Pi_{j=1}^n x_j$ subject to

$$\log \prod_{j=1}^n \frac{a_j x_j}{a_j + x_j} = C$$

where a_j, $j = 1, \ldots, n$, and C are given.

Exercise 4-16 Find integers x, y, z (positive or negative) which satisfy

$$\frac{z}{2} - \frac{x}{3} + 2y = 11$$

and which maximize

$$|x|10^2 + |y|10 + |z|$$

    Ans.: $x = 9$, $y = 9$, $z = -8$, and the maximum value is 998.

Exercise 4-17 If x and y are integers, can $x/y + y/x$ be an integer?
    Hint: if $x/y + y/x = k$, an integer, then $x^2 + y^2 = kxy$, $x^2 = y(kx - y)$; thus, y divides x^2, which is to be proved impossible unless $y = \pm x$. Thus, the sum can only be 2 or -2.

There are few criteria known for a nonnegative integer solution to a nonlinear, constrained optimization problem. The following useful criterion is due to O. Gross [15].

Theorem 4-5 *A necessary and sufficient condition that a nonnegative integer vector* $x = (x_1, \ldots, x_n)$ *provide a minimum to the expression*

$$\sum_{j=1}^n \varphi_j(x_j) \tag{4·6}$$

where φ_j, $j = 1, \ldots, n$ *are convex, subject to the constraint*

$$\sum_{j=1}^n x_j = m \tag{4-7}$$

for a given positive integer m *is that*

$$\min_{j \in I} [\varphi_j(x_j + 1) - \varphi_j(x_j)] \geq \max_{j \in S^+(x)} [\varphi_j(x_j) - \varphi_j(x_j - 1)] \tag{4-8}$$

where $I = \{1, \ldots, n\}$ *and* $S^+(x) = \{j \in I \mid x_j > 0\}$.

Proof SUFFICIENCY   Let x be a feasible solution (that is,

$\Sigma_{i=1}^{n} x_i = m$

$x_i \geq 0$, are integers) which satisfies Inequality (4-8).   Let x' be another feasible solution.   We show that

$$\sum_{j=1}^{n} \varphi_j(x_j') \geq \sum_{j=I}^{n} \varphi_j(x_j)$$

Let

$$\lambda \equiv \min_{j \in I} \left[\varphi_j(x_j + 1) - \varphi_j(x_j) \right] \tag{4-9}$$

Then

$$\lambda \leq \varphi_j(x_j + 1) - \varphi_j(x_j) \qquad \text{for all } j \in I \tag{4-10}$$

Also from Inequality (4-8) we have

$$\lambda \geq \varphi_j(x_j) - \varphi_j(x_j - 1) \qquad \text{for all } j \in S^+(x) \tag{4-11}$$

The convexity of φ_j implies

$$\tfrac{1}{2}[\varphi_j(k + 1) + \varphi_j(k - 1)] \geq \varphi_j(k) \tag{4-12}$$

Thus,

$$\varphi_j(k + 1) - \varphi_j(k) \geq \varphi_j(k) - \varphi_j(k - 1) \tag{4-13}$$

and hence $\varphi_j(k + 1) - \varphi_j(k)$ is a nondecreasing function on the integers. Thus, if $k \geq x_j$, Inequality (4-10) gives

$$\lambda \leq \varphi_j(k + 1) - \varphi_j(k) \tag{4-14}$$

and if $0 < k \leq x_j$, then $j \in S^+(x)$ and Inequality (4-11) gives

$$\lambda \geq \varphi_j(k) - \varphi_j(k - 1) \tag{4-15}$$

We sum Inequality (4-14) over values of k with $x_j \leq k \leq x_j' - 1$ for $x_j' > x_j$, and sum Inequality (4-15) over values of k with $x_j' + 1 \leq k \leq x_j$ for $x_j' < x_j$.   The first summation gives

$$\varphi_j(x_j') - \varphi_j(x_j) \geq \lambda(x_j' - x_j) \qquad x_j' > x_j$$

and the second gives

$$\varphi_j(x_j) - \varphi_j(x_j') \leq \lambda(x_j - x_j') \qquad x_j' < x_j$$

In either case, and obviously even if $x_j = x_j'$, we have

$$\varphi_j(x_j') \geq \varphi_j(x_j) + \lambda x_j' - \lambda x_j \qquad \text{for all } j \in I$$

Summing over $1 \leq j \leq n$, and using $\Sigma_{j=1}^{n} x_j' = m = \Sigma_{j=1}^{n} x_j$, we have sufficiency; that is, x minimizes expression (4-6).

Proof Necessity Let x minimize expression (4-6) and satisfy (4-7) in nonnegative integers and suppose that the sense of Inequality (4-8) is the opposite. Since $m > 0$, $S^+(x) \neq \varnothing$, the right side of Inequality (4-8) attains its maximum for an integer α, and the left side its minimum for an integer β. Since we assume the opposite of Inequality (4-8) holds, we have

$$\varphi_\beta(x_\beta + 1) - \varphi_\beta(x_\beta) < \varphi_\alpha(x_\alpha) - \varphi_\alpha(x_\alpha - 1) \tag{4-16}$$

If $\alpha = \beta$, this relation cannot hold because φ is monotone. Thus $\alpha \neq \beta$. Consider

$$x'_\alpha = x_\alpha - 1$$
$$x'_\beta = x_\beta + 1$$

and $x'_j = x_j$ for remaining indices. Obviously $x'_j \geq 0$ are integers, and $\Sigma_{j=1}^n x'_j = m$. Also,

$$\sum_{j=1}^n \varphi_j(x'_j) - \sum_{j=1}^n \varphi_j(x_j) = \varphi_\alpha(x_\alpha - 1) - \varphi_\alpha(x_\alpha) + \varphi_\beta(x_\beta + 1) - \varphi_\beta(x_\beta)$$

which <0 by Inequality (4-16) contradicting the fact that x_j, $j = 1$, . . . , n, yield the minimum. Thus, Inequality (4-8) must hold, proving necessity.

The solution is obtained iteratively, starting with

$$x_j{}^0 = 0 \qquad j = 1, \ldots, n$$

For $k \geq 0$, let $j^*(k)$ be an index, yielding

$$\min_{j \in I} [\varphi_j(x_j{}^{(k)} + 1) - \varphi_j(x_j{}^{(k)})]$$

and put

$$x_{j*}{}^{(k+1)} = x_{j*}{}^{(k)} + 1$$
$$x_j{}^{(k+1)} = x_j{}^{(k)} \qquad j \neq j^*$$

One can prove that a solution is obtained by allocating m units to the φ_i, one unit at a time, in the direction of minimum marginal increase. Thus, the vector $x^{(m)}$ satisfies the constraints and yields the minimum.

Exercise 4-18 In the problem as set in Theorem 4-5, let $\varphi_i = \varphi_j$, $i, j = 1, \ldots, n$. Show that

$$x_j = \left[\frac{m}{n}\right] \qquad j \in S$$

$$x_j = \left[\frac{m}{n}\right] + 1 \qquad \text{otherwise}$$

where $[m/n]$ is the greatest integer in m/n, and S is a subset of the integers, containing exactly $n - m + n[m/n]$ elements.

Exercise 4-19   Solve the problem of Exercise 4-18 by using Lagrange multipliers.

Exercise 4-20   Show that the foregoing is applicable to the problem of minimizing

$$\sum_{j=1}^{n} w_j p_j^{x_j}$$

subject to $\Sigma_{j=1}^{n} x_j = m$, where $x_j \geq 0, j = 1, \ldots , n$, are integers, m is a positive integer, $w_j > 0$ are real, and $0 < p_j < 1$.

Here m is the number of units of a given weapon to be allocated to destroy n enemy targets; $x_j \geq 0, j = 1, \ldots , n$, is the number assigned to the jth target, whose value is w_j, and whose probability of surviving an attack by a single unit weapon is q_j. The probability of not surviving an attack is $p_j^{x_j} = (1 - q_j)^{x_j}$, and the problem requires maximizing the expected value destroyed.

The following theorem is interesting for its usefulness in some applications and for the different methods of proof that are possible.

Theorem 4-6   *If $x_1, \ldots , x_n$ are positive integers such that*

$$\prod_{i=1}^{n} x_i = maximum \ for \ n \ to \ be \ determined \qquad (4\text{-}17)$$

and

$$\sum_{i=1}^{n} x_i = C \qquad (4\text{-}18)$$

where C is a given positive integer, and if

$C = 3k$	then	$x_i = 3$	$i = 1, \ldots , n$
$C = 3k + 2$	then	$x_1 = 2, x_i = 3$	$i = 2, \ldots , n$
$C = 3k + 1$	then	$x_1 = 2, x_2 = 2, x_i = 3$	$i = 3, \ldots , n$

Note that n must be determined.

Proof 1   Note first that for a maximum, $x_i \neq 1$. Also if $x_i = 4$ for some i, then x_i may be replaced by $x_j = 2, x_k = 2$; and if $x_i > 4$, then x_i may be replaced by $x_j = 3$ and $x_k = x_i - 3$, whose product $3(x_i - 3)$ is greater than x_i. Hence all factors are equal to 2 or 3. Now the factors in 2^3 give the same sum as those in 3^2, and thus 2^3 may be replaced by 3^2. The rest of the proof is straightforward.

Note, for example, that if $C = 100$, then since $x_i = 1$ for no i we cannot take 3^{33}, and hence we have $x_1 = 2, x_2 = 2, x_i = 3, i = 3, \ldots , 34$. The product is $2^2 \times 3^{32}$. Another solution is $x_1 = 4, x_i = 3, i = 2, \ldots , 33$.

Proof 2   Another argument demonstrates that the x_i should be equal (or nearly equal because of the end effect). For the present, we only give the proof for equality.

Consider the kth-order exponential mean

$$X_k = \left[\frac{1}{n} \sum_{i=1}^{n} x_i^k \right]^{1/k}$$

X_2 is the root mean square, X_1 is the arithmetic mean, X_0 is the geometric mean, and X_{-1} is the harmonic mean. Note, by using the first two terms of the series expansion of the exponential, that

$$X_0 = \lim_{k \to 0} X_k = \lim_{k \to 0} \left[\frac{1}{n} \sum_{i=1}^{n} e^{k \ln x_i} \right]^{1/k}$$

$$= \lim_{k \to 0} \left[1 + \frac{k}{n} \sum_{i=1}^{n} \ln x_i \right]^{1/k}$$

$$= \lim_{k \to 0} \left[1 + \frac{(1/n) \sum_{i=1}^{n} \ln x_i}{1/k} \right]^{1/k}$$

$$= \exp \left(\frac{1}{n} \sum_{i=1}^{n} \ln x_i \right) = \left(\prod_{i=1}^{n} x_i \right)^{1/n}$$

We now show that $X_k \geq X_j$ for $k > j$. Note that equality holds if $x_1 = x_2 = \cdots = x_n$. Let

$$0 < r < x \qquad r = s\alpha \qquad 0 < \alpha < 1$$
$$p_i a_i^s = u_i \qquad p_i = v_i \qquad v_i > 0$$

and

$$p_i a_i^{s\alpha} = (p_i a_i^s)^\alpha p_i^{1-\alpha} = u_i^\alpha v_i^{1-\alpha}$$

then

$$\Sigma u_i^\alpha v_i^{1-\alpha} < (\Sigma u_i)^\alpha (\Sigma v_i)^{1-\alpha}$$

unless u_i/v_i is independent of i or simply unless a_i is independent of i. This follows from the fact that [17]

$$\gamma_j > 0 \qquad j = 1, \ldots, n \qquad \sum_{j=1}^{n} \gamma_j = 1$$

imply

$$\sum a_i^{\gamma_1} b_j^{\gamma_2} \cdots l_m^{\gamma_n} < \left(\sum a_i \right)^{\gamma_1} \left(\sum b_j \right)^{\gamma_2} \cdots \left(\sum l_m \right)^{\gamma_n}$$

unless $a_i, b_j, \ldots, l_m$ are all proportional or one of them is zero for all values of its subscript. Thus,

$$\left(\frac{\Sigma p_i a_i^{s\alpha}}{\Sigma p_i} \right)^{1/s\alpha} < \left(\frac{\Sigma p_i a_i^s}{\Sigma p_i} \right)^{\frac{1}{s}}$$

We obtain the result if we replace $s\alpha$ by r and put $p_i = 1/n$.

Now our problem requires that the geometric mean be maximized subject to a constrained arithmetic mean. The foregoing shows that $X_1 \geq X_0$, and hence X_1 is obtained for those values of the constraining constant which are divisible by n if and only if all x_i are equal. To take care of the boundary condition, one proceeds as before.

Proof 3 INDUCTIVE APPROACH Partition solution set $S = \{x_1, \ldots, x_n\}$ into two sets $S_1 = \{y_1, \ldots, y_r\}$, $S_2 = \{z_1, \ldots, z_s\}$, with $r + s = n$. Suppose that $\Sigma_{i=1}^{r} y_i = Q_1$ and $\Sigma_{i=1}^{s} z_i = Q_2$, with $Q_1 + Q_2 = C$. Then $\Pi_{i=1}^{r} y_i$ is maximum for all partitions of Q_1 and $\Pi_{i=1}^{s} z_i$ is maximum for all partitions of Q_2. Otherwise, S would not be a solution since Q_1 and Q_2 are arbitrary except for $Q_1 + Q_2 = C$; thus, it is sufficient to study one product Πy_i. We are thus led to the problem of maximizing this product subject to the small value of the constraining constant Q_1.

Theorem 4-7 *Let Q_1 be an integer ≥ 2.*

a. *If $Q_1 \equiv 0 \mod 3$, then max $\Pi_{i=1}^{r} y_i = 3^k$ and $Q_1 = 3k = 3 + 3 \cdots + 3$ (k threes).*

b. *If $Q_1 \equiv 1 \mod 3$, then max $\Pi_{i=1}^{r} y_i = 4 \cdot 3^{k-1}$ and $Q_1 = 3k + 1 = 4 + (3 + 3 + \cdots + 3)$ ($k - 1$ threes) or $Q_1 = 3k + 1 = 2 + 2 + (3 + 3 + \cdots + 3)$ ($k - 1$ threes).*

c. *If $Q_1 \equiv 2 \mod 3$, then max $\Pi_{i=1}^{r} y_i = 2 \cdot 3^k$ and $Q_1 = 3k + 2 = 2 + (3 + 3 + \cdots + 3)$ (k threes).*

Proof 4 Suppose that x_i, $i = 1, \ldots n$, is a solution. Select two factors x_j and x_k and form $z_j = x_j - 1$, $z_k = x_k + 1$, assuming that $x_j \leq x_k$. Thus

$$\sum_{i \neq j, k}^{n} x_i + z_j + z_k = C$$

$$\prod_{i \neq j, k}^{n} x_i z_j z_k = (x_j - 1)(x_k + 1) \prod_{i \neq j, k}^{n} x_i \leq \prod_{i=1}^{n} x_i$$

Cancellation gives

$$x_j x_k \geq (x_j - 1)(x_k + 1) \qquad \text{or} \qquad x_k + 1 \geq x_j$$

Alternatively, writing $z_j = x_j + 1$, $z_k = x_k - 1$ yields

$$x_j x_k \geq (x_j + 1)(x_k - 1) \qquad \text{or} \qquad x_j \geq x_k - 1$$

Combining the two results, we have

$$x_k + 1 \geq x_j \geq x_k - 1$$

which holds for any two factors x_j and x_k. Thus, some (perhaps all) factors must be equal to an integer x_0, while the remaining ones are equal to $x_0 - 1$. The problem becomes one of finding x_0, n_1, and n_2 which maximize

$$x_0{}^{n_1}(x_0 - 1)^{n_2} \qquad \text{subject to} \qquad n_1 x_0 + n_2(x_0 - 1) = C$$

Having established that the factors must be 2 and 3, one may complete the proof as follows (e.g., use the case where $C = 100$): First, to estimate the powers, we write the product as $2^r 3^s$, with $2r + 3s = 100$ or $r = \frac{1}{2}(100 - 3s)$. We then find s which maximizes $2^{50-(\frac{3}{2})s}3^s$. This quantity is maximum when its logarithm is maximum. The expression

$$[50 - (\tfrac{3}{2})s] \log 2 + s \log 3 = s(\log 3 - \tfrac{3}{2} \log 2) + 50 \log 2$$

is maximum for the largest possible s, so that 3^s does not exceed 100. Since $x_i = 1$ is excluded for any of the factors, $s \neq 33$. Thus $s = 32$, and one solution is $3^{32}2^2$.

A heuristic approach   Let us ignore the requirement that x_i be integers. In addition, we reduce the inequality constraints $x_i > 0$ to equality constraints by writing $x_i - y_i{}^2 = 0$, where y_i is real. Our problem becomes: Find y_i which maximize

$$\prod_{i=1}^{n} y_i{}^2 \tag{4-19}$$

subject to

$$\sum_{i=1}^{n} y_i{}^2 = 100 \tag{4-20}$$

Note that the original problem required the determination of a point on the surface of a simplex, whereas the second is on the surface of a sphere.

To maximize $\sum_{i=1}^{n} \log y_i{}^2$ subject to $\sum_{i=1}^{n} y_i{}^2 = 100$, form the lagrangian function

$$F(y_1, \ldots, y_n, \lambda) = \sum_{i=1}^{n} \log y_i{}^2 + \lambda \left(\sum_{i=1}^{n} y_i{}^2 - 100 \right)$$

Then

$$\frac{\partial F}{\partial y_i} = \frac{2}{y_i} + 2\lambda y_i = 0 \qquad i = 1, \ldots, n$$

Thus $v_i{}^2 = -1/\lambda$, which, when substituted in Equation (4-20), gives

$\lambda = -(n/100)$, $y_i{}^2 = 100/n$. We now determine n, which maximizes

$$\prod_{i=1}^{n} \frac{100}{n} = \left(\frac{100}{n}\right)^n$$

Again, when viewed as a continuous problem, we find that $(100/x)^x$ is maximum for $x = 100/e = 36.8$. Using nearest integer approximation to obtain an estimate for n (that is, $n = 36$ or $n = 37$) and then for $y_i{}^2$, we have $y_i{}^2 = 3$. This choice for $y_i{}^2$ forces a reduction of the value of n in order to satisfy $\Sigma_{i=1}^n y_i{}^2 = 100$; however, $3^{32} \cdot 2^2 > 3^{33} \cdot 1$. The last part of the argument is a careful examination of the end effect. Note, for example, that $1^{100} < 2^{50} < e^{100/e} > 3^{1\frac{90}{3}} > 4^{25} > 5^{20} > 6^{1\frac{90}{8}} > \cdots$.

Remark It is worth noting that in the continuous case (which gives an idea of the type of answer to be expected) the following is known. If $x_1, \ldots, x_n$ are positive, and if $a_1, \ldots, a_n$, C are positive constants, then the maximum of $\Pi_{i=1}^n x_i$ subject to $\Sigma_{i=1}^n a_i x_i = C$ is attained when $a_1 x_1 = a_2 x_2 = \cdots = a_n x_n$. With the same qualifications, the minimum of $\Sigma_{i=1}^n a_i x_i$ subject to $\Pi_{i=1}^n x_i = C$ is attained when $a_1 x_1 = a_2 x_2 = \cdots = a_n x_n$. These two facts may be proven through the Lagrange-multiplier approach. If $a_i = 1$, $i = 1, \ldots, n$, then the relation between the arithmetic and geometric means (see Sec. 4-6) enables one to solve these problems.

Exercise 4-21 Minimize in nonnegative integers

$$\sum_{i=1}^{n} x_i{}^{-1} \quad \text{subject to} \quad \sum_{i=1}^{n} x_i - C$$

where C is a given positive integer.

Exercise 4-22 Maximize in nonnegative integers

$$\sum_{i=1}^{n} x_i \quad \text{subject to} \quad \sum_{i=1}^{n} x_i{}^{-1} = C$$

where C is a given positive integer.

Theorem 4-8 *The positive integers* $x_1, \ldots, x_n$ *maximize*

$$\prod_{i=1}^{n} x_i{}^i \quad \text{subject to} \quad \sum_{i=1}^{n} x_i = C$$

if and only if $x_i = 1, 2,$ *or* 3, $i = 1, \ldots, n$. *(Here C is a positive integer and n is not fixed.)*

Theorem 4-9   *If α, β, and γ are the numbers of 1s, 2s, and 3s, respectively, in the solution given in Theorem 4-8, then the maximum is obtained from the lattice points determined by* [28]

$$(2C + 1) \log 2 - (C + 1) \log 3 \leq (3\beta + 6\gamma) \log 2 - (\beta + 3\gamma) \log 3$$
$$\leq (2C + 1) \log 2 - C \log 3$$
$$(C - 1)(\log 3 - \log 2) \leq (\beta + 4\gamma) \log 3 - 3\gamma \log 2$$
$$\leq (C + 2)(\log 3 - \log 2)$$
$$(C - 2) \log 3 \leq 3\beta \log 2 + (\beta + 5\gamma) \log 3$$
$$\leq (C + 3) \log 3$$
$$(C - 4) \log 2 \leq 3(\beta + \gamma) \log 2 + \gamma \log 3$$
$$\leq (C + 2) \log 2$$

Before proving Theorems 4-8 and 4-9, we give the following lemma.

Lemma 4-1   *If the solution vector is $x^0 = (x_1{}^0, \ldots, x_n{}^0)$, then $x_i{}^0 \geq x_j{}^0$ for $i > j$.*

Proof   Obviously it is more profitable to put the largest number at the end preceded by the next largest, etc.

Proof of Theorem 4-8   If $x_i = 4$, then 4^k may be replaced in the kth position by 2^k, and another factor, 2^{k+1}, will appear in the $(k + 1)$st position, and we have $4^k < 2^k \cdot 2^{k+1}$.   If $x_i > 4$, then $x_i = 3 + (x_i - 3)$ and $x_i < 3(x_i - 3)$.   This process is continued now, using $x_i - 3$ instead of x_i.   Thus, we write $x_i - 3 = 3 + [(x_i - 3) - 3]$, $x_i - 6 = 3 + [x_i - 6] - 3$, etc.   We also note that $x_i{}^i < 3^i(x_i - 3)^i$, etc.

Proof of Theorem 4-9   Let α, β, and γ indicate the frequency with which the factors 1, 2, and 3, respectively, appear, and consider the product

$$\Pi = \prod_{i=1}^{n} x_i{}^i = 1.1^2 \cdots 1^\alpha \cdot 2^{\alpha+1} \cdots 2^{\alpha+\beta} \cdot 3^{\alpha+\beta+1} \cdots 3^{\alpha+\beta+\gamma}$$

$$= 2^{\beta(2\alpha+\beta+1)/2} \cdot 3^{\gamma(?\ \ 2\beta+\gamma+1)/2}$$

where $\alpha + 2\beta + 3\gamma = C$.   Our problem is to find α, β, and γ which maximize the product.   Suppose that some α, β, and γ yield the maximum.   We introduce the perturbations δ_1 in α, δ_2 in β, and δ_3 in γ. Then

$$\delta_1 + 2\delta_2 + 3\delta_3 = 0$$

We seek a fundamental set of solutions of this equation (there is a finite set of such solutions) such that any other solution is a linear combination of them with integer coefficients.   To obtain these solutions for the above equation, we use the generating function [20]

$$\frac{1}{(1 - \delta_1{}^m \delta_2)(1 - \delta_1{}^b \delta_3{}^a)}$$

of the equation

$$a\,\delta_1 = ma\,\delta_2 + b\,\delta_3$$

where b is prime to a.

The fundamental solutions consist of the exponents of δ_i in each factor of the denominator. For our problem $a = 1$, $m = -2$, $b = -3$, and we have two fundamental solutions, $(-2,1,0)$ and $(-3,0,1)$. Since, as we shall see later, it is our purpose to generate a region in which the solution of the optimization problem is found, we take additional solutions generated from this system. (The ideas will become clear as we continue our example.) We shall use the following solutions of the equation as small perturbations of the optimum:

$$
\begin{array}{ll}
(1,1,-1) & (-1,-1,1) \\
(1,-2,1) & (-1,2,-1) \\
(3,0,-1) & (-3,0,1) \\
(2,-1,0) & (-2,1,0)
\end{array}
$$

On substituting in Π, first α, β, γ and then $\alpha + \delta_1$, $\beta + \delta_2$, $\gamma + \delta_3$ and dividing the second by the first, we obtain an expression dominated by unity. If we apply the logarithm to both sides, we have

$$\frac{\beta + \delta_2}{2}\,[2(\alpha + \delta_1) + \beta + \delta_2 + 1]\log 2$$

$$+ \frac{\gamma + \delta_3}{2}\,[2(\alpha + \delta_1) + 2(\beta + \delta_2) + \gamma + \delta_3 + 1]\log 3$$

$$- \frac{\beta}{2}\,(2\alpha + \beta + 1)\log 2 - \frac{\gamma}{2}\,(2\alpha + 2\beta + \gamma + 1)\log 3 \le 0$$

or

$$[\alpha\,\delta_2 + \beta(\delta_1 + \delta_2) + \delta_1\delta_2 + \tfrac{1}{2}\delta_2{}^2 + \tfrac{1}{2}\delta_2]\log 2$$
$$+ [\alpha\,\delta_3 + \beta\,\delta_3 + \gamma(\delta_1 + \delta_2 + \delta_3) + \delta_1\delta_3 + \delta_2\delta_3 + \tfrac{1}{2}\delta_3{}^2 + \tfrac{1}{2}\delta_3]\log 3$$
$$\le 0$$

If we put $\alpha = C - 2\beta - 3\gamma$ and $\delta_1 = -2\delta_2 - 3\delta_3$, we have, after simplifying,

$$[3\beta(\delta_2 + \delta_3) + 3\gamma\,\delta_2]\log 2 + [\beta\,\delta_3 + \gamma(\delta_2 + 5\delta_3)]\log 3$$
$$\ge (C\,\delta_2 - \tfrac{3}{2}\delta_2{}^2 - 3\delta_2\,\delta_3 + \tfrac{1}{2}\delta_2)\log 2$$
$$+ (C\,\delta_3 - \delta_2\,\delta_3 - \tfrac{5}{2}\delta_3{}^2 + \tfrac{1}{2}\delta_3)\log 2$$

We now use values of $(\delta_1, \delta_2, \delta_3)$ and write after each the resulting inequality:

$(1, -2, 1)$:

$\quad (3\beta + 6\gamma) \log 2 - (\beta + 3\gamma) \log 3 \leq (2C + 1) \log 2 - C \log 3$

$(-1, 2, -1)$:

$\quad (3\beta + 6\gamma) \log 2 - (\beta + 3\gamma) \log 3 \geq (2C + 1) \log 2 - (C + 1) \log 3$

Combining the two results, we have

$$(2C + 1) \log 2 - (C + 1) \log 3 \leq (3\beta + 6\gamma) \log 2 - (\beta + 3\gamma) \log 3$$
$$\leq (2C + 1) \log 2 - C \log 3$$

$(1, 1, -1)$:

$\quad\quad 3\gamma \log 2 - (\beta + 4\gamma) \log 3 \geq (C + 2) \log 2 - (C + 2) \log 3$

$(-1, -1, 1)$:

$\quad\quad -3\gamma \log 2 + (\beta + 4\gamma) \log 3 \geq -(C - 1) \log 2 + (C - 1) \log 3$

Combining the two results, we have

$$(C - 1)(\log 3 - \log 2) \leq (\beta + 4\gamma) \log 3 - 3\gamma \log 2$$
$$\leq (C + 2)(\log 3 - \log 2)$$

$(3, 0, -1)$: $-3\beta \log 2 - (\beta + 5\gamma) \log 3 \geq -(C + 3) \log 3$

$(-3, 0, 1)$: $\quad 3\beta \log 2 + (\beta + 5\gamma) \log 3 \geq (C - 2) \log 3$

Combining the two results, we have

$$(C - 2) \log 3 \leq 3\beta \log 2 + (\beta + 5\gamma) \log 3 \leq (C + 3) \log 3$$

$(2, -1, 0)$: $-3(\beta + \gamma) \log 2 - \gamma \log 3 \geq -(C + 2) \log 2$

$(-2, 1, 0)$: $\quad 3(\beta + \gamma) \log 2 + \gamma \log 3 \geq (C - 4) \log 2$

Combining the two results, we have

$$(C - 4) \log 2 \leq 3(\beta + \gamma) \log 2 + \gamma \log 3 \leq (C + 2) \log 2$$

As an illustration, suppose that $C = 100$. We obtain

$\quad 27.6 \leq 0.97\beta + 0.84\gamma \leq 28.7$
$\quad 40.19 \leq 1.1\beta + 2.33\gamma \leq 41.82$
$\quad 107.8 \leq 3.17\beta + 5.5\gamma \leq 113.3$
$\quad 66.24 \leq 2.08\beta + 3.18\gamma \leq 70.7$

Note that the middle expressions remain the same for any value of C. In addition, it may be desirable to construct a larger number of inequalities by taking additional values of $(\delta_1, \delta_2, \delta_3)$. One approach is to plot these inequalities in search of the solution, which must be a lattice point in the common region of intersection. Figure 4-3 is a plot of the region determined by eight inequalities. It contains two lattice points. We have for the solution $\beta = 6$, $\gamma = 24$, and hence $\alpha = 34$. The region retains its size for any C but is translated to a new position.

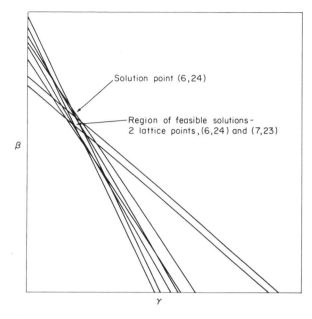

Fig. 4-3

Misuse of Lagrange multipliers   The lagrangian and hence continuous approach to this problem, with $C = 100$, yields a result which is far from the answer.   Let us briefly examine this approach.   Thus, we form the function

$$F(x_1, \ldots, x_n, \lambda) = x_1 x_2^2 x_3^3 \cdots x_n^n - \lambda(\Sigma x_i - 100)$$

$$\frac{\partial F}{\partial x_1} = x_2^2 x_3^3 \cdots x_n^n - \lambda = 0$$

$$\frac{\partial F}{\partial x_2} = x_1 2 x_2 x_3^3 \cdots x_n^n - \lambda = 0$$

$$\frac{\partial F}{\partial x_i} = x_1 x_2^2 \cdots i x_i^{i-1} x_{i+1}^{i+1} \cdots x_n^n - \lambda = 0$$

If we multiply the ith equation by x_i and add, we obtain

$$\frac{n(n+1)}{2} \prod_{i=1}^{n} x_i^i - 100\lambda = 0$$

Thus,

$$\lambda = \frac{n(n+1)}{200} \prod_{i=1}^{n} x_i^i$$

and the ith equation, on multiplying by x_i, gives

$$x_i = i \prod_{i=1}^{n} \frac{x_i{}^{i}}{\lambda}$$

or

$$x_i = \frac{200i}{n(n+1)}$$

Our problem now is to find n which maximizes $\Pi_{i=1}^{n}[200i/n(n+1)]^i$ or simply its logarithm. This yields

$$\sum_{i=1}^{n} \left(i \log \frac{200}{n(n+1)} + i \log i \right) = \frac{n(n+1)}{2} \log \frac{200}{n(n+1)} + \sum_{i=1}^{n} i \log i$$

Now, from the relation $\int_{z}^{z+1} \log \Gamma(\zeta)\, d\zeta = z \log z - z + \frac{1}{2} \log 2\pi$, $|\arg z| < \pi$, the foregoing is equal to $[n(n+1)/2][\log 200 - \log n(n+1) + 1] + \int_{1}^{n+1} \log \Gamma(\zeta)\, d\zeta - (n/2) \log 2\pi$. Differentiating with respect to n and equating to zero, we have

$$\frac{(2n+1)}{2} \left[\log \frac{200}{n(n+1)} \right] + \log \Gamma(n+1) - \frac{\log 2\pi}{2} = 0$$

or

$$\frac{\Gamma(n+1)}{\sqrt{2\pi}} = \left(\frac{n(n+1)}{200} \right)^{n+\frac{1}{2}}$$

Using Stirling's approximation, we finally obtain

$$e^{-\frac{1}{2}} = \left(\frac{200}{e(n+1)} \right)^{n+\frac{1}{2}}$$

which is satisfied for a value of n between 73 and 74. Recalling that $n = 64$ gave the correct answer, one concludes that this approach has not been very helpful in obtaining the solution. In addition, one has the difficulty of deciding what integer values to take for x_i.

The technique of Theorem 4-9 may be generalized to the problem of maximizing

$$\prod_{j=1}^{n} x_j \quad \text{subject to} \quad \sum_{j=1}^{n} x_j{}^{p} = C \quad p > 1 \text{ is an integer}$$

This leads to a solution involving α 1s, β 2s, and γ 3s such that

$$\alpha + 2^p \beta + 3^p \gamma = C$$

Perturbation leads to the equation

$$\delta_1 + 2^p\, \delta_2 + 3^p\, \delta_3 = 0$$

which has the generating function

$$\frac{1}{(1 - \delta_1^{-2^p} \delta_2)(1 - \delta_1^{-3^p} \delta_3)}$$

and fundamental solutions $(-2^p, 1, 0)$ and $(-3^p, 0, 1)$.

The same method is also applicable to maximizing $\Pi_{j=1}^n x_j{}^j$ subject to

$$\sum_{j=1}^n x_j{}^p = C, \; p > 1 \text{ is an integer.}$$ Again, the solution is a product of 1s, 2s, and 3s. When $C = 100$, the solution for the second problem is as follows:

$p = 2$	$(44,14,0)$
$p = 3$	$(52,6,0)$
$p = 4$	$(52,3,0)$
$p = 5$	$(68,1,0)$
$p = 6$	$(100,0,0)$

Remark   The maximizing solution of $\Sigma_{i=1}^n a_i x_i$ in positive integers subject to $\Pi_{i=1}^n x_i = C$, where $a_k = \max (a_1, \ldots , a_n)$ without loss of generality, is given by $x_k = C, \; x_i - 1, \; i \neq k$. An easy way to see this is to divide $\Sigma_{i=1}^n a_i x_i$ by $\Pi_{i=1}^n x_i = C$ and maximize the result. It is also easy to generalize this result to the maximization of $\Sigma_{j=1}^n a_j x_j{}^p$, with p a positive integer, subject to the same constraints.

The corresponding minimization problem may be tackled as follows. Suppose that $a_1 \leq a_2 \leq \cdots \leq a_n$, and let $C = p_1{}^{\alpha_1} p_2{}^{\alpha_2} \cdots p_s{}^{\alpha_s}$, with $p_1 < p_2 < \cdots < p_s$. If $\alpha_1 + \alpha_2 + \cdots + \alpha_s \leq n$, then the minimum is obtained by assigning one prime to each x_i in ascending ordering and then using 1s at the end if necessary. Generally, if we write $x_j = p_1{}^{\alpha_{1j}} \cdots p_s{}^{\alpha_{sj}}, \; j = 1, \ldots , n$, then the problem becomes: Find nonnegative integers α_{ij} which minimize $\Sigma_{j=1}^n a_j x_j$ subject to the linear constraints $\Sigma_{j=1}^n \alpha_{ij} = \alpha_i, \; i = 1, \ldots , s$.

Consider now the problem of maximizing in positive integers $\Sigma_{j=1}^n a_j x_j{}^p$, a_j given natural numbers, with p a positive integer, subject to $\Pi_{j=1}^n x_j{}^j = C$, with C a given positive integer.

Lemma 4-2   *Let k be an index such that $\alpha_k \geq \alpha_j, \; j = 1, \ldots , n$, then $x_j = 1, \; j = k + 1, \ldots , n$.*

Proof   Given a vector $x_1, \ldots , x_n$, we define a new vector by

$$\bar{x}_1 = x_1 x_{k+1}$$
$$\bar{x}_k = x_k x_{k+1}$$
$$\bar{x}_j = x_j \qquad j = 2, \ldots , n, \, j \neq k$$

Obviously the product is the same since

$$\prod_{j=1}^{n} \bar{x}_j{}^j = (x_1 x_{k+1})\bar{x}_2{}^2 \cdots (x_k x_{k+1})^k \times 1 \cdots \bar{x}_n{}^n$$

$$= x_1 x_2{}^2 \cdots x_k{}^k x_{k+1}^{k+1} \cdots x_n{}^n = C$$

Now we show that the sum is not less than the previous sum; i.e.,

$$\alpha_1 \bar{x}_1{}^p + \sum_{j=2}^{k-1} \alpha_j \bar{x}_j{}^p + \alpha_k \bar{x}_k{}^p + \alpha_{k+1} + \sum_{j=k+2}^{n} \alpha_j \bar{x}_j{}^p \geq \sum_{j=1}^{n} \alpha_j x_j{}^p$$

This follows from

$$\alpha_k \bar{x}_k{}^p = \alpha_k x_k{}^p x_{k+1}^p \geq \alpha_k x_k{}^p + \alpha_k x_{k+1}^p \geq \alpha_k x_k{}^p + \alpha_{k+1}^p$$

when $x_k \neq 1$, $x_{k+1} \neq 1$, and from

$$\alpha_1 \bar{x}_1 \geq \alpha_1 x_1$$

The result follows directly when $x_k = 1$, $x_{k+1} = 1$. The same argument applies to all $j \geq k$.

Lemma 4-3 *With the same assumptions as in Lemma 4-2, it follows, from*

$$\prod_{j=1}^{n} x_j{}^j = \prod_{\substack{j=1 \\ j\neq i}}^{n} x_j{}^j (x_i{}^{i/k})^k = C \qquad 1 \leq i \leq k$$

and by putting

$$\bar{x}_k = x_k x_i{}^{i/k} \qquad \bar{x}_j = x_j \qquad j \neq k \tag{4-21}$$

where x_i satisfies

$$(x_i{}^{i/k})^p > \frac{x_i{}^p - 1}{x_k{}^p} + 1 \tag{4-22}$$

such that $x_i{}^{i/k}$ is an integer, that

$$\sum_{\substack{j=1 \\ j\neq i}}^{k-1} \alpha_j \bar{x}_j{}^p + \alpha_i + \alpha_k \bar{x}_k{}^p + \sum_{j=k+1}^{n} \alpha_j \geq \sum_{j=1}^{k} \alpha_j x_j{}^p + \sum_{j=k+1}^{n} \alpha_j$$

Proof From $\alpha_k \geq \alpha_i$ and (4-22) we have

$$\alpha_k x_k{}^p x_i{}^{(j/k)p} - \alpha_k x_k{}^p \geq \alpha_i x_i{}^p - \alpha_i$$

The use of (4-21) yields

$$\alpha_k \bar{x}_k{}^p + \alpha_i > \alpha_i x_i{}^p + \alpha_k x_k{}^p$$

and the result follows.   We have the following theorem.

Theorem 4-10 *A necessary and sufficient condition for improving a feasible solution toward a maximizing solution is that it has an x_i, $1 \le i \le k$ with the property that $x_i^{i/k}$ is an integer which satisfies condition (4-22). In (4-21) we use the largest such x_i.*

Exercise 4-23 Find positive integers x_i which maximize the following:

(a) $x_1{}^m \Pi_{i=2}^n x_i$, subject to $\Pi_{i=1}^n x_i = 100$, for integer $m > 1$.

Ans.: Put $x_i = 3$, $x_1 = [mx_i]$. The brackets denote the largest integer less than mx_i such that $100 - [mx_i]$ is divisible by 3. Thus, if $m = 3$, then $mx_i = 9$, $100 - 9 \not\equiv 0 \bmod 3$, and $100 - 8 \not\equiv 0 \bmod 3$, but $100 - 7 \equiv 0 \bmod 3$; hence $x_i = 7$.

(b) $\Pi_{i=1}^n x_i$ subject to $x_i{}^p + \Sigma_{i=2}^n x_i = 100$ for integer $p > 1$.

Ans.: Put $x_1 = 1$, $x_i = 3$.

(c) $x_1{}^m \Pi_{i=2}^n x_i$ subject to $x_i{}^p + \Sigma_{i=2}^n x_i = 100$ for integers $m > 1$ and $p > 1$.

(d) $\Pi_{i=1}^n x_i{}^i$ subject to $\Sigma_{i=1}^n x_i = 100$.

(e) $\Pi_{i=1}^n x_i$ subject to $\Sigma_{i=1}^n x_i + x_i{}^2 = 100$.

(f) $\Pi_{i=1}^n x_i{}^p$ subject to $\Pi_{i=1}^n x_i{}^i = C$, C a given positive integer.

(g) $\Pi_{i=1}^n x_i{}^i$ subject to $\Pi_{i=1}^n x_i = C$, C a given positive integer.

Exercise 4-24 Let p, N, r be positive integers, with $r > 1$. Find [14] a p-part partition of N into nonnegative integers x_i which minimizes the sum of binomial coefficients $\Sigma_{i=1}^p C(x_i, r)$ where

$$C(x_i, r) = \frac{x_i!}{r!(x_i - r)!} \qquad C(x_i, r) = 0 \text{ if } r > x_i$$

Hint: Using the fact that the x_i should be as equal as possible, let $N = pq + r$, with $p > r \ge 0$. Take

$$x_1 = x_2 = \cdots = x_r = q + 1 \qquad \text{and} \qquad x_{r+1} = \cdots = x_p = q$$

4-6 USEFUL INEQUALITIES

In the analysis of many optimization problems, it is necessary to estimate and refine bounds in order to get close to the optimum. For this purpose, several classical inequality relations have proven useful. We give some of them here for ready reference.

Consider the expression

$$\sum_{i=1}^n (a_i - \lambda b_i)^2$$

which is a quadratic nonnegative expression in λ, where a_i and b_i, $i = 1$, ..., n, are arbitrary real numbers. On expanding, this expression becomes

$$\sum_{i=1}^n a_i{}^2 - 2\lambda \sum_{i=1}^n a_i b_i + \lambda^2 \sum_{i=1}^n b_i{}^2$$

Since the expression is nonnegative for all λ, the discriminant of the quadratic must be nonpositive, i.e., must satisfy the relation (called the Cauchy-Schwarz inequality)

$$\Big(\sum_{i=1}^{n} a_i b_i \Big)^2 - \sum_{i=1}^{n} a_i^2 \sum_{i=1}^{n} b_i^2 \le 0$$

A generalization of the Cauchy-Schwarz inequality is given by Hölder's inequality

$$\Big| \sum_{i=1}^{n} a_i b_i \Big| \le \Big(\sum_{i=1}^{n} |a_i|^p \Big)^{1/p} \Big(\sum_{i=1}^{n} |b_i|^q \Big)^{1/q}$$

where $1/p + 1/q = 1$ and $p > 0, q > 0$.

From this, one also has

$$\frac{1}{n} \Big| \sum_{i=1}^{n} a_i b_i \Big| \le \Big(\frac{1}{n} \sum_{i=1}^{n} |a_i|^p \Big)^{1/p} \Big(\frac{1}{n} \sum_{i=1}^{n} |b_i|^q \Big)^{1/q}$$

Minkowski's inequality gives

$$\Big(\sum_{i=1}^{n} |a_i + b_i|^p \Big)^{1/p} \le \Big(\sum_{i=1}^{n} |a_i|^p \Big)^{1/p} + \Big(\sum_{i=1}^{n} |b_i|^p \Big)^{1/p}$$

where $p \ge 1$. The opposite inequality holds for $p \le 1$. Note that equality holds if $p = 1$ or if $a_i = c b_i$ $(i = 1, \ldots, n)$, where c is a constant. Both Hölder's (hence also Cauchy-Schwarz') and Minkowski's inequalities hold if the summation is replaced by an integral, a_i by a function $f(x)$, and b_i by a function $g(x)$, where $|f(x)|^p$ and $|g(x)|^q$ are integrable in the case of Hölder's inequality and $|f(x)|^p$ and $|g(x)|^p$ are integrable in the case of Minkowski's inequality.

Jensen's inequality is given by

$$\Big(\sum_{i=1}^{n} |a_i|^r \Big)^{1/r} > \Big(\sum_{i=1}^{n} |a_i|^s \Big)^{1/s} \qquad \text{if } 0 < r < s$$

Other useful inequalities are

$$
\begin{aligned}
(1 + x)^p &> 1 + px && \text{if } x > -1, x \ne 0, \text{ and } p > 1 \\
x^p - 1 &> p(x - 1) && \text{if } x > 1 \text{ and } p \text{ is a real number } > 1 \\
x^p - 1 &< p(x - 1) && \text{if } x > 1 \text{ and } 0 < p < 1 \\
x^a y^b &< ax + by && \text{if } x \ne y \text{ and } a + b = 1, a > 0, b > 0 \\
x &\le \frac{1 - p^x}{1 - p} \le xp^{x-1} && \text{if } 0 \le x \le 1 \text{ and } 0 < p < 1
\end{aligned}
$$

In the last inequality, note that p may be an expression such as $1 - ae^{-by/x}$, where $a, b > 0$. Thus, the inequality may be applied to show that

$$\lim_{x \to 0} \frac{1 - (1 - ae^{-by/x})^x}{x} = 0$$

which is the derivative of the numerator at the origin.

The following relation holds among the harmonic, geometric, and arithmetic means of the real numbers a_i, $i = 1, \ldots, n$ (from left to right):

$$\frac{n}{1/a_1 + \cdots + 1/a_n} < \sqrt[n]{a_1 \cdots a_n} < \frac{a_1 + \cdots + a_n}{n}$$

Each of these means is bounded above by the largest of the a_i and is bounded below by the smallest of the a_i. When these three means are defined for an integrable function, the above relation becomes

$$\frac{b - a}{\int_a^b dx/f(x)} \le e^{1/(b-a)} \int_a^b \log f(x) \, dx \le \frac{1}{b - a} \int_a^b f(x) \, dx$$

The geometric mean requires that $f(x)$ be positive.

Jensen's theorem asserts that for a convex function $f(x)$ and for positive a_i ($i = 1, \ldots, n$),

$$f\left(\frac{\sum_{i=1}^{n} a_i x_i}{\sum_{i=1}^{n} a_i} \right) \le \frac{\sum_{i=1}^{n} a_i f(x_i)}{\sum_{i=1}^{n} a_i}$$

where x_i ($i = 1, \ldots, n$) are n arbitrary values of x. The definition of a convex function is obtained by letting $n = 2$, $a_1 = a_2 = 1$, and $x_1 < x_2$.

This theorem has many interesting consequences and applications, in the case of both sums and integrals. The theorem itself applies to integrals over an interval (a,b) if the sum is replaced by an integral, the x_i by a bounded function $g(x)$, and the a_i by a nonnegative function $a(x)$ with a positive integral over (a,b).

A general theorem for harmonic, geometric, and arithmetic means gives, for positive a_i and positive b_i, $i = 1, \ldots, n$,

$$\frac{\sum_{i=1}^{n} b_i}{\sum_{i=1}^{n} b_i/a_i} \le \exp\left(\frac{\sum_{i=1}^{n} b_i \log a_i}{\sum_{i=1}^{n} b_i} \right) \le \frac{\sum_{i=1}^{n} a_i b_i}{\sum_{i=1}^{n} b_i}$$

One also has

$$\exp\left[\frac{\sum_{i=1}^{n}(b_i/a_i)\log a_i}{\sum_{i=1}^{n}b_i/a_i}\right] < \frac{\sum_{i=1}^{n}b_i}{\sum_{i=1}^{n}b_i/a_i}$$

and

$$\frac{\sum_{i=1}^{n}a_ib_i}{\sum_{i=1}^{n}b_i} < \exp\left(\frac{\sum_{i=1}^{n}a_ib_i\log a_i}{\sum_{i=1}^{n}a_ib_i}\right)$$

These three results have an immediate generalization to the continuous case. For further details, the interested reader should consult Ref. 17.

4-7 THE THEORY OF MAX-MIN

There are problems of a competitive nature, involving conflict of interest between two sides, which cannot be treated through game theory. Frequently such problems involve an objective function $F(x,y)$, expressing the interests of two competitors subject to constraints on the solution vector of each competitor, for example, $x \geq 0$, $y \geq 0$, $\sum_{i=1}^{n}x_i = X$, $\sum_{i=1}^{n}y_i = Y$. The function $F(x,y)$ is given in analytic form, and a solution which gives a minimum with respect to y and then a maximum with respect to x is sought in integers. The order of optimization may not be interchanged. There is no general theory for a solution in integers.

Example   *Given:* n cities, to be defended by side A by allocating $x_i \geq 0$ weapons to the ith city with $\sum_{i=1}^{n}x_i = X$. Each city is to be attacked by side B who will allocate $y_i \geq 0$ weapons to the ith city with $\sum_{i=1}^{n}y_i = Y$. The quantity x_i/y_i denotes the ratio of effectiveness of defense to offense for the ith city. If $k_i > 0$ is the effectiveness of the defense, and if α_i with $0 < \alpha_i < 1$ is the probability that an attacking unit which survives the defense will destroy the target, then $\{1 - \alpha_i \exp[-k_i(x_i/y_i)]\}^{y_i}$ is the probability that the ith target will survive an attack by y_i weapons. If $v_i > 0$ is the value of the ith target, then B wants to minimize the expected value

$$\sum_{i=1}^{n} v_i\left[1 - \alpha_i \exp\left(-\frac{k_ix_i}{y_i}\right)\right]^{y_i}$$

while A wants to maximize this minimum value. What is the best choice of the integer-valued vectors x and y?

Danskin [4a] has developed an interesting, elaborate theory for treating this type of problem (but not for integer solutions). We summarize the material leading to his main result and also give the latter.

If $\varphi(x) = \min\limits_{y} F(x,y)$, where $F(x,y)$ and its partial derivatives $F_{x_i}(x,y)$ are continuous in x and y, and where both vectors x and y belong to subsets of Euclidean space, then $\varphi(x)$ may not be differentiable. To remedy this problem, a new tool is needed. A direction $\gamma = (\gamma_1, \ldots, \gamma_n)$ (a unit vector of directional cosines) in the x space from x^0 is *admissible* if there is an arc with one end point at x^0 which lies entirely in the set of admissible values of x (which may be the entire space or a subset defined by constraints) such that for any sequence x^m along the arc with $x^m \to x^0$ we have $\gamma^m \to \gamma$, where γ is given by

$$\gamma_i{}^m \equiv \frac{x_i{}^m - x_i}{|x^m - x^0|}$$

Theorem 4-11　*A necessary condition for a maximum at x^0 is that the directional derivative*

$$D_\gamma \varphi(x^0) = \min\limits_{y \in Y(x)} \sum_{i=1}^{n} \gamma_i F_{x_i}(x^0,y)$$

(which can be shown to exist in any admissible direction γ) is nonpositive.

Here $Y(x)$ is the set of y belonging to a closed and bounded subset which yields the minimum with respect to $x = x^0$.

REFERENCES

1. Andersson, J.: All Nonnegative Integer Solution $x + 2y + 3z + 5t = n$, *Mathesis*, p. 383, 1953.
2. Bond, James: Calculating the General Solution of a Linear Diophantine Equation, *Am. Math. Monthly*, vol. 74, pp. 955–957, October, 1967.
3. Carlitz, L.: Solution of a Problem Posed by L. Moser, *Pi Mu Epsilon J.*, vol. 3, pp. 232–233, 1961.
4. Carmichael, Robert D.: "The Theory of Numbers and Diophantine Analysis," Dover Publications, Inc., New York, 1915.
4a. Danskin, John M.: "The Theory of Max-Min," Springer-Verlag New York Inc., 1967.
5. Davenport, H., and K. F. Roth: The Solubility of Certain Diophantine Inequalities, *Mathematika*, vol. 2, pp. 81–96, December, 1955.
6. Delcourte, M.: *Mathesis*, p. 383, 1958; p. 272, 1959.

7. denBroeder, G. G., R. E. Ellison, and L. Emerling: On Optimum Target Assignments, *Operations Res.*, vol. 7, pp. 322–326, May–June, 1959.

8. Dickson, L. E.: "History of the Theory of Numbers," vols. 1–3, Chelsea Publishing Company, New York.

9. Erdös, P.: Some Results on Diophantine Approximation, *Act. Arithmet.*, pp. 359–369, 1959.

10. Fox, Bennett: Discrete Optimization Via Marginal Analysis, *Management Sci.*, vol. 13, pp. 210–216, November, 1966.

11. Garver, R.: The Solution of Problems in Maxima and Minima by Algebra, *Am. Math. Monthly*, vol. 42, pp. 435–437, 1935.

12. Gelfond, A. O.: "The Solution of Equations in Integers," P. Noordhoff, Ltd., Groningen, The Netherlands, 1960.

13. Gibrat, M. R.: Escadrilles d'avions, *Rev. Franc. Rech. Opération.*, no. 27, 1963.

14. Goldman, A. J., and E. S. Langford: Minimal Sum of Binomial Coefficients, *Am. Math. Monthly*, p. 785, September, 1965.

15. Gross, O.: Class of Discrete Type Minimization Problems, pt. 30, RM-1644, Rand Corp., Santa Monica, Calif., February, 1956.

16. Hall, H. S., and S. R. Knight: "Higher Algebra," Macmillan & Co., Ltd., London, 1948.

17. Hardy, G. H., J. E. Littlewood, and G. Polya: "Inequalities," Cambridge University Press, New York, 1934.

18. Horner, Walter W., and Alfred Brousseau: The Pancake Problem, *Math. Mag.*, p. 100, March–April, 1968.

19. Itard, Jean: "Arithmétique et Théorie Des Nombres," Presses Universitaires de France, Paris, 1963.

20. MacMahon, Percy A.: "Combinatory Analysis," vols. 1 and 2, Chelsea Publishing Company, New York, 1960.

21. Mordell, L. J.: Some Diophantine Inequalities, *Mathematika*, vol. 2, pp. 145–149, 1955.

21a. Moser, Leo, and C. M. Sandwick, Sr.: Packaged Radios, *Am. Math. Monthly*, vol. 59, pp. 637–638, November, 1952.

22. Nagell, Trygve: "Number Theory," Chelsea Publishing Company, New York, 1964.

23. Nagell, Trygve: Sur quelques catégories d'equations diophantiennes résolubles par des identités, *Act. Arithmet.*, vol. 9, pp. 227–235, 1964.

24. Netto, E.: "Lehrbuch der Combinatorik," Chelsea Publishing Company, New York, 1901.

25. Niven, Ivan: "Diophantine Approximations," Interscience Publishers, New York, 1963.

26. Olds, C. D.: "Continued Fractions," Random House, Inc., New York, 1963.

27. Ryser, Herbert J.: "Combinatorial Mathematics," John Wiley & Sons, Inc., New York, 1963.

28. Saaty, T. L.: On Nonlinear Optimization in Integers, *Naval Res. Log. Quart.*, vol. 15, no. 1, pp. 1–22, March, 1968.

29. Silverman, D. L., and Michael Goldberg: A Diophantine Equation, *Am. Math. Monthly*, vol. 74, p. 1013, October, 1967.

30. Skolem, Th.: "Diophantische Gleichungen," Chelsea Publishing Company, New York, 1950.

31. Stewart, B. M.: "Theory of Numbers," 2d ed., The Macmillan Company, New York, 1965.

32. Syski, R.: Algebraic Properties of Optimum Gradings, 3d Intern. Teletraffic Cong., Paris, 1961.

33. Takács, Lajos: "Combinatorial Methods in the Theory of Stochastic Processes," John Wiley & Sons, Inc., New York, 1967.

34. Thebault, V.: Positive Integer Solutions of $a^b = b^a$, *Mathesis*, p. 67, 1960.

35. Utz, W. R.: Diophantine Equations, *Pi Mu Epsilon J.*, November, 1954.

36. Veidinger, L.: On the Distribution of the Solutions of Diophantine Equations with Many Unknowns, *Act. Arithmet.*, 1958.

37. Weinstock, Robert: Greatest Common Divisor of Several Integers and An Associated Linear Diophantine Equation, *Am. Math. Monthly*, vol. 67, pp. 664–667, 1960.

5

Integer Programming

5-1 INTRODUCTION

One of the most general forms that an optimization problem in integers can take is the following: Find a vector x of nonnegative components x_j, $j = 1, \ldots, n$, in E_n which maximizes the "objective" function $f(x_1, \ldots, x_n)$ subject to the constraints $g_i(x_1, \ldots, x_n) \leq 0$, $i = 1, \ldots, m$. Geometrically one seeks a lattice point in the region which satisfies the constraints (called the *feasible region*) and minimizes f. We have already noted in Chap. 4 that problems in nonnegative integers and with equality constraints are often transformed to problems in inequality constraints, and hence integer programming is central to Diophantine optimization. Some problems require that only some of the components of x be integers. A requirement of the other components may be that they be rational. This case is called *mixed-integer programming*. The case where all the components of x are integers is sometimes called *all-integer integer programming*.

Some integer-programming problems require finding a vector x whose components take on the binary values 0 and 1 and are called *bivalent programs*.

Problems whose variables are nonnegative integers may be transformed to the binary variable case by replacing each variable x_j with an expression

$$x_j = x_{j1} + 2x_{j2} + 2^2 x_{j3} + \cdots + 2^{k-1} x_{jk}$$

where $x_{jp} = 0$ or 1 $(p = 1, \ldots, k)$, and where k is sufficiently large to allow x_j to assume its largest integer value in the feasible region. Thus $2^k - 1$ becomes an upper bound for x_j. This transformation rapidly increases the number of variables so that the solution of an integer program as a bivalent program becomes very cumbersome, if not physically impossible. However, a number of problems naturally occur as bivalent programs, and algorithms for solving this type of problem have been developed.

Example 5-1 [31]   Consider the integer-programming problem of minimizing, in nonnegative integers x_1, x_2, the expression

$$x_1 + 3x_2$$

subject to the constraints

$$3x_1 - x_2 \geq 4$$
$$x_1 + x_2 \leq 3$$

By noting from the second constraint that $x_1 \leq 3$, $x_2 \leq 3$, we put

$$x_1 = x_{11} + 2x_{12} \qquad x_2 = x_{21} + 2x_{22}$$

and the problem may be transformed to that of finding variables

$$x_{11}, x_{12}, x_{21}, x_{22}$$

whose values are 0 or 1 which minimize

$$x_{11} + 2x_{12} + 3x_{21} + 6x_{22}$$

subject to

$$3x_{11} + 6x_{12} - x_{21} - 2x_{22} \geq 4$$
$$x_{11} + 2x_{12} + x_{21} + 2x_{22} \leq 3$$

ON SOLVABILITY IN INTEGERS

Consider a rectangular system of equations

$$\sum_{j=1}^{n} a_{ij}x_j = b_i \qquad i = 1, \ldots, m$$

or, in matrix notation, $Ax = b$. Let $\bar{x} = (\bar{x}_1, \ldots, \bar{x}_n)$ be a solution. To each x_j corresponds a column vector of the coefficients of that x_j. Consider all nonzero $\bar{x}_j$ in $\bar{x}$. If their corresponding columns are linearly independent (that is, every relation of the form $\Sigma_{i=1}^{k}\alpha_i v_i = 0$, where v_i are the column vectors in question, implies that $\alpha_i = 0, i = 1, \ldots, k$) then $\bar{x}$ is called an *extreme solution.* Linear independence assures a unique solution for the planes intersecting at the (solution) point, whose components are these nonzero x_i's. If the system were given as a set of inequalities, then the vertices of the corresponding convex polyhedron would be the extreme solutions of the system obtained by replacing the inequalities with equalities. These vertices are called the *extreme points* of the polyhedron. We now consider conditions on matrix A such that all extreme points have integer coordinates.

Definition A basis of the $m \times n$ matrix A of integers (called an *integral matrix*) whose m rows are linearly independent is a set of m columns whose rank is m.

Definition A basis of A is said to be unimodular if its determinant is equal to $+1$ or -1.

Definition A is said to be totally unimodular if each nonsingular submatrix of A is unimodular.

Let us write

$$X(A,b) \equiv \{x: Ax = b, x \geq 0\}$$

and

$$X^*(A,b) = \{x: Ax \leq b, x \geq 0\}$$

A sufficient condition for the extreme points of $X(A,b)$ to be integral for all integral b is that each basis be unimodular. For, by Cramer's rule, one can solve for the x_i, and since the determinant of the coefficient matrix which appears in the denominator is ± 1, and since b has integral components, x_i must be integral. We now prove that unimodularity is also necessary.

Theorem 5-1 (Veinott and Dantzig) [36] *If A is an integral matrix whose rows are linearly independent, then the following statements are equivalent:*

a. *Every basis is unimodular.*
b. *The extreme points of $X(A,b)$ are integral for all integral b.*
c. *Every basis has an integral inverse.*

Proof $a \Rightarrow b$ Let B be the basis associated with the nonzero components x_B of an extreme point x of $X(A,b)$. Thus, by hypothesis, $Bx_B = b$ and $\det B = \pm 1$. Hence, by Cramer's rule, x_B is integral.

$b \Rightarrow c$ Let B be a basis, let 1_i denote the ith unit column vector, and let y be any integer vector such that

$$z \equiv y + B^{-1}1_i \geq 0$$

Now $Bz = By + 1_i \equiv b$ is integral, and z contains the nonzero components of an extreme point of $X(A,b)$; hence, z is integral.   Since the left side of $z - y = B^{-1}1_i$ is integral, the ith column of B^{-1} is integral. But the same argument applies for all i; therefore, B^{-1} is integral.

$c \Rightarrow a$ Let B be a basis.   Since B and B^{-1} are integral, their determinants must be nonzero integers, and it follows from

$$(\det B)(\det B^{-1}) = 1$$

that

$$\det B = \det B^{-1} = \pm 1$$

Corollary   (Hoffman and Kruskal)   *If A is an integral matrix, the following statements are equivalent:*

a*. *A is totally unimodular.*
b*. *The extreme points of $X^*(A,b)$ are integral for all integral b.*
c*. *Every nonsingular submatrix of A has an integral inverse.*

Proof   We augment A with an identity matrix so that the matrix $A' = (A,I)$ has m rows.   These rows are linearly independent.   If A' is used instead of A in Theorem 5-1, the statements about A' are equivalent to those about A in the corollary.   Thus $a \Rightarrow a^*$, since if C is a nonsingular submatrix of A whose rank is $m - k$, then a basis B in A' can be obtained by permuting rows and has the form

$$B = \begin{bmatrix} C & 0 \\ D & I_k \end{bmatrix}$$

where I_k is a $k \times k$ identity matrix.   Thus, $\det B = \det C$, and hence $\det B = \pm 1$ if and only if $\det C = \pm 1$.

We shall use A^T to denote the transpose matrix of A.

Exercise 5-1   Show that if any one of the matrices A, A^T, $-A$ is totally unimodular, so are all others.

The following theorem gives some sufficient conditions for establishing the unimodularity of A.

Theorem 5-2 (Heller-Tompkins)   *Every basis of A is unimodular if the rows of A can be partitioned into two disjoint sets R_1 and R_2 such that:*

  a. *Every column contains at most two nonzero entries.*
  b. *Every entry is 0, $+1$, -1.*
  c. *Two nonzero entries in a column with the same sign do not appear in the same set R_i of rows.*
  d. *Two nonzero entries in a column with different signs appear with the same set R_i of rows.*

Proof   The proof is by induction.

Exercise 5-2   Note that every column of the coefficient matrix of the transportation problem, given in Chap. 1, has two unit entries, and the remaining entries are zero. Prove that this matrix is unimodular, and hence that the problem has a solution in integers.

The foregoing three results are a special case of a general idea due to Heller [26]. A matrix in which every basis of its columns is unimodular, when viewed as a set of columns, is called a *unimodular set.* This leads to a general definition of unimodular sets of vectors in a vector space (or of elements in a free abelian group).

Definition   A set A of vectors in m-space is unimodular when, for every basis in A, the representation of every vector of A has coefficients $-1, 0, 1$.   Clearly, if A is unimodular, so is every subset of A.

Theorem 5-2a (I. Heller)

  a. *The set of edges (that is, one-dimensional faces, taken in both orientations and interpreted as vectors) of a simplex is unimodular.*
  b. *A unimodular set of dimension m contains at most $m(m + 1)$ elements (not counting the null vector); that is, if it contains $m(m + 1)$ elements, then it is maximal.*
  c. *If a unimodular set A of dimension m contains $m(m + 1)$ vectors (not counting the null vector), then A is the set of edges of an m-simplex.*
  d. *There exist, for $m \geq 4$, maximal unimodular sets of less than $m(m + 1)$ elements.*

The emphasis is on maximal sets because every subset of a unimodular set is itself unimodular.

Choosing a basis among the edges of an m-simplex, and representing a part or all of the other edges as linear combinations of that basis, yields a set of columns A in which every basis is unimodular. For example, if one chooses a star as basis (namely, all edges emanating from a given vertex), one can obtain the matrix of the transportation problem; if one chooses a hamiltonian circuit of edges, then in the matrix so obtained every column consists of a string of consecutive 1s preceded and/or followed by a string of consecutive 0s.

5-2 THE KNAPSACK PROBLEM [16]

One of the simplest integer-optimization problems which can be expressed algebraically is a linear problem in which a linear expression is to be maximized or minimized in nonnegative integers, subject to a linear inequality constraint. It has the following form. Find

$$\max \sum_{j=1}^{n} c_j x_j$$

subject to

$$\sum_{j=1}^{n} a_j x_j \leq b \qquad \begin{array}{l} x_j \geq 0 \\ x_j \text{ is an integer} \end{array}$$

In vector notation, the problem is to maximize cx subject to $Ax \leq b$, where $c = (c_1, \ldots, c_n)$, $x^T = (x_1, \ldots, x_n)^T$, $A = (a_1, \ldots, a_n)$, and where the components of the vector x are nonnegative integers. The name arises from the particular problem in which a knapsack of capacity b is to be packed with n categories of objects of value $c_1, \ldots, c_n$ and size $a_1, \ldots, a_n$, respectively, for each category object so that the value of the load is maximum.

Reflection about how to solve this problem may suggest that an item whose value per unit size is the largest should be used the most, and whatever is left over from the total capacity should be applied to the item with next largest value per unit size, and so on. Thus, without loss of generality, we assume that the variables are already labeled according to their relative value; i.e.,

$$\frac{c_1}{a_1} \geq \frac{c_2}{a_2} \geq \cdots \geq \frac{c_n}{a_n}$$

We have already mentioned the following definition.

Definition   A lexicographic ordering of a set of vectors of the same number of components is an ordering of the vectors according to the first components, and, if there is a tie, then according to the second components, and so on, the vector with the larger component being considered larger.

Thus $(3,7,1)$ is lexicographically larger than $(2,10,50)$ and smaller than $(3,8,0)$.

We start this proposed approach to the knapsack problem by constructing the lexicographically largest vector $x = (x_1, \ldots, x_n)$, and then go
on to the next largest vector, and so on, until $x = 0$ is reached. The fact
that the lexicographically largest vector does not necessarily yield the
maximum is illustrated by the problem

$$8x_1 + 5x_2 + x_3 = \max$$

subject to

$$3x_1 + 2x_2 + x_3 \leq 13 \qquad \begin{array}{l} x_i \geq 0 \\ i = 1,\ 2,\ 3 \\ x_i \text{ is an integer} \end{array}$$

Here $\frac{8}{3} \geq \frac{5}{2} \geq 1$, and the lexicographically largest vector is obtained by
taking $[\frac{13}{3}]$, that is, the largest integer in $\frac{13}{3}$, which is 4. This leaves
$13 - 4 \times 3 = 1$. Our problem now is to distribute 1 among the remaining variables; i.e., we solve $2x_2 + x_3 = 1$, which we can do by putting
$x_2 = 0,\ x_3 = 1$. Thus, $(4,0,1)$ is the desired vector. However, if instead
we take $x_1 = 3$ and solve $2x_2 + x_3 = 4$, we find that the next largest
vector is $(3,2,0)$. If we evaluate the cost or objective function at these
vectors, we find that $(4,0,1)$ gives 33 whereas $(3,2,0)$ gives 34, which can
be shown by listing all the solutions of the constraint to be the maximum.
    The lexicographically largest solution $x^0 = (x_1{}^0, \ldots, x_n{}^0)$ is obtained
as follows:

$$x_1{}^0 = \left[\frac{b}{a_1}\right] \qquad x_2{}^0 = \left[\frac{b - a_1 x_1{}^0}{a_2}\right], \ldots, x_n{}^0 = \left[\frac{b - \sum\limits_{j=1}^{n-1} a_j x_j{}^0}{a_n}\right]$$

Given a vector x^i in a lexicographic ordering which is a solution, the largest vector x^{i+1} smaller than x^i in this ordering which is also a solution is
obtained by decreasing the last positive component of x^i by unity and then
increasing the next component as much as possible, etc. If this process
does not satisfy the constraint, the last component of x^i is reduced by 2,
and the process is continued. To find the maximum, one must run
through a list of vectors from the largest to the smallest; that is, $x = 0$.
However, one need not generate all vectors in the lexicographic ordering.
We give a method for selecting possibly a smaller number. Note that
if $x_s{}^i > 0$ is the last component of x^i that is positive and

$$x_{s+1}^i = \cdots = x_n{}^i = 0$$

and if we define a vector y^i to coincide with x^i, except that

$$y_s{}^i = x_s{}^i - 1 \geq 0$$

then the maximum of $\Sigma_{j=1}^{n} c_j x_j$ would be

$$\delta^i = \sum_{j=1}^{n} c_j y_j{}^i + \frac{c_{s+1}}{a_{s+1}} \left(b - \sum_{j=1}^{n} a_j y_j{}^i \right)$$

ignoring the integer requirement on $x_{s+1}, \ldots, x_n$, and noting that $c_{s+1}/a_{s+1} \geq \cdots \geq c_n/a_n$ and that $b - \Sigma_{j=1}^{n} a_j y_j{}^i$ is the remaining capacity. With the integer requirement, the maximum could not exceed δ^i. Now, if x^* yields the maximum value among all the vectors which come on or before x^i in the ordering, and if $\delta^i \leq cx^*$, then one need not consider any vector x which has the same first s components as y^i. Thus, if $\delta^i \leq cx^*$, we put $x^{i+1} = y^i$ and proceed. If $\delta^i > cx^*$, $x^{i+1} =$ the next lexicographic vector [2,4a,16a].

From the lexicographically largest constraint solution vector $x^1 = (4,0,1)$ of our example, we have $x_3{}^1 = 1 > 0$, $y_3{}^1 = x_3{}^1 - 1 \geq 0$. Thus, $y_1{}^1 = 4$, $y_2{}^1 = 0$, $y_3{}^1 = 0$. Also, $c_1 y_1{}^1 = 32$, $c_2/a_2(13 - 4 \times 3) = \frac{5}{2}$, $\delta^1 = 32 + \frac{5}{2} = 34.5$, and $34.5 \geq 33$, where 33 corresponds to the maximum value at $x^* = (4,0,1)$. Thus, we take the next lexicographic vector which satisfies the constraint. This is $(3,2,0)$, which gives the value 34. Again we have $x_1{}^2 = 3$, $x_2{}^2 = 2$, $x_3{}^2 = 0$; $y_1{}^2 = 3$, $y_2{}^2 = 1$, $y_3{}^2 = 0$; $c_1 y_1{}^2 = 24$, $c_2 y_2{}^2 = 5$. This gives

$$\delta^2 = 29 + \tfrac{5}{2}[13 - (3 \times 3 + 1 \times 2)] = 34$$

which is the same value as that obtained at x^2. Thus, we take

$$x^3 = y^2 = (3,1,0)$$

from which we have $y^3 = (3,0,0)$, $\delta^3 = 24 + 1(13 - 3 \times 3) = 28 \leq 34$. This implies that x^4 is given as $(2,3,1)$, which yields a value of 31. We have $y^4 = (2,3,0)$ and $\delta^4 = 31 + \frac{5}{2}(13 - 12) = 33 \times 5 < 34$, which implies that $x^5 = (2,3,0)$ is the next lexicographic vector. This gives the value 31. Now $y^5 = (2,2,0)$, $\delta^5 = 29 < 34$, and $x^6 = (2,2,0)$. Again, $x^7 = (2,1,5)$, with value 26; $y^7 = (2,1,4)$; $\delta^7 = 25 < 34$; $x^8 = (2,1,4)$; $x^9 = (2,1,3)$; etc.

Exercise 5-3   Maximize in nonnegative integers

$2x_1 + 7x_2 + 3x_3 + x_4$

subject   to

$6x_1 + 3x_2 + 2x_3 + x_4 \leq 20$

Ans. (0,6,1,0).

When minimization is the object, the first assignment is made to the variable whose corresponding relative value is least, etc. (Note that the criterion for the minimum problem may be obtained by multiplying the objective function by -1 and then maximizing.)

Exercise 5-4   Show that the solution to

$$x_1 + x_2 + x_3 + x_4 + x_5 + x_6 = \min$$

subject to

$$16x_1 + 17x_2 + 23x_3 + 24x_4 + 39x_5 + 40x_6 = 100 \qquad \text{(note the equality)}$$

where $x_i \geq 0$ and x_i is an integer, $i = 1, \ldots, 6$, is given by $(2,4,0,0,0,0)$.

This is the algebraic statement of a problem which appeared in an April, 1967, issue of *The New Yorker* magazine.   The problem asked for the number of darts which one must use on the dartboard in Fig. 5-1 in order to score 100.   Note that because there is a unique answer it did not ask for the minimum number.

Exercise 5-5   Maximize $3x_1 - x_2$ subject to

$$
\begin{aligned}
3x_1 - 2x_2 &\leq 3 \\
-5x_1 - 4x_2 &\leq -10 \\
2x_1 + x_2 &\leq 5
\end{aligned}
\qquad
\begin{aligned}
&x_i \text{ is an integer} \\
&i = 1, 2
\end{aligned}
$$

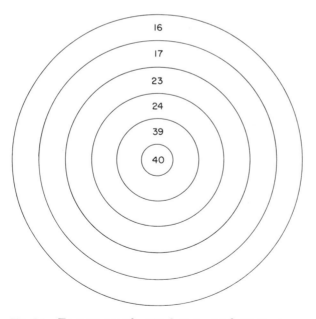

Fig. 5-1   To score exactly 100, how many darts must you use?

Optimal solution (1,2)   *Hint:* Reduce the constraints to

$$3x_1 - 2x_2 + x_3 = 3$$
$$-5x_1 - 4x_2 + x_4 - x_6 = -10$$
$$2x_1 + x_2 + x_5 = 5$$

Then eliminate variables down to a single constraint. The optimal solution here is (1,2,4,3,1,0).

Exercise 5-6   Maximize $3x_1 + x_2$ subject to

$$2x_1 + 3x_2 \leq 6 \qquad x_i \text{ is an integer}$$
$$2x_1 - 3x_2 \leq 3 \qquad i = 1, 2$$

5-3 GENERAL LINEAR PROGRAMMING

The simplex process is the most widely used method for solving linear-programming problems without integer requirements. However, the method remains viable and is used by the new algorithms for integer programming. It is essential to understand the workings of this process in order to be prepared for the ensuing discussion for solving integer problems.

In a linear-programming problem, the function f to be maximized, called the *objective function*, and the constraints g_i, $i = 1, \ldots, m$, given in Sec. 5-1 are linear; that is, $f(x) = c_1x_1 + \cdots + c_nx_n$, and

$$g_i(x) \leq 0 \qquad \text{or} \qquad a_{i1}x_1 + \cdots + a_{in}x_n - b_i \leq 0$$

$i = 1, \ldots, m$, $x_j \geq 0$, $j = 1, \ldots, n$. We shall not discuss this well-known problem except for a brief summary of the simplex process, the algorithm most frequently used for solving such a problem; it is sometimes used also as an auxiliary tool for solving a nonlinear-programming problem.

In the linear-programming problem, the *feasible region*, which is the region common to all the constraint inequalities, is polyhedral (since the g_i's are linear and hence are hyperplanes in n-dimensional space); the objective function defines a hyperplane in $(n + 1)$-space. For each constant value of f, we obtain a contour in n-space. Weyl showed that the solution is on the boundary and usually is a vertex of the polyhedron. This is intuitively obvious in three dimensions. If one is maximizing, the contour passing through this vertex (the contours can be made to cover n-space) has the greatest distance from the origin. It is conceivable that all the vertices can be tested for the solution since the number of vertices is finite; however, shorter methods are used in practice.

Figure 5-2 gives the geometric representation of the following linear-

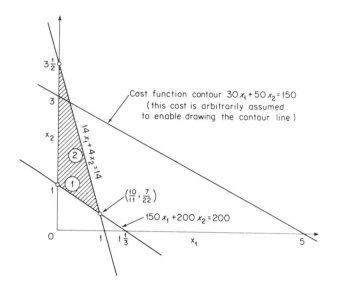

Fig. 5-2

programming problem:

$$30x_1 + 50x_2 = \min$$
$$150x_1 + 200x_2 \geq 200$$
$$14x_1 + 4x_2 \leq 14$$
$$x_1,\ x_2 \geq 0$$

Exercise 5-7   Determine which vertex of the polygon defined by the constraints gives the minimum.

In matrix notation a linear-programming problem requires that a column vector $x \geq 0$, that is, with components $x_j \geq 0$, $j = 1, \ldots, n$, be found which satisfies the constraints $Ax \leq b$ and also maximizes the linear function cx, where $A = (a_{ij})$, $i = 1, \ldots, m$, $j = 1, \ldots, n$, $c = (c_1, \ldots, c_n)$, and b is a column vector with components $b_1, \ldots, b_m$. With the original problem, known as the *primal*, is associated a *dual* problem $yA \geq c$, $y \geq 0$; yb is minimum where $y = (y_1, \ldots, y_m)$.

A well-known duality theorem of linear programming asserts that if either the primal or the dual has a solution, then the values of the objective functions of both problems at the optimum are the same. The solution of either problem can be obtained from the solution of the other. It is sometimes computationally convenient to solve the dual problem.

The simplex process of G. B. Dantzig currently used to solve linear programs begins by choosing basis vectors in m dimensions, where m is the number of inequalities.   Successive bases are chosen; one is finally obtained which solves the problem.   With each iteration, i.e., new basis, the value of the objective function improves toward the optimum value or, at worst, remains the same, for iterations in the feasible region. Since the number of possible bases is finite, it is clear that, barring pathological cases (e.g., a process known as *cycling*, in which bases may recur), the optimum is reached in a finite number of steps.   There are methods devised to avoid these difficulties.   We shall now give some theory and illustrate the simplex process.   The following existence theorems are well known.

Theorem 5-3   *If one feasible solution exists, then there exists a feasible solution (called a basic feasible solution) with, at most, m points P_i, with positive weights x_i and $n - m$ or more points P_i with $x_i = 0$.*

Remark   A basic solution is called *degenerate* if at least one of the x_i corresponding to a basis vector is zero.

Theorem 5-4   *If the values of the objective function for the class of feasible solutions have a finite upper bound, then there exists a maximum feasible solution which is a basic feasible solution.*

The simplex method will be applied to an illustrative problem.   The long method of calculation is used here to clarify the ideas.   A tableau method will be illustrated in solving a quadratic programming problem in a later section.   The constraint set for the problem is

$$x_1 + 4x_2 + 2x_3 \geq 6$$
$$3x_1 + x_2 + 2x_3 \geq 5$$
$$x_i \geq 0 \qquad i = 1, 2, 3$$

and the form (cost function) to be minimized is

$$2x_1 + 9x_2 + x_3$$

This problem has the geometric representation shown in Fig. 5-3.

Step 1   Change to equalities by introducing slack variables which are nonnegative variables used to reduce the inequalities to equalities.

$$x_1 + 4x_2 + 2x_3 - x_4 = 6 \qquad x_4 \geq 0$$
$$3x_1 + x_2 + 2x_3 - x_5 = 5 \qquad x_5 \geq 0 \Big\} \text{ slack variables}$$
$$-2x_1 - 9x_2 - x_3 = \max$$

Step 2   Write out the matrix

$$[P_1, P_2, P_3, P_4, P_5; P_0] = \begin{bmatrix} 1 & 4 & 2 & -1 & 0 & | & 6 \\ 3 & 1 & 2 & 0 & -1 & | & 5 \end{bmatrix}$$

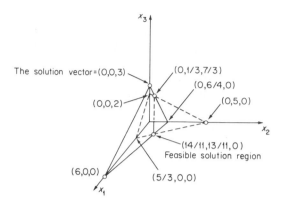

Fig. 5-3

and write

$$c_1 = -2 \qquad c_2 = -9 \qquad c_3 = -1 \qquad c_4 = 0 \qquad c_5 = 0$$

Step 3 Start by selecting a basis, which is a set of linearly independent vectors (i.e., the determinant of their matrix does not vanish); every other vector can be expressed as a linear combination of the basis vectors. A linear combination of vectors P_1 and P_2, for example, may be given as $aP_1 + bP_2$, where a and b are real numbers. In this case, two vectors are needed to form a basis, as can be seen from the matrix.

Remark Using a set of artificial vectors as a basis avoids an initial choice of nonfeasible vectors, i.e., a set of vectors for which the corresponding variables are negative. A simple example of an artificial vector basis is (1,0) and (0,1).

Suppose that the initial choice is P_1 and P_2 as a basis. Express P_0 as a linear combination of them. (See below for how to do this.) Obtain $P_0 = \frac{14}{11}P_1 + \frac{13}{11}P_2$ here. In this problem the cost function will be negative for positive x_i. Hence, if a positive cost is obtained for P_0 as a combination of the basis vectors chosen, then at least one basis vector must be changed. Also, express the remaining vectors as a linear combination of P_1 and P_2, obtaining

	P_1	P_2
P_1	1	0
P_2	0	1
P_3	$\frac{6}{11}$	$\frac{4}{11}$
P_4	$\frac{1}{11}$	$-\frac{3}{11}$
P_5	$-\frac{4}{11}$	$\frac{1}{11}$

Let β_{ij} be the coefficient in the above array whose first subscript is the same as that of the vector on top and whose second subscript is the same as that of the vector to its left. For example, to obtain P_4 as a linear combination of P_1 and P_2, write $P_4 = aP_1 + bP_2$. Note that $\beta_{14} = a$, $\beta_{24} = b$. To show how a and b are obtained, the relation among the vectors may be written as

$$
\overset{P_4}{\begin{bmatrix} -1 \\ 0 \end{bmatrix}} = a \overset{P_1}{\begin{bmatrix} 1 \\ 3 \end{bmatrix}} + b \overset{P_2}{\begin{bmatrix} 4 \\ 1 \end{bmatrix}} = \begin{bmatrix} a \\ 3a \end{bmatrix} + \begin{bmatrix} 4b \\ b \end{bmatrix} = \begin{bmatrix} a + 4b \\ 3a + b \end{bmatrix}
$$

or, by equating sides: $-1 = a + 4b$, $0 = 3a + b$. On solving these two simultaneous equations in a and b, one has $a = \frac{1}{11}$, $b = -\frac{3}{11}$. Similarly, all other vectors are expressed as linear combinations of the basis P_1 and P_2.

Step 4   Consider $z_j = \beta_{1j}c_1 + \beta_{2j}c_2$ $(j = 1, \ldots, 5)$.

Remark   In general, if the basis vectors have subscripts p, q, r, etc., write

$z_j = \beta_{pj}c_p + \beta_{qj}c_q + \beta_{rj}c_r + \cdots$

$z_1 = c_1$	$= -2$	compare with $c_1 = -2$
$z_2 = c_2$	$= -9$	compare with $c_2 = -9$
$z_3 = \frac{6}{11}c_1 + \frac{4}{11}c_2$	$= -\frac{48}{11}$	compare with $c_3 = -1$
$z_4 = \frac{1}{11}c_1 - \frac{3}{11}c_2$	$= \frac{25}{11}$	compare with $c_4 = 0$
$z_5 = -\frac{4}{11}c_1 + \frac{1}{11}c_2$	$= -\frac{1}{11}$	compare with $c_5 = 0$

Compare z_j with c_j as indicated.

If $z_j \geq c_j$ for all j, the process is finished; that is, $P_0 = \frac{14}{11}P_1 + \frac{13}{11}P_2$, and the cost would be (when maximizing, negative) given as follows: If $P_0 = aP_1 + bP_2$, then the cost is $ac_1 + bc_2$. In this case, one has

$$
\tfrac{14}{11}(-2) + \tfrac{13}{11}(-9) = -\tfrac{145}{11} \text{ units}
$$

that is, 11 units for the minimum. If one were directly minimizing, then the criterion would be $z_j \leq c_j$.

Remark   It is clear that $z_j < c_j$ for some j. Then consider max $(c_j - z_j)$. In this case $c_3 - z_3 = $ max. Hence for a next choice of basis one uses P_3 along with either P_1 or P_2. One decides which of P_1 or P_2 to use by the following method (if $c_j \geq z_j$ for all j, and $\beta_{ij} \leq 0$ for all i, the maximum feasible solution is infinite).

Step 5   Express P_0 as a linear combination of P_1 and P_2:

$P_0 = \tfrac{14}{11}P_1 + \tfrac{13}{11}P_2$

Express P_3 as a linear combination of P_1 and P_2, and multiply by θ:

$$\theta P_3 = \theta \tfrac{6}{11} P_1 + \theta \tfrac{4}{11} P_2$$

Subtract the second equation from the first:

$$P_0 = \theta P_3 + (\tfrac{14}{11} - \tfrac{6}{11}\theta)P_1 + (\tfrac{13}{11} - \tfrac{4}{11}\theta)P_2$$

Choose

$$\theta = \min\left(\frac{\tfrac{14}{11}}{\tfrac{6}{11}}, \frac{\tfrac{13}{11}}{\tfrac{4}{11}}\right) = \tfrac{14}{6}$$

Hence obtain

$$P_0 = \tfrac{14}{6}P_3 + \tfrac{2}{6}P_2$$

and the new basis will consist of P_2 and P_3. The cost in this case is given by

$$\tfrac{14}{6}c_3 + \tfrac{2}{6}c_2 = \tfrac{14}{6}(-1) + \tfrac{2}{6}(-9) = -\tfrac{32}{6}$$

which is clearly an improvement on the previous cost, since one is maximizing.

Remark In general, if $P_0 = \alpha_1 P_1 + \cdots + \alpha_q P_q$, $P_1, \ldots, P_q$ being the basis vectors, and if $c_j - z_j = \max$ yields P_j for the new vector, and

$$P_j = \beta_{1j}P_1 + \cdots + \beta_{qj}P_q$$

then choose

$$\theta = \min_i \left(\frac{\alpha_i}{\beta_{ij}}\right) \qquad \beta_{ij} > 0$$

In this manner one of the vectors in

$$P_0 = \theta P_j + (\alpha_1 - \theta\beta_{1j})P_1 + \cdots + (\alpha_q - \theta\beta_{qj})P_q$$

is eliminated.

Step 6 Again, express the remaining vectors as a linear combination of P_2 and P_3:

	P_2	P_3
P_1	$-\tfrac{2}{3}$	$\tfrac{11}{6}$
P_2	1	0
P_3	0	1
P_4	$-\tfrac{1}{3}$	$\tfrac{1}{6}$
P_5	$\tfrac{1}{3}$	$-\tfrac{2}{3}$

Consider now $z_j = \beta_{2j}c_2 + \beta_{3j}c_3$.

$$z_1 = (-\tfrac{2}{3})(-9) + \tfrac{11}{6}(-1) = \tfrac{25}{6} \qquad \text{compare with } c_1 = -2$$
$$z_2 = c_2 \qquad\qquad\qquad\quad\ = -9 \qquad \text{compare with } c_2 = -9$$
$$z_3 = c_3 \qquad\qquad\qquad\quad\ = -1 \qquad \text{compare with } c_3 = -1$$
$$z_4 = (-\tfrac{1}{3})(-9) + \tfrac{1}{6}(-1) = \tfrac{17}{6} \qquad \text{compare with } c_4 = 0$$
$$z_5 = \tfrac{1}{3}(-9) - \tfrac{2}{3}(-1) \quad\ = -\tfrac{7}{3} \qquad \text{compare with } c_5 = 0$$

Here one has $c_5 - z_5 = \max$. Hence P_5 is to replace either P_2 or P_3 in the next choice of basis. To decide which, write

$$P_0 = \tfrac{14}{6}P_3 + \tfrac{2}{6}P_2$$
$$\theta P_5 = -\theta\tfrac{2}{3}P_3 + \theta\tfrac{1}{3}P_2$$

Subtracting the second from the first, one has

$$P_0 = \theta P_5 + (\tfrac{14}{6} + \tfrac{2}{3}\theta)P_3 + (\tfrac{2}{6} - \tfrac{1}{3}\theta)P_2$$

Thus, $\theta = 1$, since one considers only those values of β_{ij} that are greater than zero. This choice gives

$$P_0 = P_5 + \tfrac{18}{6}P_3$$

and the cost is given by

$$1(0) + \tfrac{18}{6}(-1) = -3$$

which is greater than the preceding costs.

Step 7 Again, express the remaining vectors as a linear combination of P_3 and P_5:

	P_3	P_5
P_1	$\tfrac{1}{2}$	-2
P_2	2	3
P_3	1	0
P_4	$-\tfrac{1}{2}$	-1
P_5	0	1

Consider once more $z_j = \beta_{3j}c_3 + \beta_{5j}c_5$.

$$z_1 = -\tfrac{1}{2} \qquad \text{compare with } c_1 = -2$$
$$z_2 = -2 \qquad \text{compare with } c_2 = -9$$
$$z_3 = -1 \qquad \text{compare with } c_3 = -1$$
$$z_4 = \tfrac{1}{2} \qquad \text{compare with } c_4 = 0$$
$$z_5 = 0 \qquad \text{compare with } c_5 = 0$$

It is clear that all $z_j \geq c_j$, and the solution is complete. In other words, since $P_0 = \tfrac{18}{6}P_3 + P_5$, one has $(x_1,x_2,x_3,x_4,x_5) = (0,0,\tfrac{18}{6},0,1)$. The total cost is 3 (the sign having been changed to obtain the minimum). The vector P_5, which has zero cost, contributes nothing. There is no item corresponding to it. In Fig. 5-3, the vertex $(0,0,3)$ yields the solution.

Note that the simplex process guarantees no integer values for the solution vector. There is no a priori reason why any vertex of the polyhedron of feasible solutions should be a lattice point, i.e., have integer coordinates. Approximating the coordinate values with integers does not necessarily yield a feasible vector since the vertex yielding a solution may be nearest to a lattice point outside the region of feasible solutions and the nearest feasible lattice point may not be near enough to justify any approximation.

SOLUTION OF THE DUAL

If the basis leading to a maximum solution of the primal has been obtained by the simplex process, then the solution of the dual is obtained as follows: Let B be the matrix whose column vectors constitute the basis vectors leading to the solution with inverse B^{-1}, and let C^* be the cost vector corresponding to the solution basis. Then the solution of the dual is $y = C^*B^{-1}$ where the components of the vector y comprise the solution $(y_1{}^0, \ldots, y_m{}^0)$.

Proof Note that $z_j = C^*(B^{-1}A)$. Since $z_j - c_j \geq 0$, $C^*(B^{-1}A) - c \geq 0$, which becomes (on substituting $y = C^*B^{-1}$) $yA - c \geq 0$ or $yA \geq c$, which is the dual problem.

Given a linear-programming problem with three constraints and n variables, it is possible to obtain the simplex solution by forming the dual and solving geometrically. To show this, suppose for simplicity that (y_1, y_2, y_3) are the values constituting the solution. Then P_1, P_2, and P_3 are the basis vectors in the simplex solution of the dual; when the submatrix comprised of these vectors is taken from the matrix of the problem, inverted, and multiplied by the vector whose components are the cost coefficients corresponding to P_1, P_2, P_3, the solution (x_1, x_2, x_3) of the primal is obtained; i.e.,

$$(x_1, x_2, x_3) = (\text{cost vector})(B^{-1})$$

Once the values of x_1, x_2, and x_3 are known, the corresponding vectors from the matrix constitute the basis vectors leading to the solution of the primal. A similar argument applies for the simpler case of two constraints in the primal.

Exercise 5-8 Following the above description of the simplex process, show that

$$2x_1 + 3x_2 + x_3$$

is minimized at $(0,\frac{7}{20},\frac{51}{40})$ subject to the constraints

$$4x_1 + x_2 + 6x_3 \geq 8$$
$$3x_1 + 7x_2 + 2x_3 \geq 5$$
$$x_1, x_2, x_3 \geq 0$$

Exercise 5-9 Obtain the solution to Exercise 5-8 by geometric means; i.e., draw a picture of the problem.

Exercise 5-10 Find the dual of the foregoing problem; obtain the solution geometrically and algebraically, using the solution of the primal.

JUSTIFICATION OF THE SIMPLEX SOLUTION

1. For the problem, maximize $f = cx$ subject to $Ax \leq b$, $x \geq 0$, introduce the slack variables, $x_{n+1}, \ldots, x_{n+m}$, with corresponding cost coefficients $c_{n+1} = \cdots = c_{n+m} = 0$. The problem then becomes: Maximize $f = cx$, subject to $[A;I] x = b \geq 0$, where now

$$c = \{c_1, \ldots, c_n, c_{n+1}, \ldots, c_{n+m}\}$$

and $x^T = \{x_1, \ldots, x_{n+m}\} \geq 0$, and where I is an $m \times m$ identity matrix.

2. We use the fact that the solution to the linear-programming problem lies at a vertex of the region defined by the constraints, and that at any vertex n of the $(n + m)$ components of x will be zero. The remaining m components of x which can be positive constitute the "basis," and the simplex method essentially consists of moving from one vertex to an adjacent one, thereby changing the set of nonzero components by forcing one to zero in the "old" basis and replacing it by a nonzero choice of a component formerly set to zero. The change from a given basis to a new basis is made so as to both satisfy the constraints and effect an increase in the objective function f. The possibility of moving from one vertex to an adjacent one while satisfying the constraints is assured by the convexity of the "feasibility region" defined by the constraints. If a basic solution is degenerate, then there is a possibility of making a change in basis without increasing f.

A brief justification of the simplex process proceeds as follows: Let the trial solution selected at some point in the iterative procedure be x, where we define x' such that

$$x'^T = \{\bar{y}^T; \bar{\bar{y}}^T\}$$

that is, x' is a rearrangement of x such that $\bar{y}$ is the basis selected for the trial solution and $\bar{\bar{y}}$ includes the components of x not in the basis ($\bar{\bar{y}}_j = 0$, $j = 1, \ldots, n$).

Defining similar appropriate rearrangements of the matrices c and $[A;I]$, we may write for the objective function and the right side, respectively:

$$f = \bar{c}\bar{y} + \bar{\bar{c}}\bar{\bar{y}} \tag{5-1}$$
$$b = \bar{A}\bar{y} + \bar{\bar{A}}\bar{\bar{y}} \tag{5-2}$$

We now wish to change one of the components of $\bar{\bar{y}}$ in such away that the following occur:

1. f undergoes an increase
2. The constraint (5-2) remains satisfied
3. One of the components of $\bar{y}$ vanishes, while the constraint $x \geq 0$ remains satisfied.

The constraint (5-2) requires that for any change $\Delta\bar{\bar{y}}$ in the vector $\bar{\bar{y}}$, we have

$$\Delta b = \bar{A}\,\Delta\bar{y} + \bar{\bar{A}}\,\Delta\bar{\bar{y}} = 0, \tag{5-3}$$

or

$$\Delta\bar{y} = -(\bar{A})^{-1}\bar{\bar{A}}\,\Delta\bar{\bar{y}} = -D\,\Delta\bar{\bar{y}} \tag{5-4}$$

where

$$D \equiv (\bar{A})^{-1}\bar{\bar{A}} \tag{5-5}$$

and the existence of $(\bar{A})^{-1}$ is assured by the existence of a solution to Equation (5-2), with $\bar{y}$ as the solution vector. Since only one component of $\bar{\bar{y}}$, say $\bar{\bar{y}}_\alpha$, is to be made positive, (5-4) may be written as

$$\Delta\bar{y}_i = -D_{i\alpha}\,\Delta\bar{\bar{y}}_\alpha \tag{5-6}$$

The corresponding change in the objective function f is readily seen to be, from (5-1) and using (5-6),

$$\Delta f_0 = (\bar{\bar{c}}_\alpha - z_\alpha)\,\Delta\bar{\bar{y}}_\alpha \tag{5-7}$$

where

$$z_\alpha = \sum_{i=1}^{m} \bar{c}_i D_{i\alpha} \tag{5-8}$$

or equivalently

$$z = \bar{c}D \tag{5-8a}$$

Thus, if one wishes to produce an increase in f, the component of $\bar{\bar{y}}$ to be made positive should be the one for which $(\bar{\bar{c}}_\alpha - z_\alpha)$ is positive. Assuming no degeneracy, it is natural to select the component with the largest positive difference. If none of the differences $(\bar{\bar{c}}_\alpha - z_\alpha)$ is positive, the solution cannot be improved, and $\bar{y}$ is the solution vector. Since one of the components of $\bar{y}$ is to be annihilated, $\Delta\bar{\bar{y}}_\alpha$ must be chosen as [see

(5-6)]

$$\Delta \bar{y}_\alpha = \left(\frac{\bar{y}_\beta}{D_{\beta\alpha}} \right) \tag{5-9}$$

for some β. In order to ensure that the constraint $x \geq 0$ will be met by the new trial solution, β must be selected such that

$$\left(\frac{\bar{y}_\beta}{D_{\beta\alpha}} \right) = \min_i \left(\frac{\bar{y}_i}{D_{i\alpha}} \right) \tag{5-10}$$

since then the new components of the old basis $\bar{y}$ will be

$$\bar{y}_i^* = \bar{y}_i + \Delta \bar{y}_i = \bar{y}_i - D_{i\alpha} \left[\min_i \frac{\bar{y}_i}{D_{i\alpha}} \right] \geq 0 \tag{5-11}$$

Finally, the new basis is

$$\begin{aligned} \bar{y}_i^* &= \bar{y}_i - D_{i\alpha} \frac{\bar{y}_\beta}{D_{\beta\alpha}} \qquad i \neq \alpha \\ \bar{y}_\alpha^* &= \frac{\bar{y}_\beta}{D_{\beta\alpha}} \end{aligned} \tag{5-12}$$

The iteration procedure is then continued until the solution is found.

We now interpret the algorithm as it was described before.

Step 1   This step is the introduction of slack variables to go from inequalities to equations.

Step 2   This step involves writing the partitioned matrix $[A;I]$ and the constraint vector b which can be used to evaluate the objective function at each stage of the iteration.

Step 3   This step is the determination of the matrix D given in (5-5), although the procedure actually defines a matrix $\beta = [I;D]$. However, the identity matrix part of the β matrix is not useful in the subsequent steps of the procedure. The correspondence between β and D is made obvious by writing (5-5) in the form

$$\bar{A} = \bar{A}D \tag{5-5a}$$

Step 4   This corresponds to the calculation of the quantities z_α (or the vector z) [(5-8) or (5-8a)] and the differences $(\bar{c}_\alpha - z_\alpha)$. In addition, the objective function,

$$f = \bar{c}\bar{y}$$

is evaluated as

$$f = \bar{c}(\bar{A})^{-1}b$$

since $\bar{y}$ must satisfy $\bar{y} = (\bar{A})^{-1}b$ from Equation (5-2). [The coefficients a,b of the linear combination are the components of the vector $(\bar{A})^{-1}b$.]

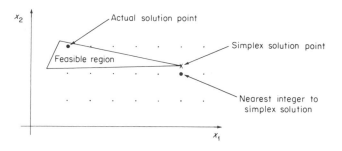

Fig. 5-4

Step 5 This corresponds to the determination of β [for which $(\bar{y}_\beta/D_{\beta\alpha})$ is the minimum of $(\bar{y}_i/D_{i\alpha})$], and the calculation of $\Delta\bar{\bar{y}}_\alpha = \bar{y}_\beta/D_{\beta\alpha}$. The rest is obvious.

WHY NEAREST–INTEGER APPROXIMATIONS USUALLY DO NOT WORK

One reason why nearest-integer approximations in linear programming do not yield the correct answer is illustrated in Fig. 5-4, where two constraints meet at a vertex between two rows of lattice points of the plane. Suppose that the simplex process yields this vertex (marked with a cross in Fig. 5-4) as the solution. The nearest-integer approximation to this vertex lies outside the (shaded) feasible region and hence is not even feasible. The integer solution to the problem may actually be far removed from the simplex solution, which can also be seen in the figure. Here, there is only one lattice point in the feasible region.

5-4   THE SIMPLEX PROCESS APPLIED TO A TRANSPORTATION PROBLEM [10,13]

When the simplex process is applied to a "transportation" problem with integral coefficients, integer solutions are obtained. This is illustrated in the following example. Let

$$a_1 = \sum_{j=1}^{5} x_{1j} = 24 \qquad b_1 = \sum_{i=1}^{4} x_{i1} = 10$$

$$a_2 = \sum_{j=1}^{5} x_{2j} = 18 \qquad b_2 = \sum_{i=1}^{4} x_{i2} = 20$$

$$a_3 = \sum_{j=1}^{5} x_{3j} = 20 \qquad b_3 = \sum_{i=1}^{4} x_{i3} = 10$$

$$a_4 = \sum_{j=1}^{5} x_{4j} = 16 \qquad b_4 = \sum_{i=1}^{4} x_{i4} = 18$$

$$b_5 = \sum_{i=1}^{4} x_{i5} = 20$$

and let the cost matrix be

$$(c_{ij}) = \begin{bmatrix} 4 & 9 & 8 & 10 & 12 \\ 6 & 10 & 3 & 2 & 3 \\ 3 & 2 & 7 & 10 & 3 \\ 3 & 5 & 5 & 4 & 8 \end{bmatrix}$$

Thus, the cost to ship a unit from the second origin to the first destination is 6, from the fourth origin to the fifth destination is 8, etc. One is faced with the problem of choosing the quantities x_{ij} to be shipped (i.e., choosing the values in the shipping matrix) subject to the constraints, such that the cost function which now can be written as

$$4x_{11} + 9x_{12} + 8x_{13} + 10x_{14} + 12x_{15} + 6x_{21} + 10x_{22} + 3x_{23} + 2x_{24}$$
$$+ 3x_{25} + 3x_{31} + 2x_{32} + 7x_{33} + 10x_{34} + 3x_{35} + 3x_{41} + 5x_{42}$$
$$+ 5x_{43} + 4x_{44} + 8x_{45}$$

is a minimum.

The constraints constitute a set of $4 + 5 = 9$ equations in 20 unknowns. Of the equations, $m + n - 1$ are independent (recall that $\Sigma_{i=1}^{4}a_i = \Sigma_{j=1}^{5}b_j$). The minimizing solution, therefore, requires, at most, $m + n - 1$ routes of positive shipments.

To find a feasible solution containing eight or fewer nonzero shipping values is simple. It is done as follows: Form a table with the proper number of origins and the proper number of destinations. Place the given values of a_i in an additional column on the right and b_j as an additional row on the bottom, as illustrated in Table 5-1.

The cells in this table must be assigned numbers which add up to the row and column indicated. To do this, put in space (1,1) the minimum of (a_1,b_1), that is, the minimum of the two values 24 and 10; here the value is 10. Move one space in the direction of the maximum of (a_1,b_1),

Table 5-1

j		Destinations					
i		1	2	3	4	5	Totals
Origins	1						$24 = a_1$
	2						$18 = a_2$
	3						$20 = a_3$
	4						$16 = a_4$
	Totals	$10 = b_1$	$20 = b_2$	$10 = b_3$	$18 = b_4$	$20 = b_5$	78

that is, to position (1,2), the first row and second column. Record in this position the minimum of $(a_1 - 10, b_2)$, with $a_1 = 24$, $b_2 = 20$, which is 14. Next, move one space n the direction of the maximum of $(a_1 - 10, b_2)$, namely, to position (2,2), and record in that position the minimum of

$$(b_2 - 14, a_2) = (20 - 14, 18) = 6$$

Continuing this process will give a feasible solution. It is clear that, at most, $(m + n - 1) = 8$ nonzero shipping values will be required.

While the above method will always give a feasible solution, and hence a starting point for the simplex routine, a better feasible solution can generally be obtained by a little more thought, often greatly reducing the work which follows. This means choosing more than the positions with the lowest shipping costs for the positive shipments; it means choosing the positions whose shipping costs seem, by inspection, to give the "best bargain." To illustrate, consider the first column of the cost matrix; the third and fourth positions are the ones with lowest cost in the column, yet the best choice seems to be the first position. This follows from the fact that, in the third row, there is a better choice than 3, that is, 2, and in the fourth row there is a choice almost as good as 3, that is, 4. However, in the first row if one fails to use the first element, which is 4, one must choose between costs exceeding this number by from 4 to 8. With this in mind, Table 5-1 will now be filled with a feasible solution, as given in Table 5-2. The vacant positions represent zero shipments. Note that fewer than $m + n - 1$ nonzero values have been used. Note also that the cost of this choice is

$$40 + 80 + 40 + 54 + 40 + 56 + 16 = 326$$

In order to improve this feasible solution, form a new table containing the same number of elements as the cost matrix, place the cost values

Table 5-2   First shipping table

i \ j	Destinations 1	2	3	4	5	Totals
1	10		10	4		24
2					18	18
3		20				20
4				14	2	16
Totals	10	20	10	18	20	78

Origins

Table 5-3   First pseudocost table

$$(\bar{c}_{ij}) = \begin{array}{|c|c|c|c|c|}
\hline
④ & 4 & ⑧ & ⑩ & 14 \\
\hline
-7 & -7 & -3 & -1 & ③ \\
\hline
2 & ② & 6 & 8 & 12 \\
\hline
-2 & -2 & 2 & ④ & ⑧ \\
\hline
\end{array}$$

c_{ij} in each position containing a nonzero shipment, and put a circle around each. (See the circled values in Table 5-3.) The elements in this "pseudocost" table will be labeled $\bar{c}_{ij}$. Hence $c_{ij} = \bar{c}_{ij}$ for all values which have the same subscripts as those of a nonzero shipping value. As for the remaining values, form an auxiliary table with spaces for values U_i $(i = 1, \ldots , m)$ and V_j $(j = 1, \ldots , n)$. To see how this is done, choose any circled value $\bar{c}_{ij}$, and arbitrarily assign real values to U_i and V_j so that

$$U_i + V_j = \bar{c}_{ij} = c_{ij}$$

Find a circled value having one subscript the same as c_{ij}, say c_{ik}, and choose V_k such that the previously chosen U_i plus V_k equals c_{ik}. If no such circled value exists, choose at random a new c_{kp} from the circled values, and assign to U_k and V_p values such that $U_k + V_p = c_{kp}$. Continue this until the auxiliary Table 5-4 is complete.

To see how this table is developed, choose position (1,1) and arbitrarily let $U_1 = c_{11} = 4$. Since $U_1 + V_1 = c_{11}$, it follows that $V_1 = 0$. Position (1,3) is also occupied by a nonzero shipping value. Since U_1 and V_3 correspond to that position, one must have $U_1 + V_3 = c_{13}$ or $4 + V_3 = 8$, yielding $V_3 = 4$. Similarly, $U_1 + V_4 = c_{14}$ which gives $V_4 = 6$. However, in that column one also has a nonzero shipping value in position (4,4). Hence $U_4 + V_4 = c_{44}$. Since $V_4 = 6$, it follows that $U_4 = -2$,

Table 5-4   First auxiliary table

	U_i	V_j
1	4	0
2	-7	0
3	2	4
4	-2	6
5		10

Table 5-5

$$(\bar{c}_{ij} - c_{ij}) = \begin{bmatrix} 0 & -5 & 0 & 0 & 2 \\ -13 & -17 & -6 & -3 & 0 \\ -1 & 0 & -1 & -2 & 9 \\ -5 & -7 & -3 & 0 & 0 \end{bmatrix}$$

etc.   With the auxiliary table completed in this manner, all $\bar{c}_{ij} = U_i + V_j$ may now be computed and then compared with the original costs c_{ij}. If all $\bar{c}_{ij} \leq c_{ij}$, the shipping allocation yields the minimum cost.   Otherwise, consider only those positions for which the difference $\bar{c}_{ij} - c_{ij}$ is positive, and choose the position for which this difference is maximum. We have Table 5-5.

In this case $\bar{c}_{ij} > c_{ij}$ only in positions (1,5) and (3,5), and the latter gives the maximum difference.   Rewrite the old shipping table with a θ_1 placed in position (3,5).   In order to obtain the total a_3, θ_1 must be subtracted from the nonzero shipping value in position (3,2).   However, it must also be placed somewhere in the second column to yield b_2.   Hence it is placed in the (4,2) position and subtracted from the value in the (4,5) position. The totals are now correctly obtained everywhere.   When there are two possible nonzero values to which θ_1 may be added, as is the case in the fourth row, the value with the smaller total cost is used.   This gives Table 5-6.

Among the expressions in which θ_1 appears, select those which have the form $\alpha - \theta_1$.   Then assign to θ_1 the smallest of these α's, and introduce this value in the table.   This gives a new shipping table.   In the present example $\theta_1 = 2$, which leaves the shipping table with eight nonzero shipping values, as required by the condition that $m + n - 1$ of the constraints be independent, and one has shipping Table 5-7.

The process is now repeated until all $\bar{c}_{ij} \leq c_{ij}$.   When this occurs, the

Table 5-6   Shipping table

	j	Destinations					
i		1	2	3	4	5	$Totals$
Origins	1	10		10	4		24
	2					18	18
	3		$20 - \theta_1$			θ_1	20
	4		θ_1		14	$2 - \theta_1$	16
	$Totals$	10	20	10	18	20	78

Table 5-7   Second shipping table

i \ j	1	2	3	4	5	Totals
Destinations (header)						
1	10		10	4		24
2					18	18
3		18			2	20
4		2		14		16
Totals	10	20	10	18	20	78

solution yields the minimum shipping cost.   The steps are given in Tables 5-8 to 5-17 without further elaboration.

The new cost associated with Table 5-7 is

$$40 + 80 + 40 + 54 + 36 + 6 + 10 + 56 = 322$$

Table 5-8   Second pseudocost table

④	11	⑧	⑩	12
−5	2	−1	1	③
−5	②	−1	1	③
−2	⑤	2	④	6

Table 5-9 Second auxiliary table

U_i	V_i
4	0
−5	7
−5	4
−2	6
	8

The only $\bar{c}_{ij} > c_{ij}$ is $\bar{c}_{12} = 11$, where $c_{12} = 9$.

Table 5-10   Shipping table

i \ j	1	2	3	4	5	Totals
Destinations (header)						
1	10	θ_2	10	$4 - \theta_2$		24
2					18	18
3		18			2	20
4		$2 - \theta_2$		$14 + \theta_2$		16
Totals	10	20	10	18	20	78

The smallest $\theta_2 > 0$ is $\theta_2 = 2$, and the table is given as Table 5-11.

Table 5-11   Third shipping table

j \ i	1	2	3	4	5	Totals
		Destinations				
1	10	2	10	2		24
2					18	18
3		18			2	20
4				16		16
Totals	10	20	10	18	20	78

The cost is now

$$40 + 18 + 80 + 20 + 54 + 36 + 6 + 64 = 318$$

which is an improvement on the previous cost.

Table 5-12   Third pseudocost table

④	⑨	⑧	⑩	10
−3	2	1	3	③
−3	②	1	3	③
−2	3	2	④	4

**Table 5-13
Third auxiliary table**

U_i	V_i
4	0
−3	5
−3	4
−2	6
	6

Here $\bar{c}_{24} > c_{24}$.

Table 5-14   Shipping table

j \ i	1	2	3	4	5	Totals
		Destinations				
1	10	$2 + \theta_3$	10	$2 - \theta_3$		24
2				θ_3	$18 - \theta_3$	18
3		$18 - \theta_3$			$2 + \theta_3$	20
4				16		16
Totals	10	20	10	18	20	78

The minimum $\theta_3 > 0$ is $\theta_3 = 2$, giving Table 5-15.

Table 5-15   Final shipping table

	j	Destinations					
i		1	2	3	4	5	Totals
Origins	1	10	4	10			24
	2				2	16	18
	3		16			4	20
	4				16		16
	Totals	10	20	10	18	20	78

The cost is now

$$40 + 36 + 80 + 4 + 48 + 32 + 12 + 64 = 316$$

still lower than before.

Table 5-16   Final pseudocost table

④	⑨	⑧	9	10
-3	2	1	②	③
-3	②	1	2	③
-1	4	3	④	5

Table 5-17   Final auxiliary table

U_i	V_i
4	0
-3	5
-3	4
-1	5
	6

Every $\bar{c}_{ij} \le c_{ij}$ so that the last shipping table gives the optimum solution with cost 316.

If the supply exceeds the demand in the formulation of the problem, then

$$\sum_{i=1}^{m} a_i > \sum_{j=1}^{n} b_j$$

If the demand exceeds the supply, the above inequality is reversed.   In the former case, one can add an extra column to the shipping and cost matrices with the costs being zero (indicating storage).   In the latter case, an extra row may be added to the shipping and to the cost matrices, with costs M in each space.   This M will be considered a very high cost so that the row will be used only to indicate the destinations that are left without their demands fulfilled.

It is a characteristic feature of transportation problems that they need not have unique solutions, and there may exist a whole family of shipping programs, each of which costs no more than any program not contained in this family.

5-5 AN INTEGER-PROGRAMMING ALGORITHM

There are a number of ways of approaching integer-programming problems. A number of expository articles have presented and compared these methods [2,3,4,15,17,20,31,45]. Our purpose here is to open the door slightly by presenting a main algorithm due to Gomory so that the student who has such a problem to solve will approach the subject with a modicum of sophistication. Throughout the book we have intentionally avoided deep involvement with algorithms because of space limitations, choosing to give the subject of integer mathematics greater breadth and variety. Later in the chapter we shall give another, more general, approach through zero-one or bivalent programming. For large problems, that method is unwieldy because of the number of manipulations.

Consider, now, the problem of maximizing the linear objective function, which, for convenience, we write as

$$z = c_0 - \sum_{j=1}^{n} c_j x_j \qquad \text{(often } c_0 \text{ can be transformed to zero)} \qquad (5\text{-}13)$$

subject to the constraints

$$y_i \equiv b_i - \sum_{j=1}^{n} a_{ij} x_j \geq 0 \qquad i = 1, \ldots, m \qquad (5\text{-}14)$$

with $x_j \geq 0$, which can be written as

$$x_j = -1(-x_j) \geq 0 \qquad j = 1, \ldots, n \qquad (5\text{-}15)$$

where the components of the vector $x = (x_1, \ldots, x_n)$ are integers. This problem is known as an *all-integer–integer-programming problem* if a_{ij}, b_i, c_j and x_j are integers, and as an *all-integer-programming problem* if the requirement is only that x_j be integers. Problems in which only some of the x_j's are required as integers are called *mixed-integer-programming problems.*

Note that if we drop the integrality requirement for the solution vector x, then we are left with an ordinary linear-programming (LP) problem which can be solved by the simplex method. The basic integer-programming method was to solve the desired integer-programming (IP) problem by ignoring the integrality requirement. If the solution so obtained has the desired integral properties, then it must be an optimal solution to the given IP problem since every feasible solution of the IP problem is also a feasible solution of the corresponding LP problem, obtained by relaxing the integral requirements. However, if the optimal solution of the LP problem is not a feasible solution to the IP problem (the integral restriction is violated), then the method consists of forming a new LP problem by adding a new constraint. The new constraint is selected to have the property that the set of feasible solutions to the new LP problem does not include the optimal solution of the original LP problem, but does include all feasible solutions to the IP problem. The new LP problem is then solved. If the optimal solution obtained is a feasible solution of the IP problem, then we are done. Otherwise, we repeat the process by adding another constraint. Such additional constraints are called *cuts*. The cuts cut off a part of the set of feasible solution to the LP problem. Gomory's algorithm provides a systematic way in which these cuts are selected, so that the cutting process converges to the optimal solution of the IP problem in a finite number of steps [19]. (Ref. 4 summarizes several other algorithms besides cutting methods. Examples are rounding, branch and bound, and partition methods. An additive algorithm is described in Ref. 1.)

To see how cuts are introduced, consider a typical constraint equation, which we write as follows (with $a_{i0} = b_i$):

$$y_i = a_{i0} + \sum_{j=1}^{n} a_{ij}(-x_j) \qquad (5\text{-}16)$$

or (dropping the ith subscript for convenience)

$$0 = a_0 + \sum_{j=1}^{n} a_j(-x_j) + 1(-y)$$

Let λ be a positive number to be determined later. Expressing each number a_j/λ, $j = 0, 1, \ldots , n$, as the sum of its integral and fractional parts, we can write

$$a_j = \left[\frac{a_j}{\lambda}\right]\lambda + r_j \qquad j = 0, 1, \ldots , n$$

Obviously, we have

$$1 = \left[\frac{1}{\lambda}\right]\lambda + r$$

where

$$0 \leq r_j < \lambda \qquad \text{and} \qquad 0 \leq r < \lambda$$

Substituting and rearranging terms of Equation (5-16), we obtain

$$\sum_{j=1}^{n} r_j x_j + ry = r_0 + \lambda \left\{ \left[\frac{a_0}{\lambda}\right] + \sum_{j=1}^{n} \left[\frac{a_j}{\lambda}\right](-x_j) + \left[\frac{1}{\lambda}\right](-y) \right\} \qquad (5\text{-}17)$$

Since r_j, $j = 1, \ldots, n$, and r are nonnegative, the left-hand side of (5-17) is nonnegative. Hence the right-hand side is also nonnegative. Again, for integer values of x_j and y, the expression in the braces on the right side of (5-17) is an integer since all coefficients are integral. Since $r_0 > \lambda$, a negative integral value of the expression in the braces will make the right side negative, contradicting the fact that the entire right side is nonnegative. Thus the term in the braces is both integral and nonnegative. Therefore,

$$y' = \left[\frac{a_0}{\lambda}\right] + \sum_{j=1}^{n} \left[\frac{a_j}{\lambda}\right](-x_j) + \left[\frac{1}{\lambda}\right](-y) \qquad (5\text{-}18)$$

is a new nonnegative integer variable implied by (5-16). For Gomory's first algorithm, $\lambda = 1$, but we shall omit this case. For Gomory's second algorithm, $\lambda > 1$, from which we have $[1/\lambda] = 0$. Thus,

$$y' = \left[\frac{a_0}{\lambda}\right] + \sum_{j=1}^{n} \left[\frac{a_j}{\lambda}\right](-x_j) \equiv a_0' - \sum_{j=1}^{n} a_j' x_j \qquad (5\text{-}19)$$

Equation (5-19) represents a new equation that must be satisfied by any integer solution to the original IP problem. In order to show how λ is chosen and hence also give a geometric illustration of the method, we must give the steps of the algorithm which justify the selection of λ.

We proceed to cast the problem into tableau form. A typical ith constraint is written as a row array

$$(b_i \mid a_{i1}, a_{i2}, \ldots, a_{in}) \qquad i = 1, \ldots, m \qquad (5\text{-}20)$$

All the arrays (5-20) are now stacked systematically to yield the tableau given below. The objective function may be considered as a $y_0 \equiv z$ and put at the top of the tableau. The bottom row is reserved for a constraint to be added.

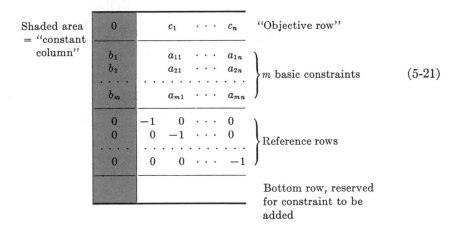

Shaded area = "constant column"

"Objective row"

m basic constraints (5-21)

Reference rows

Bottom row, reserved for constraint to be added

The tableau (5-21) is called *primal feasible* if the constant column, with the possible exception of the top element, contains only non-negative entries. Clearly, primal feasibility means that the point $x = 0$ is feasible. Similarly, a tableau is called *dual feasible* if the objective row, again with the possible exception of the first element, contains only nonnegative entries.

Lemma *If the tableau is primal and dual feasible, then $x = 0$ is the optimal-integer solution of the integer-programming problem.*

Proof Given the tableau

	1	$-x_1$	$-x_2$	$\cdots$	$-x_n$
$z =$	c_0	c_1	c_2	$\cdots$	c_n
$y_1 =$	b_1	a_{11}	a_{12}	$\cdots$	a_{1n}
$y_2 =$	b_2	a_{21}	a_{22}	$\cdots$	a_{2n}
$\cdots$	$\cdots$				
$y_m =$	b_m	a_{m1}	a_{m2}	$\cdots$	a_{mn}

suppose that it is primal feasible; that is, $b_i \geq 0$, $i = 1, \ldots, m$. Now $x_j = 0$, $j = 1, \ldots, n$, is a feasible solution because $y_i = b_i \geq 0$. If the tableau is dual feasible, too, then $c_j \geq 0$, $j = 1, \ldots, m$. The maximum values of the expression $z = c_0 - \Sigma_{j=1}^{n} c_j x_j$ is attained at $x = (0, \ldots, 0)$ because x_j are restricted to take nonnegative value. This implies that $x = 0$ is an optimal solution. This completes the proof.

An ex-step   As we have previously shown in the discussion of the simplex method, a programming problem may be transformed by performing an exchange step (ex-step), which consists of introducing a new variable

$$y = d_0 - d_1 x_1 - d_2 x_2 - \cdots - d_n x_n$$

at the expense of one of the original variables, say x_r, which will be eliminated. Thereby, a linear expression

$$\alpha_0 - \alpha_1 x_1 - \cdots - \alpha_n x_n$$

is transformed into the expression

$$\bar{\alpha}_0 - \bar{\alpha}_1 x_1 - \cdots - \bar{\alpha}_{r-1} x_{r-1} - \bar{\alpha}_r y - \bar{\alpha}_{r+1} x_{r+1} - \cdots - \bar{\alpha}_n x_n$$

with

$$\bar{\alpha}_i = \begin{cases} \alpha_i - \dfrac{d_i}{d_r} a_r & \text{for } i \neq r \\[2ex] -\dfrac{a_r}{d_r} & \text{for } i = r \end{cases}$$

Note an ex-step is simply a Gauss-Jordan transformation step applied to the row

$$(\alpha_0 \mid \alpha_1, \ldots, \alpha_n)$$

of a condensed tableau with respect to the "pivot row"

$$(d_0 \mid d_1, \ldots, d_n)$$

and the "pivot" d_r.

We shall now elaborate further on the ex-step in order to make the foregoing concepts clear. Consider two linear forms in two variables x_1, x_2.

$$y_1 = \alpha_0 - \alpha_1 x_1 - \alpha_2 x_2 \tag{5-22}$$
$$y_2 = \beta_0 - \beta_1 x_1 - \beta_2 x_2 \tag{5-23}$$

Suppose $\alpha_1 \neq 0$. From Equation (5-22),

$$x_1 = \frac{\alpha_0}{\alpha_1} - \frac{1}{\alpha_1} y_1 - \frac{\alpha_2}{\alpha_1} x_2 \tag{5-24}$$

Substituting for x_1 in Equation (5-23), we obtain

$$y_2 = \beta_0 - \beta_1 \left[\frac{\alpha_0}{\alpha_1} - \frac{1}{\alpha_1} y_1 - \frac{\alpha_2}{\alpha_1} x_2 \right] - \beta_2 x_2$$

or

$$y_2 = \left(\beta_0 - \frac{\beta_1 \alpha_0}{\alpha_1} \right) + \frac{\beta_1}{\alpha_1} y_1 - \left(\beta_2 - \frac{\beta_1 \alpha_2}{\alpha_1} \right) x_2 \tag{5-25}$$

In Equations (5-24) and (5-25) we have two new linear forms, which are characterized by the fact that the formerly independent variable x_1 has now become a function (dependent variable), while y_1 has become an independent variable. In other words, x_1 and y_1 have been exchanged. This is called an *ex-step*. In our tableau notation we have

Initial tableau

	1	$-x_1$	$-x_2$
$y_1 =$	α_0	α_1	α_2
$y_2 =$	β_0	β_1	β_2

$$(5\text{-}26)$$

After an ex-step

	1	$-y_1$	$-x_2$
$x_1 =$	$\dfrac{\alpha_0}{\alpha_1}$	$\dfrac{1}{\alpha_1}$	$\dfrac{\alpha_2}{\alpha_1}$
$y_2 =$	$\left(\beta_0 - \dfrac{\beta_1 \alpha_0}{\alpha_1}\right)$	$-\dfrac{\beta_1}{\alpha_1}$	$\left(\beta_2 - \dfrac{\beta_1 \alpha_2}{\alpha_1}\right)$

$$(5\text{-}27)$$

Definition The column x and the row y of the variables being exchanged intersect in the element α_1; this element is called the *pivot element* of the step.

RULES FOR AN EX-STEP

1. The pivot element is replaced by its reciprocal value.
2. The other elements of the pivot column are to be divided by the pivot element.
3. The other elements of the pivot row are to be divided by the pivot element and given the opposite sign.
4. An element in the remaining part of the matrix is transformed as follows: Add the new pivot row beneath the tableau (called the *basement row*). The rule says add to an element the product of the element vertically beneath it in the basement row with that element in the pivot column which is in the same row as the given element.

As noted, this ex-step is simply a Gauss-Jordan transformation. For the Gomory algorithm the starting tableau is required to have some special properties.

1. The columns C_i, $i = 1, \ldots , n$, of the starting tableau, that is, all columns but the constant column, must be lexicographically positive.

A column is called *lexicographically positive* if its top nonzero element is positive. One column is lexicographically greater than another if their difference is lexicographically positive.

2. At every step, the constant entry b_i of the ith reference row will denote the value x_i assumes for that point at which all current nonbasic variables vanish. Clearly, the starting tableau is dual feasible. If it is also primal feasible, then it is optimal. Otherwise, consider a constraint having a negative entry in the constant column, and follow the following rules.

Rule 1   Consider a constraint having a negative entry in the constant column. Let us denote it by

$$(p_0 \mid p_1, \ldots, p_n) \tag{5-28}$$

Rule 2   Choose as pivot column C_r the lexicographically smallest column which has a negative entry p_r in the line chosen in (5-28).

Rule 3   For each column C_k with $p_k < 0$, find the largest integer $u_k \le C_k/C_r$; that is, take the ratios of corresponding elements and compute $\lambda_k = -p_k/u_k$. Finally, choose

$$\lambda = \max_k \lambda_k$$

Note that $u_r = 1$.

Rule 4   Add the constraint $d_0 - d_1 x_1 - \cdots - d_n x_n$ with

$$d_j = \left[\frac{p_j}{\lambda} \right] \qquad j = 0, 1, \ldots, n$$

That is, write the coefficients d_j into the bottom row of the tableau. By rule 3, λ makes $d_r = -1$. We use this d_r as a pivot for an ex-step.

Remarks
1. Since at every step the pivot chosen is -1, the integer character of the tableau will be preserved during a transformation.
2. The following can be shown:
   a. The columns of the new tableau remain lexicographically positive.
   b. The constant column decreases lexicographically.
3. The algorithm terminates if
   a. The tableau is primal feasible.
   b. All entries in the row

   $$(p_0 \mid p_1, \ldots, p_n)$$

   chosen according to rule 1, are negative except p_0; these conditions imply that the problem is not feasible.

4. Finally, it can be shown that the algorithm terminates after a finite number of steps, provided there exists a feasible integer solution.

Note in this algorithm that the only rows where pivoting takes place are those in which the constant terms b_i are negative. Further, in the tableau form only the negative elements are eligible pivot elements. Thus, a row is eligible for pivoting only if it starts with a negative constant and contains other negative elements.

But $a_j < 0$ implies $[a_j/\lambda] < 0$; therefore, if a row appearing in Equation (5-16) is eligible, then clearly the row in Equation (5-19), which is derived from it, is eligible.

We are thus assured that if there are any eligible rows left in the tableau, we can create from any one of them a new eligible row of the form of Equation (5-19). If there are no eligible rows, the problem has been completed, or it has no solution.

Remark The selection of λ (rule 3) enables us to adjust the new row so that the pivot element will become -1. Of course, this is possible, as can be seen from the fact that for λ sufficiently large, all negative d_j's become -1s and all others vanish. The rules for determining λ were obtained by satisfying the following two requirements.

1. It should produce a pivot of -1.
2. λ should be as small as possible.

ALGORITHM

Assume that the all-integer starting tableau is dual feasible. If the initial tableau does not have $c_1 > 0, \ldots, c_n > 0$, then some special device is necessary. One way is to append the extra constraint

$$y_{m+1} = b_{m+1} - x_1 - x_2 - \cdots - x_n \geq 0$$

with b_{m+1} very large, then pivot in this row and in the smallest lexicographic column. The solution to this enlarged linear program is the solution to the original one.

We choose a row having a negative constant term (if there is none, the problem has been solved); for this row we choose λ_{min} and the pivot column by the first three rules given above. Create a new row of type (5-19) and adjoin this row to the bottom of the tableau. Then perform an ex-step on the new row. Because the pivot element is -1, the matrix remains in integers. Repeat the steps until either a primal solution is found or a constraint appears, implying that no feasible solution exists.

Example 5-2 Consider the problem whose initial tableau is given below. The first trial solution is $x_1 = 0$, $x_2 = 0$, which is not feasible. Therefore, choose the row x_5,

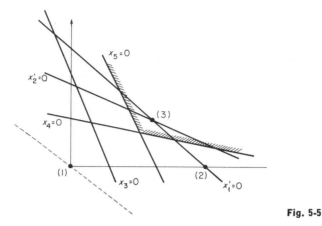

Fig. 5-5

corresponding to the maximum infeasibility, and generate the new constraint x_1'. The next trial solution $x_1 = 3$, $x_2 = 0$ is on the hyperplane $x_1' = 0$. Again, this is not feasible, so choose the row x_4, with maximum infeasibility, and generate the constraint x_2'. The next trial point $x_1 = 2$, $x_2 = 1$ is on the hyperplane $x_2' = 0$, and this happens to be a feasible solution, hence an optimal solution. (See Fig. 5-5 and the tables.)

Table 5-18

	1	$-x_1$	$-x_2$	
x_0	0	4	5	(a) Pivot column 1
x_3	-2	-3	-1	(b) $(1/1)\,4 \geq 4$, $\lambda_1 = 3$
x_4	-5	-1	-4	$(1/1)\,5 \geq 4$, $\lambda_2 = 2$
x_3	-7	-3	-2	←
x_1	0	-1	0	(c) $\lambda = 3$
x_2	0	0	-1	
x_1'	-3	-1*	-1	

Table 5-19

	1	$-x_1'$	$-x_2$	
x_0	-12	4	1	
x_3	7	-3	2	
x_4	-2	-1	-3	←
x_5	2	-3	1	
x_1	3	-1	1	
x_2	0	0	-1	
x_2'	-1	-1	-1*	

Table 5-20

	1	$-x_1'$	x_2'
x_0	-13	3	1
x_3	5	-5	2
x_4	1	2	-3
x_5	1	-4	1
x_1	2	-2	1
x_2	1	1	-1

5-6 AN ALL-INTEGER-PROGRAMMING ALGORITHM WITH PARABOLIC CONSTRAINTS [40]

It will be shown that the integer-programming problem of minimizing a linear objective function subject to linear and parabolic constraints can be solved in a finite number of steps by a simple modification of Gomory's algorithm, given above.

Problem   Minimize

$$z = \sum_{i=1}^{n} c_i x_i - c_0 \tag{5-29}$$

for nonnegative integers $x_1, \ldots, x_n$, subject to parabolic constraints, with integer coefficients

$$P_i(x) \geq 0 \qquad j = 1, \ldots, m \tag{5-30}$$

The coefficients c_i, $i = 0, 1, \ldots, n$, are integers.

Definition   (parabolic constraints)   A parabolic constraint of rank k is of the form

$$a_{00} - L_0(x) - \sum_{s=1}^{k} b_s (L_s(x))^2 \geq 0 \tag{5-31}$$

where b_s denotes positive numbers, and $L_s(x)$, $s = 0, 1, \ldots, k$, are $(k + 1)$ linearly independent, homogeneous linear forms of n variables of the type

$$L_s(x) = \sum_{i=1}^{n} a_{si} x_i \tag{5-32}$$

Just as in Gomory's algorithm, we proceed to cast the program in a tableau form:

$$
\begin{array}{c|ccc|c}
a_{10} = 0 & a_{11} & \cdots & a_{1n} & b_1 \\
\cdots\cdots & \cdots\cdots\cdots\cdots & & & \cdots \\
a_{k0} = 0 & a_{k1} & \cdots & a_{kn} & b_k \\
\hline
a_{00} & a_{01} & \cdots & a_{0n} &
\end{array}
\qquad (5\text{-}33)
$$

The k top rows represent the coefficients of the linear forms

$$
L_s(x) = \sum_{i=1}^{n} a_{si} x_i
$$

$s \neq 0$, which occur in squares. Their homogeneity is indicated by setting $a_{s0} = 0$. The bottom row stands for the linear part.

Clearly, if the constraint is linear, then it occupies just one line.

Transformation   A parabolic expression

$$
a_{00} - L_0(x) - b_1(L_1(x))^2 - \cdots - b_k(L_k(x))^2 \qquad (5\text{-}34)
$$

is transformed by an ex-step (as shown in Gomory's algorithm).

A Gauss-Jordan step with the pivot d_r in the array

$$
\begin{array}{c|ccc|c}
0 & a_{11} & \cdots & a_{1n} & b_1 \\
\cdots & \cdots\cdots\cdots\cdots & & & \cdots \\
0 & a_{k1} & \cdots & a_{kn} & b_k \\
\hline
a_{00} & a_{01} & \cdots & a_{0n} & \\
\hline
d_0 & d_1 & \cdots & d_n &
\end{array}
\qquad (5\text{-}35)
$$

leaving the entries b_s unchanged, arrives at the representation

$$
\begin{array}{cccc|c}
\bar{a}_{10} & \bar{a}_{11} & \cdots & \bar{a}_{1n} & b_1 \\
\cdots\cdots\cdots\cdots\cdots\cdots & & & & \cdots \\
\bar{a}_{k0} & \bar{a}_{k1} & \cdots & \bar{a}_{kn} & b_k \\
\hline
\bar{a}_{00} & \bar{a}_{01} & \cdots & \bar{a}_{0n} &
\end{array}
\qquad (5\text{-}36)
$$

of the parabolic expression in terms of the new variables. However, the constant column entries $\bar{a}_{s0} \neq 0$, $s \neq 0$. Thus, we need a restoration step to bring the inhomogeneous forms to the standard form.

Rule for restoration step   Replace

$$\bar{a}_{0i} \quad \text{by} \quad \bar{a}_{0i} - 2 \sum_{s=1}^{k} b_s \bar{a}_{s0} \bar{a}_{si} \qquad \text{for } i \neq 0$$

$$\bar{a}_{00} \quad \text{by} \quad \bar{a}_{00} - \sum_{s=1}^{k} b_s \bar{a}_{s0}^2 \qquad\qquad\qquad (5\text{-}37)$$

$$\bar{a}_{s0} \quad \text{by} \quad 0 \qquad\qquad\qquad\qquad \text{for } s \neq 0$$

Leave $\bar{a}_{s1}$ and b_s unchanged for $i \neq 0$ and $s \neq 0$.

THE ALGORITHM

As in the algorithm of Gomory, we shall require the tableau to have the following special properties:

1. We require that the n uppermost constraints be linear and linearly independent. Whenever possible, one will choose reference rows or given linear basic constraints, but sometimes it will be necessary to add suitable dummy constraints. The reason which may forbid choosing the reference rows as the uppermost rows of the tableau stems from condition (2).

2. We require that all columns, except the constant column, be lexicographically positive (cf. Gomory). We assume that the starting tableau meets all the requirements. Then the algorithm will consist of a sequence of transformations applied to a tableau. Consider the topmost constraint, having a negative entry in the constant column. If it is a linear constraint

$$(a_0 \mid a_1, \ldots, a_n)$$

treat it as in Gomory's algorithm. If it is a parabolic constraint, treat its linear part, using the rules of Gomory's algorithm. It can be shown that the algorithm terminates after a finite number of steps.

Example 5-3   Minimize $z = 3x + y$ for nonnegative integers x, y subject to

$$6x - 2y - x^2 - 3 \geq 0$$
$$5(x + y) - (x - y)^2 - 16 \geq 0$$

Solution   The first step is to form the tableau. A constraint

$$5(x + y) - (x - y)^2 - 16 \geq 0$$

is written, as shown below:

	0	−1	1	1
Linear → part	−16	−5	−5	

Without changing the problem, we add the constraints $x \geq 0$, $y \geq 0$. These constraints will serve simultaneously as the reference rows and the two topmost linearly independent constraints. Thus, our starting tableau appears as shown in Table 5-21. Find the pivot needed for an ex-step: Pick the topmost constraint, having a negative entry in the constant column.   Note that it is

−3	−6	2

Table 5-21

Constant column

	0	3	1	
Reference { rows {	0	−1	0	
	0	0	−1	
First constraint {	0	−1	0	1
	−3	−6	2	
Second constraint {	0	−1	1	1
	−16	−5	−5	
	−1	−1*	0	

Here the pivot column is C_1, corresponding to the negative entry $−6$.   Rule 3 $\Rightarrow$
$$u_1 = \left[\frac{3}{3}\right] = 1, \text{ and } \lambda = \left[\frac{+6}{1}\right] = 6. \text{ Rule 4} \Rightarrow: \text{Add the constraint } d_0 − d_{1x} −$$
$d_{2y},$ here

$$d_0 = \left[\frac{-3}{6}\right] = \left[-\frac{1}{2}\right] = -1 \qquad \begin{matrix} d_1 = -1 \\ d_2 = 0 \end{matrix}$$

With d_1 as the pivot, apply the ex-step, which results in Table 5-22; then apply the restoration step, which yields Table 5-23.   It is left to the reader to verify the application of the restoration step.

Table 5-22

−3	3	1	
1	−1	0	
0	0	−1	
1	−1	0	1
3	−6	2	
1	−1	1	1
−11	−5	−5	

Table 5-23

−3	3	1	
1	−1	0	
0	0	−1	
0	−1	0	1
2	−4	2	
0	−1	1	1
−12	−3	−7	
−2	−1	−1*	

The process is continued, with $d_2 = -1$ being the new pivot entry.   The new tableaux are listed below.

Table 5-24

−5	2	1	
1	−1	0	
2	1	−1	
0	−1	0	1
−2	−6	2	
0	−2	1	1
−2	−4	−3	
−1	−1*	0	

Table 5-25

−7	2	1	
2	−1	0	
1	1	−1	
0	−1	0	1
3	−4	2	
0	−2	1	1
−2	4	−7	
−1	0	−1*	

Table 5-26

	−6	2	1	
$x \rightarrow$	2	−1	0	
$y \rightarrow$	2	1	−1	
	0	−1	0	1
	1	−4	2	
	0	−2	1	1
	4	2	−5	
	*	*	*	

Table 5-26 is optimal and yields the solution

$$x = y = 2$$

For a practical application, see the satellite problem below.

5-7 ALGEBRAIC FORMULATION OF PROBLEMS

THE SATELLITE–COMMUNICATION PROBLEM [33]

In Chap. 1 we gave the example of a satellite-communication problem. Here we formulate the problem in a binary-programming framework.

Before presenting our model, we shall give a three-dimensional dia-

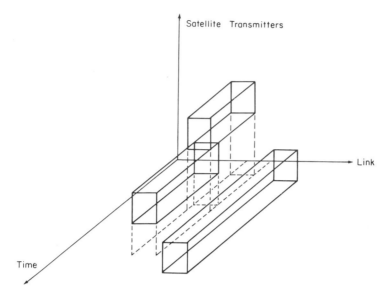

Fig. 5-6

gram (Fig. 5-6), illustrating the availability of a satellite transmitter to a given link at time t, where t is divided into discrete units of equal duration. We assume that the links and satellites have been ordered and labeled, and that there are n links and m satellites. Without loss of generality, we may assume that there are k transmitters in each satellite, and hence that all km transmitters are labeled in natural order. Figure 5-6 indicates the fact that the satellites may have different numbers of transmitters. Our model is applicable to any number of transmitters in a satellite. A transceiver is a transmitter-receiver system.

As an initial step, we give a simplified formulation of the problem for a single period and a simple objective function. We then expand the formulation to include more time and broader objectives.

We denote a satellite transmitter by i, $i = 1, \ldots, m$, a link by j, $j = 1, \ldots, n$, and time in discrete units by t. We then let

$$a_{ijt} = \begin{cases} 1 & \text{if } i \text{ is available to } j \text{ at time } t \text{ and satisfies the transmission requirement} \\ -p & \text{otherwise (where } p \text{ is an arbitrary positive number)} \end{cases}$$

and

$$X_{ijt} = \begin{cases} 1 & \text{if } i \text{ is assigned to } j \text{ at } t \\ 0 & \text{in the opposite case} \end{cases}$$

and let r_{jt} denote the number of satellite transmitters required by link j

at time t.   If c_{ijt} is the profit derived from the use of i by j at t we have the following allocation problem at time t_0.

Problem   Find X_{ijt_0} such that

$$\sum_j X_{ijt_0} = 1$$

(a transmitter is assigned to only one link),

$$\sum_i X_{ijt_0} = r_{jt_0}$$

(the requirements must be satisfied), and

$$\sum_{i,j} c_{ijt_0} a_{ijt_0} X_{ijt_0} = \max$$

Remark   Note in the above formulation that the constraints are given as equalities.   It is obvious that this need not be the case since availability may exceed the requirements or conversely.   Our assignment problem is a special case of the transportation problem.   The constraints of such a problem require the following:

1. If the requirements at any time for all the links are greater than the availability, then one artificial (or dummy) satellite transmitter should be used in the algorithm to write the requirement-availability constraint as an equation rather than an inequality.
2. If the requirements are less than the availability, then an artificial link should be used to take the slack and reduce the inequality to an equation.   For an artificial transmitter q, we have $a_{qjt} = 1$ for all j and t.   The profit coefficient of a dummy transmitter is assumed to equal zero.

If the number of transceivers associated with an antenna is limited, one can apply this restriction by imposing, in addition to the above sums, constraints on the $\Sigma_i X_{ijt_0}$.   In that case this sum would be less than or equal to the numbers of transceivers available to j.   The imposition of such constraints could still be within the transportation problem format.

The modified model   We shall modify the model in two essential ways. First, we reformulate it in such a manner as to permit allocation over several periods.   We then use an objective function which includes other important factors besides what has been considered previously.   If we denote the availability matrix $(a_{ij,t+u})$ at time $t + u$ by A_{t+u}, we then have a larger assignment problem for several periods by using a block-diagonal availability matrix of the form

$$
\begin{array}{c}
\\
\text{Satellite} \\
\text{transmitters}
\end{array}
\overset{\text{Links}}{
\begin{bmatrix}
A_t & 0 & \cdots & 0 & I \\
0 & A_{t+1} & \cdots & 0 & I \\
\multicolumn{5}{c}{\cdots\cdots\cdots\cdots\cdots\cdots\cdots} \\
0 & 0 & \cdots & A_{t+s} & I \\
R_t & R_{t+1} & \cdots & R_{t+s} &
\end{bmatrix}}
$$

where the quantities I on the right are column vectors, consisting entirely of unit elements indicating the availability of the transmitters at the indicated times. The quantity R_{t+u} is a row vector whose elements are the requirements $r_{j,t+u}$.

The problem here is as follows.

Problem   Find $X_{ij,t+u}$ such that

$$\sum_j X_{ij,t+u} = 1$$

$$\sum_i X_{ij,t+u} = r_{j,t+u} \qquad \text{for all } j \text{ and } u$$

and

$$\sum_{i,j,u} c_{ij,t+u} a_{ij,t+u} X_{ij,t+u} = \max$$

The objective function is modified by including two additional factors. The first is to allocate in such a manner that a station would not in general be required to switch from one satellite to another while there is requirement and availability of a satellite already in use, since switching imposes additional costs. Let $d_{ij,t+u}$ be the cost associated with switching. Thus, another element of the objective is to minimize the effect of switching. This can be expressed by the function

$$\sum_{i,j} \sum_{u=0}^{s} d_{ij,t+u} (a_{ij,t+u+1} X_{ij,t+u+1} - a_{ij,t+u} X_{ij,t+u})^2$$

The reason for the quadratic factor is that if there is switching, we want the cost to be positive. If the requirement is for only one time period, this imposes a switching cost when the requirement ends and possibly also when the assignment begins. This is probably not a serious shortcoming. (If it is, the switching factor must be accounted for by some other relationship.) Yet another objective is to minimize the unsatisfied availability of transmitters and the requirements for these transmitters. If the "costs" associated with this objective are $e_{j,t+u}$, then we minimize

$$\sum_{j,u} e_{j,t+u} \left(\sum_i a_{ij,t+u} X_{ij,t+u} - r_{j,t+u} \right)^2$$

The profit, switching, and availability-requirement objectives may be combined by multiplying the first objective function by (-1) to change the maximization problem to a minimization problem and then combining the three objectives into a single one by taking a weighted average.

Now the problem is as follows.

Problem   Find $X_{ij,t+u}$ such that

$$\sum_j X_{ij,t+u} = 1$$

$$\sum_i X_{ij,t+u} = r_{j,t+u}$$

and

$$-\alpha \sum_{i,j,u} c_{ij,t+u} a_{ij,t+u} X_{ij,t+u}$$

$$+ \beta \sum_{i,j,u} d_{ij,t+u} (a_{ij,t+u+1} X_{ij,t+u+1} - a_{ij,t+u} X_{ij,t+u})^2$$

$$+ (1 - \alpha - \beta) \sum_{j,u} e_{j,t+u} \left(\sum_i a_{ij,t+u} X_{ij,t+u} - r_{ij,t+u} \right)^2 = \min$$

where $\alpha + \beta < 1$, $\alpha \geq 0$, $\beta \geq 0$.

The above is an assignment problem with a quadratic objective function. Note that because of the binary values of $X_{ij,t+u}$, one may write $X_{ij,t+u}^2 = X_{ij,t+u}$; however, this is insufficient for linearizing the objective function.

On introducing the variable

$$z = a + \sum_{i=1}^n a_i X_i + \sum_{i,j=1}^n a_{ij} X_i X_j$$

we have a problem in a linear-objective function z to be minimized subject to the additional parabolic constraint

$$z - a - \sum_{i=1}^n a_i X_i - \sum_{i,j=1}^n a_{ij} X_i X_j \geq 0$$

to which the method discussed in Sec. 5-6 is applicable.

The block-diagonal availability matrix may be used to allocate for one or more time periods, e.g., for the period $[t,\ t + v]$, where $v \leq s$. The block matrices of the remaining periods are then used in the necessary time order for the next block-diagonal matrix, which has for its remaining terms availability blocks corresponding to subsequent time periods. In this manner future requirements and availability are used to influence the present allocation, particularly to give the desired smoothing for switching.

Linearization   Work by many investigators on the solution (in integers) of quadratic assignment models such as the one developed above is in progress. However, for the present, the most useful algorithm which yields integer values is that of the transportation problem, which can be applied to the assignment problem with a linear objective function.

Since our objective function is quadratic, it would be desirable to reformulate this function so that it is linear. For example, if $\alpha = 1$, then $\beta = 0$, and the object is to maximize profits, then the problem is linear. However, an additional linear term may be introduced by a proper choice of the cost coefficients. Consider the time interval $(t, t + s)$ in which s is chosen sufficiently small for feasible allocation. Let b_{jt} be the time remaining in $[t, t + s]$ until the jth link's transmitter need is terminated. Let f_{ijt} be the length of time the ith transmitter will be available to the jth link at time t. Define

$$g_{ijt} = \begin{cases} b_{jt} - f_{ijt} & \text{when} \geq 0 \\ 0 & \text{otherwise} \end{cases}$$

In this case the linear cost function to minimize (to which the transportation algorithm is applicable) is

$$-\alpha \sum_{i,j,u} c_{ij,\,+u} a_{ij,t+u} X_{ij,t+u} + (1 - \alpha) \sum_{i,j,u} g_{ij,t+u} X_{ij,t+u}$$

where $0 \leq \alpha \leq 1$.

Bivalent programming, given in Sec. 5-8, is a relevant technique for seeking solutions to the various foregoing formulations.

Remark   If the problem is solved for a single availability period, that is, X_{ijt} are obtained for a single value of t, then switching can be reduced by modifying the availability matrix $(a_{ij,t+1})$ of the next period in terms of the allocation of the present period. In this case we use

$$a^*_{ij,t+1} = a_{ij,t+1}(1 + C X_{ijt})$$

where C is a constant which may be chosen as a balance between switching cost and the cost of unsatisfied demand. We have $0 \leq C \leq 1$. The objective function in this case is (only to maximize) profit, subject to the constraints at $t + 1$.

A NETWORK–FLOW PROBLEM

Let vertices v_0 and v_n of a directed graph be designated as the origin and destination of a conceptual substance flowing through the arc. Assume, moreover, that an arc from vertex v_i to vertex v_j has an associated capacity, or upper limit, on flow c_{ij}. Finally, let C_{ij} be the cost per unit of flow in the arc. Our flow problem becomes a linear-programming problem, requiring the minimization of $\Sigma_{i,j} C_{ij} x_{ij}$ for a total flow c from v_0 to

v_n, subject to

$$\sum_j (x_{0j} - x_{j0}) = c$$

$$\sum_j (x_{ij} - x_{ji}) = 0 \qquad \text{for } i = 1, \ldots, n - 1$$

$$\sum_j (x_{nj} - x_{jn}) = -c$$

$$0 \leq x_{ij} \leq c_{ij} \qquad \text{for every arc}$$

The network flow is sometimes a convenient method for solving this type of linear-programming problem, which has a transportation-problem setting.

THE TRAVELING–SALESMAN PROBLEM [11,31a]

We assume that the matrix d_{ij}, $i \neq j$, of the distances between every pair of vertices is given. Starting at a "base city" with index 0, we seek a tour whose routes have specific directions according to the way they are to be traveled and which returns to the starting point. If we let $x_{ij} = 1$ or 0, according to whether or not a directed arc (of the map representing the possible routes) goes from vertex i to vertex j, we have the following conditions on the tour (a specialization of an elegant formulation in Ref. 31a):

$$\sum_{\substack{i=0 \\ i \neq j}}^{n} x_{ij} = 1 \qquad j = 1, \ldots, n$$

$$\sum_{\substack{j=0 \\ j \neq i}}^{n} x_{ij} = 1 \qquad i = 1, \ldots, n$$

$$\sum_{i=1}^{n} x_{i0} = 1$$

$$u_i - u_j + n x_{ij} \leq n - 1 \qquad u_i, i = 1, \ldots, n, \text{ arbitrary reals}$$

$$\sum_{0 \leq i \neq j \leq n} \sum d_{ij} x_{ij} = \min \qquad \text{the length of the tour is minimum}$$

THE FOUR–COLOR PROBLEM [11]

Let the regions of a planar map be labeled $r = 1, 2, \ldots, n$. Let the variable t_r be integer-valued $0 \leq t_r \leq 3$. Thus, t_r assigns one of the four colors, labeled 0, 1, 2, 3, to the region whose number is r. If two regions r and s have a boundary in common, then $t_r - t_s \neq 0$. Such a relation is written down for every pair of adjacent regions. The relation for one pair may be reduced to two inequalities as follows:

$$\text{either } t_r - t_s \geq 1 \qquad \text{or} \qquad t_s - t_r \geq 1$$

This pair of inequalities may now be written as

$$t_r - t_s \geq 1 - 4\delta_{rs}$$

and

$$t_s - t_r \geq -3 + 4\delta_{rs}$$

where $\delta_{rs} = 0$ or 1. We obtain a system of such inequalities by allowing r and s to vary from 1 to n. The problem then is to determine whether it is possible to choose the integers $0 \leq t_r \leq 3$, $r = 1, \ldots, n$, and the binary variables δ_{rs}, $r, s = 1, \ldots, n$, such that the system of inequalities has a solution. If not, then our assumption that t_r take on only four values is untenable.

ALGEBRAIC FORMULATION OF THE CROSSING PROBLEM FOR COMPLETE GRAPHS

We have already discussed (in Chap. 2) the intersection problem for complete graphs, and now we give an elegant algebraic formulation due to Stanley Basin [4b]. It is easy to show that there is always a hamiltonian circuit in a complete graph. However, Basin's approach assumes that a minimum-intersection graph contains a hamiltonian circuit H, with the additional stipulation that there are no crossings on its edges. Motivation for this was provided by a realization scheme (given in Ref. 5 of Chap. 2). This scheme is an alternative one to the polygonal representation described in Chap. 2. Considering H, which is a simple closed curve, the edges not on H may lie either interior to or exterior to H. All the edges interior to H, together with any subset of edges of H, define a subgraph G_1. The edges exterior to H with the remaining edges on H define a subgraph G_2 which is the complement of G_1 relative to the entire graph; i.e., the two taken together yield the whole graph. The vertices which are all on H are labeled $1, 2, \ldots, n$ in clockwise direction. Figure 5-7 illustrates the complete graph on five vertices, with G_1 drawn in boldface.

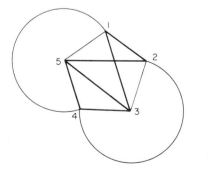

Fig. 5-7

Note that a crossing of edges can only occur between edges interior to or exterior to H. Because of the method of labeling, edges cross if and only if the labels of their corresponding vertices interlace; i.e., the edges e_{ij} and e_{kl} intersect if and only if both are in the same subgraph (G_1 or G_2) and $1 \le i < l < j < k \le n$. For all i and j which satisfy $1 \le i < j \le n$, let

$$a_{ij} = \begin{cases} 1 & \text{if } e_{ij} \in G_1 \\ 0 & \text{if } e_{ij} \in G_2 \end{cases}$$

and for all i and j which satisfy $1 \le j < i \le n$, let

$$a_{ij} = \begin{cases} 1 & \text{if } e_{ij} \in G_2 \\ 0 & \text{if } e_{ij} \in G_1 \end{cases}$$

As an illustration consider the matrix (a_{ij}) of Fig. 5-7:

$$(a_{ij}) = \begin{array}{c|ccccc} & 1 & 2 & 3 & 4 & 5 \\ \hline 1 & 0 & 1 & 1 & 0 & 0 \\ 2 & 0 & 0 & 0 & 0 & 1 \\ 3 & 0 & 1 & 0 & 1 & 1 \\ 4 & 1 & 1 & 0 & 0 & 1 \\ 5 & 1 & 0 & 0 & 0 & 0 \end{array}$$

On the main diagonal, all entries are zero because there are no loops in the graph. The two diagonals on either side of the main diagonal specify whether an edge of H belongs to G_1 or G_2. Note that the entries in the upper triangle above the main diagonal specify G_1; those below specify G_2. This follows from the manner in which a_{ij} is defined, according to the interlacing property.

Now $a_{ij}a_{kl} = 1$ if both e_{ij} and e_{kl} belong to the same subgraph. Furthermore, they will intersect provided that $1 \le i < k < j < l \le n$ (that is, their labels interlace). Thus, the total number of intersections can be written as follows:

Intersections in G_1 Intersections in G_2
$$\sum_{1 \le i < k < j < l \le n} a_{ij}a_{kl} + \sum_{1 \le l < j < k < i \le n} a_{ij}a_{kl}$$

Note that if an edge joining i to j belongs to G_1, then the edge joining j to i, which is the same edge, does not belong to G_2; hence $a_{ji} = 1 - a_{ij} \equiv \bar{a}_{ij}$. To facilitate computing with this formula, we note that in order to have intersections between e_{ij} and e_{kl}, there must be interlacing of labels. Hence in e_{ij}, j must exceed i by two, and i cannot go beyond $n - 3$ because then j can only assume the values $n - 1$ (and n) and, to obtain an intersection, k must equal $n - 2$ and l must equal n and hence j in fact cannot equal n. Thus j can at most equal $n - 1$. Similarly, k varies between $i + 1$ and $j - 1$, and l varies between $j + 1$ and n. Thus, we simply have

$$\sum_{i=1}^{n-3} \sum_{j=i+2}^{n-1} a_{ij} \left\{ \sum_{k=i+1}^{j-1} \sum_{l=j+1}^{n} a_{kl} \right\} + \sum_{i=1}^{n-3} \sum_{j=i+2}^{n-1} \bar{a}_{ij} \left\{ \sum_{k=i+1}^{j-1} \sum_{l=j+1}^{n} \bar{a}_{kl} \right\}$$

Using $\bar{a}_{ij} = 1 - a_{ij}$, the crossing number is given by

$$\binom{n}{4} - \sum_{i=1}^{n-2} \sum_{j=i+2}^{n} (j - i - 1)(n - j + i - 1)a_{ij}$$

$$+ 2 \sum_{i=1}^{n-3} \sum_{j=i+2}^{n-1} a_{ij} \left\{ \sum_{k=i+1}^{j-1} \sum_{l=j+1}^{n} a_{kl} \right\}$$

The problem now is to assign the binary values 0 and 1 to the a_{ij} in order to minimize the foregoing expression. Note that $\binom{n}{4}$ gives the maximum crossing number for a complete graph. This method implies "taking out" edges selectively from the interior of the maximum-intersection polygon, described in Chap. 2.

ON THE TREATMENT OF DICHOTOMIES [11]

Suppose that a problem is given in such a way that an either-or condition occurs in it; e.g., either the condition $G(x_1, \ldots, x_n) \geq 0$ or the condition $H(x_1, \ldots, x_n) \geq 0$ holds for $x_1, \ldots, x_n$, belonging to some set S. Let L_G be a lower bound for G, and let L_H be a lower bound for H. Let δ be a binary variable which assumes the values 0, 1. Then the problem becomes: Find $x_1, \ldots, x_n \in S$ and δ such that

$$G(x_1, \ldots, x_n) - \delta L_G \geq 0$$

and

$$H(x_1, \ldots, x_n) - (1 - \delta)L_H \geq 0$$

are satisfied. Note that if $\delta = 1$, the first condition is satisfied, and if $\delta = 0$, the second condition is satisfied. The conditions $0 \leq x_1 \leq 2$, $0 \leq x_2 \leq 2$, and either $x_1 \leq 1$ or $x_2 \leq 1$ can be replaced by

$$0 \leq x_1 \leq 1 + \delta \qquad 0 \leq x_2 \leq 2 - \delta \qquad 0 \leq \delta \leq 1 \qquad \delta = 0, 1$$

In general, if a solution of

$$G_1(x_1, \ldots, x_n) \geq 0, \ldots, G_m(x_1, \ldots, x_n) \geq 0$$

is required in which at least k of the conditions must hold simultaneously, then the system may be replaced by

$$G_1 - \delta_1 L_1 \geq 0, \; \ldots \; , G_m - \delta_m L_m \geq 0$$

where L_i is a lower bound for G_i, $i = 1, \; \ldots \; , m$, and δ_i are integer-valued variables which satisfy

$$\delta_1 + \delta_2 + \; \cdots \; + \delta_m = m - k \qquad 0 \leq \delta_i \leq 1 \qquad i = 1, \; \ldots \; , m$$

For example, the condition that x_1 take on one of the values $a_1, a_2, \; \ldots \; , a_k$ may be written as

$$x_1 = a_1 \delta_1 + \; \cdots \; + a_k \delta_k \qquad \delta_1 + \; \cdots \; + \delta_k = 1 \qquad \delta_i = 0 \text{ or } 1$$

If other variables are similarly restricted, they can also be represented in this manner.

5-8 PSEUDO-BOOLEAN METHODS FOR BIVALENT PROGRAMMING†

The method of bivalent programming will be divided into three parts, the first of which concerns the solution of linear systems of pseudo-Boolean equations and inequalities. The second section treats the case of nonlinear systems of pseudo-Boolean equations and inequalities, whereas the final section treats the problem of minimizing rather than maximizing a pseudo-Boolean function with and without constraints. Our main source of information is the work by Hammer (Ivănescu) and Rudeanu [22].

A Boolean algebra B_2 of two elements consists of the set $\{0,1\}$, upon which are defined two binary and a unitary operations called *disjunction* ($\cup$), *conjunction* ($\cap$), and *complementation* ($\bar{x}$), respectively. These operations are defined by the following tables.

Disjunction			Conjunction			Complementation		
$\cup$	0	1	$\cap$	0	1	x	0	1
0	0	1	0	0	0	$\bar{x}$	1	0
1	1	1	1	0	1			

Definition A pseudo-Boolean function is a mapping, f, such that

$$f: B_2{}^n \to \text{Re}$$

where $B_2{}^n = \{(x_1, \; \ldots \; , x_n) \mid x_i \in B_2, i = 1, \; \ldots \; , n\}$, and Re is the field of real numbers.

† The author is particularly grateful to Alan R. Curtis for his diligent contribution in preparing this section.

By making the correspondence

$$x \cup y = x + y - xy$$
$$x \cap y = xy$$

and

$$\bar{x} = 1 - x$$

any Boolean function g, $g: B_2{}^n \rightarrow B_2$, can be considered as a pseudo-Boolean function.

Since the arguments of a pseudo-Boolean function are bivalent, every pseudo-Boolean function can be shown to be linear in each of its variables and hence to have a representation as a polynomial, with coefficients in Re. Thus, one has the following theorem.

Theorem 5-5   *Every pseudo-Boolean function f is linear in each of its variables and, furthermore, can be represented as a polynomial over Re, which, after a reduction of similar terms, is uniquely determined up to the order of sums and products.*

Proof   For $f(x_1, \ldots, x_n)$ to be linear in each of its variables x_i, $i = 1, \ldots, n$, one must show that there exist pseudo-Boolean functions h_i, g_i such that

$$
\begin{aligned}
f(x_1, \ldots, x_n) &= x_i g_i(x_1, \ldots, x_{i-1}, x_{i+1}, \ldots, x_n) \\
&\quad + h_i(x_1, \ldots, x_{i-1}, x_{i+1}, \ldots, x_n) \qquad i = 1, \ldots, n
\end{aligned}
\qquad (5\text{-}38)
$$

Choose

$$
\begin{aligned}
g_i(x_1, \ldots, x_{i-1}, x_{i+1}, \ldots, x_n) &= f(x_1, \ldots, x_{i-1}, 1, x_{i+1}, \ldots, x_n) \\
&\quad - f(x_1, \ldots, x_{i-1}, 0, x_{i+1}, \ldots, x_n)
\end{aligned}
$$

and

$$h_i(x_1, \ldots, x_{i-1}, x_{i+1}, \ldots, x_n) = f(x_1, \ldots, x_{i-1}, 0, x_{i+1}, \ldots, x_n)$$

Then one has

$$
\begin{aligned}
f(x_1, \ldots, x_n) &= x_i g_i(x_1, \ldots, x_{i-1}, x_{i+1}, \ldots, x_n) \\
&\quad + h_i(x_1, \ldots, x_{i-1}, x_{i+1}, \ldots, x_n)
\end{aligned}
$$

Thus, $f(x_1, \ldots, x_n)$ is linear in each of its variables x_i. Since, by the definition of

$$g_i(x_1, \ldots, x_{i-1}, x_{i+1}, \ldots, x_n)$$

and

$$h_i(x_1, \ldots, x_{i-1}, x_{i+1}, \ldots, x_n)$$

the left-hand side of Equation (5-38) is a pseudo-Boolean function of the variables $x_1, \ldots, x_n$, by repeated applications of the reduction Equation (5-38), one can express $f(x_1, \ldots, x_n)$ as a polynomial in the variables $x_1, \ldots, x_n$ whose coefficients are sums and products of $f(\alpha_1^i, \ldots, \alpha_n^i)$, where $\alpha_k^i \in B_2$, and are obtained in the reduction process. After reduction of similar terms, the uniqueness of the representation follows from the fact that the polynomial is a pseudo-Boolean function and hence linear in each of its variables. Thus, if $P_1(x_1, \ldots, x_n)$ and $P_2(x_1, \ldots, x_n)$ are two polynomial representations for $f(x_1, \ldots, x_n)$, then

$$P_1(x_1, \ldots, x_n) = x_i Q_1 + R_1 = x_i Q_2 + R_2 = P_2(x_1, \ldots, x_n)$$
$$(5\text{-}39)$$

where Q and R are polynomials in $x_1, \ldots, x_{i-1}, x_{i+1}, \ldots, x_n$. Then, from Equation (5-39), one has $R_1 = R_2$ and $Q_1 = Q_2$. Thus, the representation is unique since Q_1, R_1, Q_2, R_2 are minimal polynomials and only divisible by 1 and themselves. This completes the proof.

As in the case of Boolean functions, there exists a canonical form of a pseudo-Boolean function which is analogous to the disjunction form of a Boolean function. This is given in the following theorem.

Theorem 5-6 (M. Carvallo) *Every pseudo-Boolean function can be written in the form*

$$f(x_1, \ldots, x_n) = \sum_{\text{all } \alpha \in B_2{}^n} C(\alpha) x_1^{\alpha_1} \cdots x_n^{\alpha_n} \qquad (5\text{-}40)$$

where

$$\alpha = (\alpha_1, \ldots, \alpha_n)$$

and

$$x_i^1 = x_i, \ x_i^0 = \bar{x}_i$$

and

$$C(\alpha) = f(\alpha_1, \ldots, \alpha_n)$$

As an example of a pseudo-Boolean function, let us take $n = 2$ and define f by

$$f(x_1, x_2) = e^{x_1 + x_2}$$

By Theorem 5-5,

$$f(x_1,x_2) = (e^2 - 2e + 1)x_1x_2 + (e - 1)x_1 + (e - 1)x_2 + 1$$

and by Theorem 5-6, one can form the following table:

$\alpha = (\alpha_1,\alpha_2)$	$c(\alpha) = e^{\alpha_1+\alpha_2}$
(0,0)	1
(0,1)	e
(1,0)	e
(1,1)	e^2

Using Equation (5-40), one obtains

$$f(x_1,x_2) = 1x_1{}^0x_2{}^0 + ex_1{}^0x_2{}^1 + ex_1{}^1x_2{}^0 + e^2x_1{}^1x_2{}^1$$
$$= \bar{x}_1\bar{x}_2 + e\bar{x}_1x_2 + ex_1\bar{x}_2 + e^2x_1x_2$$

Using the relationship $\bar{x}_i = 1 - x_i$, one can show that the two forms for $f(x_1,x_2)$ are equivalent.

I. LINEAR PSEUDO–BOOLEAN EQUATIONS, INEQUALITIES, AND SYSTEMS

LINEAR PSEUDO–BOOLEAN EQUATIONS

Let $f(x_1, \ldots, x_n)$ denote a pseudo-Boolean function of the n variables $x_1, \ldots, x_n$. A pseudo-Boolean equation is then defined as the form $f(x_1, \ldots, x_n) = 0$. Since every pseudo-Boolean function $f(x_1, \ldots, x_n)$ is representable as a polynomial in the variables $x_i, \bar{x}_i$, one now considers the general linear pseudo-Boolean equation of the form

$$\sum_{i=1}^{n} a_ix_i + b_i\bar{x}_i = k \qquad \begin{array}{l} k, a_i, b_i \in \text{Re} \\ x_i, \bar{x}_i \in B_2 \\ \text{for } i = 1, \ldots, n \end{array} \qquad (5\text{-}41)$$

Without loss of generality, one can assume that $a_i \neq b_i$ since

$$a_ix_i + b_i\bar{x}_i = (a_i - b_i)x_i + b_i$$

would reduce to a constant if $a_i = b_i$ and hence could be absorbed into k.

Using the transformation T, defined by

$$y_i = \begin{cases} x_i & \text{if } a_i > b_i \\ \bar{x}_i & \text{if } a_i < b_i \end{cases}$$
$$a_ix_i + b_i\bar{x}_i = \begin{cases} (a_i - b_i)y_i + b_i & \text{if } a_i > b_i \\ (b_i - a_i)y_i + a_i & \text{if } a_i < b_i \end{cases} \qquad (5\text{-}42)$$

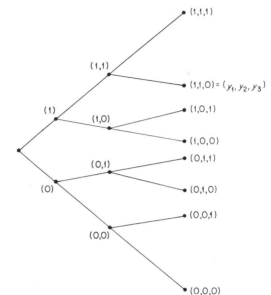

Fig. 5-8

Equation (5-41) can be rewritten in the form

$$\sum_{i=1}^{n} c_i y_i = d \qquad \begin{array}{l} c_i > 0 \\ c_i,\, d_i \in \text{Re} \\ y_i \in B_2 \\ i = 1, \ldots, n \end{array} \qquad (5\text{-}43)$$

By reindexing the c_i's, one can assume that $c_1 \geq \cdots \geq c_n > 0$, and Equation (5-43) is then called the canonical form of Equation (5-41).

Instead of checking all of the 2^n possible solutions of Equation (5-43), a more systematic approach of tracking the solutions through the binary tree, as in Fig. 5-8, will be given.

Upon examination of Equation (5-43), one can determine eight mutually exclusive cases concerning the c_i's and d, from which conclusions can be drawn concerning the solutions of Equation (5-43).

Theorem 5-7 *All solutions of the linear pseudo-Boolean equation (5-43) are characterized by the following eight disjoint cases:*

1. *If $d < 0$, then there exist no solutions.*
2. *If $d = 0$, then there exists a unique solution, $y_1 = \cdots = y_n = 0$.*
3. *If $d > 0$ and $c_1 \geq \cdots \geq c_p > d \geq c_{p+1} \geq \cdots \geq c_n$, then the solutions, if any exist, are $y_1 = \cdots = y_p = 0$ and the solutions of the equation $\Sigma_{i=p+1}^{n} c_i y_i = d$.*

4. *If $d > 0$ and $c_1 = \cdots = c_p = d > c_{p+1} \geq \cdots \geq c_n$, then there are $p + 1$ possible solutions: (1) $y_1 = \cdots = y_{j-1} = y_{j+1} = \cdots = y_n = 0$ and $y_j = 1$ for $j = 1, \ldots, p$ are solutions; and (2) the other possible solutions (if any) are $y_1 = \cdots = y_p = 0$ and the solutions of $\Sigma_{i=p+1}^{n} c_i y_i = d$.*

5. *If $d > 0$ and $c_i < d$ for $i = 1, \ldots, n$, and $\Sigma_{i=1}^{n} c_i < d$, then there are no solutions.*

6. *If $d > 0$ and $c_i < d$ for $i = 1, \ldots, n$, and $\Sigma_{i=1}^{n} c_i = d$, then the unique solution is $y_1 = \cdots = y_n = 1$.*

7. *If $d > 0$ and $c_i < d$ for $i = 1, \ldots, n$, and $\Sigma_{i=1}^{n} c_i > d$, $\Sigma_{i=2}^{n} c_i < d$, then the solutions (if any) are $y_1 = 1$ and the solutions of*

$$\sum_{j=2}^{n} c_i y_i = d - c_1$$

8. *If $d > 0$ and $c_i < d$ for $i = 1, \ldots, n$, and $\Sigma_{i=1}^{n} c_i > d$, $\Sigma_{i=2}^{n} c_i > d$, then the solutions are (1) $y_1 = 1$, together with the solutions of*

$$\sum_{i=2}^{n} c_i y_i = d - c_1$$

(if any); and (2) $y_1 = 0$, together with the solutions of $\Sigma_{i=2}^{n} c_i y_i = d$ (if any exist).

Theorem 5-7 provides a systematic method for finding the solutions to a pseudo-Boolean equation. This method is stated in the form of an algorithm as follows.

ALGORITHM FOR SOLVING LINEAR PSEUDO–BOOLEAN EQUATIONS

Step 1 Transform the linear pseudo-Boolean equation into the canonical form [Equation (5-43)], with $c_1 \geq \cdots \geq c_n > 0$. Go to step 2.

Step 2 By comparing the canonical equation (5-43) with the cases in Theorem 5-7, one can obtain the following conclusions:

a. If Equation (5-43) is as in case 1 or 5, there are no solutions. Go to step 3.

b. If Equation (5-43) is as in case 2 or 6, there is a unique solution, given in the conclusion for case 2 or 6. Go to step 3.

c. If Equation (5-43) is as in case 3, 4, or 7, then Equation (5-43) is replaced with a similar equation, given in the conclusion for case 3, 4, or 7 along with the values of the missing variables. Go to step 3.

d. If Equation (5-43) is as in case 8, then Equation (5-43) is replaced by two equations in one less variable, given in the conclusions for case 8 along with the value of the missing variable for each new equation. Go to step 3.

Step 3   If no new equations of the form of Equation (5-43) result from step 2 and there are no remaining equations to be resolved, one is finished and, by applying T^{-1} to the solution obtained, one obtains the solution to the original equation.   If new equations are formed in step 2 or there are remaining equations which have not been resolved, repeat step 2 until all equations have been resolved.

The above algorithm yields all solutions to the linear pseudo-Boolean equation since it exhausts all possibilities.

Example 5-4   Find the solutions of the linear pseudo-Boolean equation

$$6x_1 + 3\bar{x}_1 + 5x_2 - 4\bar{x}_3 + 2x_4 + \bar{x}_5 - x_6 = 7$$

Solution   Applying the transformation T and reindexing the variables, one obtains the equation

$$5y_1 + 4y_2 + 3y_3 + 2y_4 + y_5 + y_6 = 9 \qquad \text{case 8} \qquad\qquad (5\text{-}44)$$

where $y_1 = x_2$, $y_2 = x_3$, $y_3 = x_1$, $y_4 = x_4$, $y_5 = \bar{x}_5$, $y_6 = \bar{x}_6$.

					Partial Solution
Since Equation (5-44) is as in case 8 of Theorem 5-7, one has the following two partial solutions and new equations:					$(y_1, y_2, \ldots, y_i)$

$y_1 = 1$ and $\quad 4y_2 + 3y_3 + 2y_4$
$\qquad\qquad\qquad\qquad\quad + y_5 + y_6 = 4 \qquad$ case 4 $\quad$ (5-44a) $\qquad$ (1)
$y_1 = 0$ and $\quad 4y_2 + 3y_3 + 2y_4$
$\qquad\qquad\qquad\qquad\quad + y_5 + y_6 = 9 \qquad$ case 7 $\quad$ (5-44b) $\qquad$ (0)

Equation (5-44a) is as in case 4 of Theorem 5-7, and one obtains the following solutions:

$y_2 = 1$ and $\quad y_3 = y_4 = y_5 = y_6 = 0 \qquad\qquad$ (1,1,0,0,0,0)
$\qquad\qquad\qquad\qquad\qquad\qquad\qquad\qquad$ (5-44c)
$y_2 = 0$ and $\quad 3y_3 + 2y_4 + y_5 + y_6 = 4 \qquad\qquad$ (1,0)

Equation (5-44c) is as in case 8 of Theorem 5-7, and one obtains the following partial solutions and new equations:

$y_3 = 1$ and $\quad 2y_4 + y_5 + y_6 = 1 \qquad$ case 3 $\quad$ (5-44d) $\qquad$ (1,0,1)
$y_3 = 0$ and $\quad 2y_4 + y_5 + y_6 = 4 \qquad$ case 6 $\quad$ (5-44e) $\qquad$ (1,0,0)

Equation (5-44d) is as in case 3, and one obtains the following equation and partial solution:

$y_4 = 0$ and $\quad y_5 + y_6 = 1 \qquad$ case 4 $\qquad\qquad$ (5-44f) $\qquad$ (1,0,1,0)

Equation (5-44f) is as in case 4, and one obtains the following solutions:

$y_5 = 0 \qquad y_6 = 1$

$(1,0,1,0,0,1)$

$y_5 = 1 \qquad y_6 = 0$

$(1,0,1,0,1,0)$

Equation (5-44e) is as in case 6, and one obtains the solution

$y_4 = y_5 = y_6 = 1$

$(1,0,0,1,1,1)$

Equation (5-44b) is as in case 7, and one obtains the following equation and partial solution:

$y_2 = 1 \qquad$ and $\qquad 3y_3 + 2y_4$
$$+ y_5 + y_6 = 5 \qquad \text{case 7} \quad (5\text{-}44g)$$

$(0,1)$

Equation (5-44g) is as in case 7, and one obtains the following equation and partial solution

$y_3 = 1 \qquad$ and $\qquad 2y_4 + y_5 + y_6 = 2 \qquad \text{case 4} \qquad (5\text{-}44h)$

$(0,1,1)$

Equation (5-44h) is as in case 4, and one obtains the following solution and new equation and partial solution:

$y_4 = 1 \qquad$ and $\qquad y_5 = y_6 = 0$

$(0,1,1,1,0,0)$

$y_4 = 0 \qquad$ and $\qquad y_5 + y_6 = 2 \qquad \text{case 6} \qquad (5\text{-}44i)$

$(0,1,1,0)$

Equation (5-44i) is as in case 6 and yields the solution

$y_5 = y_6 = 1$

$(0,1,1,0,1,1)$

	Solutions to Equation (5-44)							Solutions to original problem				
y_1	y_2	y_3	y_4	y_5	y_6		x_1	x_2	x_3	x_4	x_5	x_6
1	1	0	0	0	0		0	1	1	0	1	1
1	0	1	0	0	1		1	1	0	0	1	0
1	0	1	0	1	0		1	1	0	0	0	1
1	0	0	1	1	1		0	1	0	1	0	0
0	1	1	1	0	0		1	0	1	1	1	1
0	1	1	0	1	1		1	0	1	0	0	0

Exercise 5-11 Find the pseudo-Boolean function of the four variables x_1, x_2, x_3, x_4 defined by the following tables.

Hint: Use Theorem 5-6.

x_1	x_2	x_3	x_4	$f(x_1,x_2,x_3,x_4)$
0	0	0	0	-5
0	0	0	1	0
0	0	1	0	7
0	0	1	1	4
0	1	0	0	2
0	1	0	1	-11
0	1	1	0	1
0	1	1	1	0

x_1	x_2	x_3	x_4	$f(x_1,x_2,x_3,x_4)$
1	0	0	0	3
1	0	0	1	0
1	0	1	0	0
1	0	1	1	-3
1	1	0	0	8
1	1	0	1	5
1	1	1	0	0
1	1	1	1	-4

Exercise 5-12   Find the solutions to the pseudo-Boolean equation

$$4x_1 + \bar{x}_1 - 3x_2 + \bar{x}_2 + 5x_3 - 2x_4 + 5x_5 + 2x_6 - x_7 = 7$$

LINEAR PSEUDO–BOOLEAN INEQUALITIES

Instead of considering the equation $f(x_1, \ldots, x_n) = 0$, consider the general linear pseudo-Boolean inequalities

$$\sum_{i=1}^{n} a_i x_i + b_i \bar{x}_i \geq k \qquad\qquad\qquad (5\text{-}45)$$

and

$$a_i, b_i, k \in \text{Re}, x_i, \bar{x}_i \in B_2 \qquad i = 1, \ldots, n$$
$$\sum_{i=1}^{n} a_i x_i + b_i \bar{x}_i > k \qquad a_i \neq b_i \qquad\qquad (5\text{-}46)$$

If $a_i b_i$ and k are integers, Inequality (5-46) reduces to Inequality (5-45), with k replaced by $k - 1$.

Inequalities (5-45) and (5-46) can be rewritten in a canonical form by applying the transformation T, defined by (5-42). This gives

$$\sum_{i=1}^{n} c_i y_i \geq d \qquad c_1 \geq \cdots \geq c_n > 0 \qquad c_i, d \in \text{Re}, y_i \in B_2 \qquad (5\text{-}47)$$

$$\sum_{i=1}^{n} c_i y_i > d \qquad c_1 \geq \cdots \geq c_n > 0 \qquad c_i, d \in \text{Re}, y_i \in B_2 \qquad (5\text{-}48)$$

Upon examination of all solutions of (5-47) and (5-48), one observes that these solutions can be grouped into families characterized by the fact that each family is generated by fixing a certain number of variables and allowing the remaining variables to take on arbitrary values of 0 or 1.

Definition   Let $\alpha^* \in B_2{}^n$ satisfy Inequality (5-47) or (5-48), and let K denote a subset of the set of integers $\{1, 2, \ldots, n\}$.   Define

$$\Omega(\alpha^*, K) = \{\beta = (\beta_1, \ldots, \beta_n) \mid \beta \in B_2{}^n, \beta \text{ is a solution of (5-47) or}$$
$$(5\text{-}48)\}$$

and

$$\beta_i = \begin{cases} \alpha_i^* & \text{if } i \in K \\ \text{arbitrary} & \text{if } i \notin K \end{cases} \qquad\qquad\qquad (5\text{-}49)$$

We shall call the set $\Omega(\alpha^*, K)$ the family of solutions of Inequality (5-47) or (5-48) generated by α^*, and we shall call α^* the generator of $\Omega(\alpha^*, K)$, with index set K; the number of elements in K will be called the index of $\Omega(\alpha^*, K)$.

Definition   A solution $\alpha^* = (\alpha_1^*, \ldots, \alpha_n^*)$ of the Inequality (5-47) or (5-48) is called a *basic solution* of Inequality (5-47) or (5-48) if and only if, for each i such that $x_i = 1$, the vector

$$\alpha' = (\alpha_1^*, \ldots, \alpha_{i-1}^*, 0, \alpha_{i+1}^*, \ldots, \alpha_n^*)$$

is not a solution of Inequality (5-47) or (5-48).

Using the definition of a basic solution, one can easily prove the following theorem, concerning some properties of a basic solution.

Theorem 5-8   (Properties of basic solutions)

a. *If* $y = (y_1^*, \ldots, y_n^*)$ *is a basic solution of Inequality* (5-47) *[or* (5-48)]*, then* $(y_{p+1}^*, \ldots, y_n^*)$, $1 \leq p \leq n$, *is a basic solution of the inequality*

$$\sum_{i=p+1}^{n} c_i y_i \geq d - \sum_{i=1}^{p} c_i y_i \qquad \left(> d - \sum_{i=1}^{p} c_i y_i \right) \tag{5-50}$$

b. *If* $(y_{p+1}^*, \ldots, y_n^*)$ *is a basic solution of the inequality*

$$\sum_{i=p+1}^{n} c_i y_i \geq d \qquad (>d) \tag{5-51}$$

then the vector $(0, \ldots, 0, y_{p+1}^*, \ldots, y_n^*)$ *is a basic solution of Inequality* (5-47) *[or* (5-48)]*.*

c. *If* $(y_2^*, \ldots, y_n^*)$ *is a basic solution of the inequality*

$$\sum_{i=2}^{n} c_i y_i \geq d - c_1 \qquad (>d - c_1) \tag{5-52}$$

then the vector $(1, y_2^*, \ldots, y_n^*)$ *is a basic solution of Inequality* (5-47) *[or* (5-48)]*.*

Using Theorem 5-8 and upon examination of Inequalities (5-47) and (5-48), one obtains the following theorems analogous to Theorem 5-7.

Theorem 5-9   [Basic solutions of Inequality (5-47)]   *All of the basic solutions of the pseudo-Boolean inequality* (5-47) *are characterized by the following six disjoint cases.*

1. *If* $d \leq 0$, *the unique basic solution is* $y_1 = \cdots = y_n = 0$.

2. *If* $d > 0$ *and* $c_1 \geq \cdots \geq c_p \geq d > c_{p+1} \geq \cdots \geq c_n$, *then the basic solutions, if any, are the following:*

  a. $y_k = 1$, *for some integer* $k \leq p$.
   $y_1 = \cdots = y_{k-1} = y_{k+1} = \cdots = y_n = 0$ *is a basic solution.*

(*There is a different solution for each $k \leq p$.*)

$b.$ $y_1 = \cdots = y_p = 0$, *and* $(y_{p+1}, \ldots, y_n)$ *is a basic solution of*

$$\sum_{i=p+1}^{n} c_i y_i \geq d$$

3. *If $d > 0$ and $c_i < d$, for $i = 1, \ldots, n$, $\Sigma_{i=1}^{n} c_i < d$, then there are no solutions.*

4. *If $d > 0$ and $c_i < d$, for $i = 1, \ldots, n$, and $\Sigma_{i=1}^{n} c_i = d$, then the unique basic solution is $y_1 = \cdots = y_n = 1$.*

5. *If $d > 0$ and $c_i < d$, for $i = 1, \ldots, n$, $\Sigma_{i=1}^{n} c_i > d$ and $\Sigma_{i=2}^{n} c_i < d$, then the basic solutions, if any exist, are $y_1 = 1$ and the basic solutions of $\Sigma_{i=2}^{n} c_i y_i \geq d - c_1$.*

6. *If $d > 0$ and $c_i < d$, for $i = 1, \ldots, n$, $\Sigma_{i=1}^{n} c_i > d$ and $\Sigma_{i=2}^{n} c_i y_i \geq d$, then the basic solutions, if any exist, are given by either of the following:*

$a.$ $y_1 = 1$ *and* $(y_2, \ldots, y_n)$ *is a basic solution of* $\Sigma_{i=2}^{n} c_i y_i \geq d - c_1$.

$b.$ $y_1 = 0$ *and* $(y_2, \ldots, y_n)$ *is a basic solution of* $\Sigma_{i=2}^{n} c_i y_i \geq d$.

For inequalities of the form of Inequality (5-48), a theorem similar to Theorem 5-9 can be written, which splits the discussion concerning basic solutions of Inequality (5-48) into five disjoint cases. If the inequality has integral coefficients, then, as mentioned before, one can transform the strict inequality to the form of Inequality (5-47).

Using Theorem 5-9, an algorithm analogous to the algorithm for solving linear pseudo-Boolean inequalities can be formulated as follows.

ALGORITHM FOR FINDING THE BASIC SOLUTIONS TO LINEAR PSEUDO-BOOLEAN INEQUALITIES

Step 1 Apply transformation, T, given by (5-42) to the inequality to obtain the canonical form [Inequality (5-47)]. Go to step 2.

Step 2 Compare the canonical form of the inequality to the cases contained in Theorem 5-9.

a. If Inequality (5-47) is as in case 3 of Theorem 5-9, there exist no solutions. Go to step 3.

b. If Inequality (5-47) is as in case 1 or 4 of Theorem 5-9, there exists a unique basic solution given in the conclusions of the appropriate case. Go to step 3.

c. If Inequality (5-47) is as in case 2 or 5 of Theorem 5-9, then the original inequality is replaced by a similar inequality in less variables contained in the conclusion of the appropriate case along with the values of the missing variables. If Inequality (5-47) is as in case 2, one also obtains a set of basic solutions given in the conclusions to case 2. Go to step 3.

d. If Inequality (5-47) or (5-48) is as in case 6 of Theorem 5-9, the original inequality is replaced by two similar inequalities with one less variable given in the conclusion of the appropriate case, along with the value of the missing variable for each inequality. Go to step 3.

Step 3 If no new inequalities result from step 2 and there are no remaining inequalities to be solved, apply T^{-1} to the basic solutions obtained in step 2, if any exist, to obtain the solutions to the original inequalities. If new inequalities arise in step 2, repeat step 2 until all inequalities have been resolved. If some inequality has no solution, the corresponding partial solution and that inequality are deleted.

The above-described algorithm determines all of the basic solutions of Inequalities (5-45) since it exhausts all possible solutions.

After having determined the basic solutions to Inequalities (5-47) or (5-48), one can construct the set of all solutions of (5-47) or (5-48) as follows.

Theorem 5-10 *The set of all basic solutions α^j, $j = 1, \ldots, m$, of Inequality (5-47) [or (5-48)] generates a class of disjoint families $\Omega(\alpha^j, K_j)$, $j = 1, \ldots, m$, and every solution of Inequality (5-47) [or (5-48)] must belong to one of these families.*

Proof Define

$$K_j = \left\{ p \,\middle|\, 0 < p \leq q \text{ where } q \text{ is the index of the last nonzero component of } \alpha^j \right\}$$

If $x = (x_1, \ldots, x_n) \in \Omega(\alpha^j, K_j)$, for some j, then x satisfies (5-47) [or (5-48)] since $\sum_{i=1}^{r} c_i \alpha_i \geq d \,(> d)$, where r is the index of $\Omega(\alpha^j, K_j)$, to which x belongs. Since $c_i \geq 0$, $i = 1, \ldots, n$, one has

$$\sum_{i=1}^{n} c_i \alpha_i = \sum_{i=1}^{r} c_i \alpha_i + \sum_{i=r+1}^{n} c_i \alpha_i \geq d \qquad (> d)$$

Because of the construction of the basic solutions α^j, $j = 1, \ldots, m$, the families $\Omega(\alpha^j, K_j)$ must be distinct. Every solution must belong to one of the above families since either it is a basic solution and hence a generator of some $\Omega(\alpha^j, K_j)$ (since all basic solutions are determined by the algorithm), or else it can be shown to belong to some $\Omega(\alpha^j, K_j)$ by changing the last nonzero components of the vector $x = (x_1, \ldots, x_n)$ until it is a basic solution.

Example 5-5 Find the solutions of the pseudo-Boolean inequality

$$2\bar{x}_1 - 8x_2 + 7\bar{x}_3 + 5x_3 - 6\bar{x}_4 + 8x_5 \geq 8 \tag{5-53}$$

Applying T to Inequality (5-53) and reindexing, one obtains

$$15y_1 + 8y_2 + 6y_3 + 5y_4 + 2y_5 \geq 22 \qquad \text{(case 5 of Theorem 5-9)} \tag{5-54}$$

where $y_1 = \bar{x}_2$, $y_2 = x_5$, $y_3 = x_4$, $y_4 = x_3$, $y_5 = \bar{x}_1$.

Inequality (5-54) is as in case 5 of Theorem 5-9, and one obtains the following partial solution and new inequality:

Partial Basic Solution

$$8y_2 + 6y_3 + 5y_4 + 2y_5 \geq 7 \text{ (case 2)}$$
$$\text{and} \quad y_1 = 1 \quad (5\text{-}54a)$$

(1)

Inequality (5-54a) is as in case 2 of Theorem 5-9, and one obtains the following basic solution and a new inequality and partial solution:

$$y_2 = 1 \quad y_3 = y_4 = y_5 = 0$$
$$6y_3 + 5y_4 + 2y_5 \geq 7 \text{ (case 6)} \quad \text{and} \quad y_2 = 0 \quad (5\text{-}54b)$$

(1,1,0,0,0)
(1,0)

Inequality (5-54b) is as in case 6 of Theorem 5-9, and one obtains the following two new inequalities and partial solutions:

$$5y_4 + 2y_5 \geq 1 \text{ (case 2)} \quad \text{and} \quad y_3 = 1 \quad (5\text{-}54c)$$
$$5y_4 + 2y_5 \geq 7 \text{ (case 4)} \quad \text{and} \quad y_3 = 0 \quad (5\text{-}54d)$$

(1,0,1)
(1,0,0)

Inequality (5-54c) is as in case 2 of Theorem 5-9, and one obtains the following basic solutions:

$$y_4 = 1 \quad y_5 = 0$$
$$y_4 = 0 \quad y_5 = 1$$

(1,0,1,1,0)
(1,0,1,0,1)

Inequality (5-54c) is as in case 4 of Theorem 5-9, and one obtains the basic solution $y_4 = y_5 = 1$.

(1,0,0,1,1)

The basic solutions are $\alpha^1 = (1,1,0,0,0)$, $\alpha^2 = (1,0,1,1,0)$, $\alpha^3 = (1,0,1,0,1)$, and $\alpha^4 = (1,0,0,1,1)$. Using these basic solutions, one can construct the index K_i: $K_1 = \{1,2\}$, $K_2 = \{1,2,3,4\}$, $K_3 = \{1,2,3,4,5\}$, and $K_4 = \{1,2,3,4,5\}$. From the K_i's and the α_i's, one constructs the following four families of solutions to Inequality (5-54):

$$\Omega(\alpha^1, K_1) = \begin{Bmatrix} (1,1,0,0,0), & (1,1,1,0,0), & (1,1,0,1,0), & (1,1,1,1,0) \\ (1,1,0,0,1), & (1,1,1,0,1), & (1,1,0,1,1), & (1,1,1,1,1) \end{Bmatrix}$$
$$\Omega(\alpha^2, K_2) = \{(1,0,1,1,0), (1,0,1,1,1)\}$$
$$\Omega(\alpha^3, K_3) = \{(1,0,1,0,1)\}$$
$$\Omega(\alpha^4, K_4) = \{(1,0,0,1,1)\}$$

Upon applying the transformation T^{-1}, one obtains the solution to Inequality (5-53), as shown in the following table, where "—" indicates an arbitrary value, either 0 or 1:

y_1	y_2	y_3	y_4	y_5	x_1	x_2	x_3	x_4	x_5
1	1	—	—	—	—	0	—	—	1
1	0	1	1	—	—	0	1	1	0
1	0	1	0	1	0	0	0	1	0
1	0	0	1	1	0	0	1	0	0

Exercise 5-13 Using Theorem 5-9, solve the strict pseudo-Boolean inequality

$$2\bar{x}_1 - 5x_2 + 3x_3 + 4\bar{x}_4 - 7x_5 + 16x_6 - x_7 - 4$$

Exercise 5-14   If the c_i's and d in Inequality (5-47) are integers, construct the families of solutions to the strict Inequality (5-48), knowing the basic solutions to Inequality (5-47).

  Hint: Use the solutions to $\Sigma_{i=1}^n c_i y_i = d$ to modify the families of solution of Inequality (5-48).   Solve Exercise 5-13, using the above results.

SYSTEMS OF LINEAR PSEUDO-BOOLEAN EQUATIONS AND/OR INEQUALITIES

A brief outline of techniques used to solve systems of pseudo-Boolean equations and/or inequalities will now be presented; the more interested reader should consult Ref. 22 to obtain the details.

  Having developed techniques for solving pseudo-Boolean equations and inequalities, one observes that the solutions to a system of such equations and inequalities must satisfy each of the equations and inequalities.   If each family F of solutions of each equation or inequality is treated separately, one takes the solution J of the system as the intersection of all the families F_i; that is,

$$J = \bigcap_{i=1}^{m} F_i \tag{5-55}$$

where m is the number of equations or inequalities in the system and F_i is the family of solutions to the ith equation or inequality.

  Instead of computing the family of solutions to each of the members of the system, a more systematic approach can be taken.   By judiciously choosing a particular member of the system, one can solve for one or possibly more variables and reduce the original system to one or more new systems, involving fewer variables.   By repeated applications of this technique, one can determine all of the solutions to the original system. Details of this technique can be found in Ref. 22, pages 37 to 52.

II. NONLINEAR PSEUDO-BOOLEAN EQUATIONS AND INEQUALITIES

The techniques presented above for obtaining solutions to linear pseudo-Boolean equations, inequalities, and systems of equations and/or inequalities will now be applied to nonlinear problems.

THE CHARACTERISTIC FUNCTION FOR PSEUDO-BOOLEAN EQUATIONS, INEQUALITIES, AND SYSTEMS

Corresponding to every pseudo-Boolean equation, inequality, or system, $G(x_1, \ldots, x_n) \geq 0$, is a corresponding Boolean equation which has the same solutions as $G \geq 0$ whose form is given in the following theorem.

Theorem 5-11   *Associated with every pseudo-Boolean equation, inequality, or system, $G(x_1, \ldots, x_n) \geq 0$, is a Boolean function ψ, called the characteristic function of $G(x_1, \ldots, x_n)$, $\psi \colon B_2^n \to B_2$ such that the solutions of $G(x_1, \ldots, x_n) \geq 0$ are the solution of the Boolean equation*

$$\psi(x_1, \ldots, x_n) = 1 \tag{5-56}$$

Proof Define $\psi(x_1, \ldots, x_n)$ as follows:

$$\psi(x_1, \ldots, x_n) = \bigcup_{F \in \mathfrak{F}} \chi_F \tag{5-56a}$$

(the union being taken over all $F \in \mathfrak{F}$), where

$$\chi_F = \bigcup_{\alpha \in F} (x_1^{\alpha_1} \cap x_2^{\alpha_2} \cap \cdots \cap x_n^{\alpha_n}) = \bigcup_{\alpha \in F} x_1^{\alpha_1} x_2^{\alpha_2} \cdots x_n^{\alpha_n}$$

and $\mathfrak{F}$ is the class of all families F of solutions of $G(x_1, \ldots, x_n) \geq 0$ and

$$x_i^{\alpha_i} = \begin{cases} x_i & \text{if } \alpha_i = 1 \\ \bar{x}_i & \text{if } \alpha_i = 0 \end{cases}$$

where α_i is the ith component of the solution $\alpha \in F$ of $G(x_1, \ldots, x_n) \geq 0$. If α is a solution of $G(x_1, \ldots, x_n) \geq 0$, then, by the definition of ψ, α is a solution of Equation (5-56). Conversely, if α is a solution of Equation (5-56), then, by the definition of ψ, there exists at least one χ_F such that $\chi_F = 1$. Since χ_F is, by definition, a union of minimal Boolean polynomials (see Birkhoff and MacLane [5a]), α must satisfy one of the members of the union, and hence, by the definition of χ_F, α is a solution of $G(x_1, \ldots, x_n) \geq 0$.

The characteristic function $\psi(x_1, \ldots, x_n)$ may be rewritten in other forms, depending upon the form of $G(x_1, \ldots, x_n) \geq 0$. Examples of several of these forms are given below.

ψ For linear pseudo-Boolean inequalities $G(x_1, \ldots, x_n) \geq 0$ For

$$\psi(x_1, \ldots, x_n) = \bigcup_{\alpha^p \in Q} x_{p_1}^{\alpha_{p_1}} \cdots x_{p_m}^{\alpha_{p_m}} \tag{5-57}$$

$p_i \in K_p = $ index set of $\Omega(\alpha^p, K_p)$ and Q is the set of all generators of the solutions of $G(x_1, \ldots, x_n) \geq 0$ and $\alpha^p \in Q$ is a generator. Note that only the elements contained in the generators of the solutions of $G(x_1, \ldots, x_n) \geq 0$ determine the characteristic function.

ψ For linear pseudo-Boolean systems of inequalities and equations Let $G(x_1, \ldots, x_n) \geq 0$ be defined as the following system of linear pseudo-Boolean equations and inequalities:

$$\begin{aligned}
g_j(x_1, \ldots, x_n) &= 0 & j &= 1, \ldots, m & &\tag{5-58a} \\
g_j(x_1, \ldots, x_n) &\geq 0 & j &= m + 1, \ldots, p & &\tag{5-58b} \\
g_j(x_1, \ldots, x_n) &> 0 & j &= p + 1, \ldots, q & &\tag{5-58c}
\end{aligned}$$

If $\psi_j(x_1, \ldots, x_n)$ is the characteristic function for $g_j(x_1, \ldots, x_n)$, $j = 1, \ldots, q$, one then has the characteristic function associated with the system $G(x_1, \ldots, x_n) \geq 0$:

$$\psi(x_1, \ldots, x_n) = \bigcap_{j=1}^{q} \psi_j(x_1, \ldots, x_n) \tag{5-59}$$

Exercise 5-15   Verify Eqs. (5-57), (5-58a), (5-58b), and (5-58c), using the definition of a characteristic function.

Examples of characteristic functions   The characteristic function for Example 5-4 is

$$\psi(x_1, \ldots, x_6) = \bar{x}_1 x_2 x_3 \bar{x}_4 x_5 x_6 \cup x_1 x_2 \bar{x}_3 \bar{x}_4 x_5 \bar{x}_6 \cup x_1 x_2 \bar{x}_3 \bar{x}_4 \bar{x}_5 x_6$$
$$\cup \; \bar{x}_1 x_2 \bar{x}_3 x_4 \bar{x}_5 \bar{x}_6 \cup x_1 \bar{x}_2 x_3 x_4 x_5 x_6 \cup x_1 \bar{x}_2 x_3 \bar{x}_4 \bar{x}_5 \bar{x}_6$$

The characteristic function for Example 5-5 is

$$\psi(x_1, \ldots, x_5) = \bar{x}_2 x_5 \cup \bar{x}_2 x_3 x_4 \bar{x}_5 \cup \bar{x}_1 \bar{x}_2 \bar{x}_3 x_4 \bar{x}_5 \cup \bar{x}_1 \bar{x}_2 x_3 \bar{x}_4 \bar{x}_5$$

SOLUTIONS OF NONLINEAR PSEUDO–BOOLEAN EQUATIONS, INEQUALITIES, AND SYSTEMS OF EQUATIONS AND/OR INEQUALITIES

Using the results of Theorem 5-6, one can write the general pseudo-Boolean equation with n variables, $x_1, \ldots, x_n$, as

$$a_1 P_1(x_1, \ldots, x_n) + \cdots + a_m P_m(x_1, \ldots, x_n) = b$$
$$a_i, b \in \text{Re} \quad (x_1, \ldots, x_n) \in B_2 \tag{5-60}$$

where

$$P_i(x_1, \ldots, x_n) = x_{i_1}{}^{\beta_{i_1}} \cdots x_{i_{k(i)}}{}^{\beta_{i_{k(i)}}} \qquad x_i^{\beta_i} = \begin{cases} x_i & \text{if } \beta_i = 1 \\ \bar{x}_i & \text{if } \beta_i = 0 \end{cases}$$

In general, $P_i(x_1, \ldots, x_n)$ does not depend on all the variables $x_1, \ldots,$ x_n, and is indicated in the definition of $P_i(x_1, \ldots, x_n)$. By letting $y_j = P_j(x_1, \ldots, x_n), j = 1, \ldots, n$, Equation (5-60) becomes

$$a_1 y_1 + \cdots + a_m y_m = b \tag{5-61}$$

Since $P_j(x_1, \ldots, x_n) \in B_2$, the y_j's can be considered as new bivalent variables, and Equation (5-61) can be considered as a linear pseudo-Boolean equation in $y_1, \ldots, y_m$. Using the techniques of part I, one can find all of the solutions of Equation (5-61).

To recover the solutions of Equation (5-60), knowing the solutions of Equation (5-61), one considers the characteristic equation associated with Equation (5-61)

$$\psi(y_1, \ldots, y_m) = 1 \tag{5-62}$$

By replacing y_j with $P_j(x_1, \ldots, x_n)$ in Equation (5-62), $j = 1, \ldots, m$, one obtains a new characteristic equation whose solutions are those of Equation (5-60):

$$\psi[P_1(x_1, \ldots, x_n), \ldots P_m(x_1, \ldots, x_n)] = 1 \tag{5-63}$$

By solving the Boolean Equation (5-63), one obtains all of the solutions of Equation (5-60); if some of the variables $x_1, \ldots, x_n$ do not appear in a solution, they may be chosen arbitrarily.

For nonlinear inequalities and systems, one applies the same linearization techniques, as in the case of the nonlinear equation, and upon solving the linear inequality or system, one forms the corresponding characteristic equation which is solved to recover the solutions to the nonlinear problem.

SOLVING THE CHARACTERISTIC EQUATION

By applying the laws of Boolean algebra, one can reduce any characteristic function $\psi(x_1, \ldots, x_n)$ into the form

$$\psi(x_1, \ldots, x_n) = Q_1 \cup \cdots \cup Q_m \tag{5-64}$$

where Q_i is of the form

$$Q_i = x_{i_1}{}^{\beta_{i_1}} \cdots x_{i_{k(i)}}^{\beta_{i_{k(i)}}} \qquad i = 1, \ldots, m$$

$$x_i{}^{\beta_i} = \begin{cases} x_i & \text{if } \beta_i = 1 \\ \bar{x}_i & \text{if } \beta_i = 0 \end{cases}$$

Upon having reduced $\psi(x_1, \ldots, x_n)$ to the form of Equation (5-64), the solutions of the characteristic equation (5-56) can be obtained by setting each $Q_i = 1$ and finding the solutions by inspection. This procedure yields all of the solutions for nonlinear pseudo-Boolean equations but only the basic solutions of nonlinear pseudo-Boolean inequalities and systems. The set of all solutions of nonlinear pseudo-Boolean inequalities can be constructed as follows.

For each solution, α^i, of Equation (5-64), construct $\Omega(\alpha^i, K_i)$, where K_i is the set of subscripts corresponding to the components of α^i. It is obvious that each family $\Omega(\alpha^i, K_i)$ is a family of solutions, and if

$$\hat{\alpha} = (\hat{\alpha}_1, \ldots, \hat{\alpha}_n)$$

is a solution to the nonlinear problem, it must belong to at least one $\Omega(\alpha, K)$; if it does not, by the definition of $\psi(x_1, \ldots, x_n)$, one would have

$$Q_1 = \cdots = Q_m = 0$$

which implies that $\psi(\hat{\alpha}_1, \ldots, \hat{\alpha}_n) = 0$, which contradicts Equation (5-56).

Since the families $\Omega(\alpha^i, K_i)$ may not be distinct, as a matter of convenience (see discussion of minimization problems), one deletes common families as follows.

Before solving Equation (5-64), check $Q_i, i = 1, \ldots, m$, as follows: If $Q_i \cap Q_j = \varnothing, i \neq j$, keep Q_i. If $Q_i \cap Q_j \neq \varnothing, i \neq j$, delete Q_i from Equation (5-64).

The above procedure yields (using $R_i = Q_i$ or $R_i = \emptyset$ as explained above)

$$\psi(x_1, \ldots, x_n) = R_1 \cup \cdots \cup R_m \tag{5-65}$$

which has distinct solutions; hence the families $\Omega(\alpha^j, K_j)$ will be distinct.

Example 5-6　Find the solutions of the nonlinear pseudo-Boolean inequality

$$-10x_1x_2x_3 + 6x_1x_2 - 5x_1x_3 + 7x_2x_3 - 2x_1 - 2x_2 - 2x_3 \leq 2 \tag{5-66}$$

Let $y_1 = x_1x_2x_3$, $y_2 = \bar{x}_2\bar{x}_3$, $y_3 = \bar{x}_1\bar{x}_2$, $y_4 = x_1x_3$, $y_5 = x_1$, and $y_6 = x_2$, $y_7 = x_3$; then, Inequality (5-66) becomes

$$10y_1 + 7y_2 + 6y_3 + 5y_4 + 2y_5 + 2y_6 + 2y_7 \geq 11 \tag{5-67}$$

The solutions of Inequality (5-67) are as follows:

y_1	y_2	y_3	y_4	y_5	y_6	y_7
1	1	—	—	—	—	—
1	0	1	—	—	—	—
1	0	0	1	—	—	—
1	0	0	0	1	—	—
1	0	0	0	0	1	—
1	0	0	0	0	0	1
0	1	1	—	—	—	—

y_1	y_2	y_3	y_4	y_5	y_6	y_7
0	1	0	1	—	—	—
0	1	0	0	1	1	—
0	1	0	0	1	0	1
0	1	0	0	0	1	1
0	0	0	1	1	1	1
0	0	1	1	—	—	—
0	0	1	0	1	1	1

where — indicates an arbitrary bivalent value.　Then the characteristic function associated with Inequality (5-67) is

$$\psi(y_1, \ldots, y_7) = y_1y_2 \cup y_1\bar{y}_2y_3 \cup y_1\bar{y}_2\bar{y}_3y_4 \cup y_1\bar{y}_2\bar{y}_3\bar{y}_4y_5 \cup y_1\bar{y}_2\bar{y}_3\bar{y}_4\bar{y}_5y_6 \cup$$
$$\cup\, y_1\bar{y}_2\bar{y}_3\bar{y}_4\bar{y}_5\bar{y}_6y_7 \cup \bar{y}_1y_2y_3 \cup \bar{y}_1y_2\bar{y}_3y_4 \cup \bar{y}_1y_2\bar{y}_3\bar{y}_4y_5y_6 \cup \bar{y}_1y_2\bar{y}_3\bar{y}_4y_5\bar{y}_6y_7 \cup$$
$$\cup\, \bar{y}_1y_2\bar{y}_3\bar{y}_4\bar{y}_5y_6y_7 \cup \bar{y}_1\bar{y}_2\bar{y}_3y_4y_5y_6y_7 \cup \bar{y}_1\bar{y}_2y_3y_4 \cup \bar{y}_1\bar{y}_2y_3\bar{y}_4y_5y_6y_7$$

Upon substituting for $y_1, \ldots, y_7$ in terms of x_1, x_2, x_3, one obtains, after reduction,

$$\psi(x_1, x_2, x_3) = x_1 \cup \bar{x}_1\bar{x}_2 \cup \bar{x}_1x_2\bar{x}_3 \tag{5-68}$$

Solving $\psi(x_1, x_2, x_3) = 1$, one obtains the solutions

$$(x_1, x_2, x_3) = (1, —, —), \ (0, 0, —), \ (0, 1, 0)$$

Exercise 5-16　Solve the pseudo-Boolean inequality

$$7x_1x_2x_3 + 5x_2x_4x_6x_7x_8 - 3x_3x_8 - 2\bar{x}_1x_4x_8 - x_4\bar{x}_5x_6 \leq 3$$

III.　MINIMIZATION OF PSEUDO–BOOLEAN FUNCTIONS

MINIMIZATION PROBLEMS WITHOUT CONSTRAINTS

A vector $x^* = (x_1^*, \ldots, x_n^*)$ is defined to be a minimizing point of the pseudo-Boolean function $f(x_1, \ldots, x_n)$, if and only if

$$f(x_1^*, \ldots, x_n^*) \leq f(x_1, \ldots, x_n) \qquad \text{for all } x \in B_2^n \tag{5-69}$$

Using the definition of a minimizing point, one finds the following necessity condition for a vector x^* to be a minimizing point:

$$f(x_1^*, \ldots, x_n^*) \leq f(x_1^*, \ldots, x_{i-1}^*, \bar{x}_i^*, x_{i+1}^*, \ldots, x_n^*)$$
$$\text{for } i = 1, \ldots, n \quad (5\text{-}70)$$

By applying Theorem 5-5, relation (5-70) can be written as

$$(x_i^* - \bar{x}_i^*)g_i(x_1^*, \ldots, x_{i-1}^*, x_{i+1}^*, \ldots, x_n^*) \leq 0$$
$$\text{for } i = 1, \ldots, n \quad (5\text{-}71)$$

where

$$f(x_1^*, \ldots, x_n^*) = x_i^* g_i(x_1^*, \ldots, x_{i-1}^*, x_{i+1}^*, \ldots, x_n^*)$$
$$+ h_i(x_1^*, \ldots, x_{i-1}^*, x_{i+1}^*, \ldots, x_n^*)$$

Exercise 5-17   Prove that relation (5-71) is not a sufficient condition.
   Hint: (5-71) characterizes a local minimum.

Upon examination of condition (5-71), one notes that

$$x_i^* = \begin{cases} 1 & \text{if } g_i < 0 \\ 0 & \text{if } g_i > 0 \\ p_i & \text{if } g_i = 0, \text{ where } p_i \text{ is an arbitrary bivalent} \\ & \text{parameter} \end{cases} \quad (5\text{-}72)$$

Using relation (5-72), one can define a Boolean function $\Omega_i(x_1, \ldots, x_{i-1}, p_i, x_{i+1}, \ldots, x_n)$ such that

$$\Omega_i(x_1, \ldots, x_{i-1}, p_i, x_{i+1}, \ldots, x_n)$$
$$= \begin{cases} 1 & \text{if } g_i < 0 \\ 0 & \text{if } g_i > 0 \\ p_i & \text{if } g_i = 0, \text{ where } p_i \text{ is an arbitrary bivalent parameter} \end{cases} \quad (5\text{-}73)$$

If one replaces $x \cup y$ by $x + y - xy$ and $x \cap y$ by xy, relation (5-73) can be considered as a pseudo-Boolean function, and hence one has

$$x_i = \Omega_i(x_1, \ldots, x_{i-1}, p_i, x_{i+1}, \ldots, x_n) \quad (5\text{-}74)$$

Relations (5-71) through (5-74) yield the following result.
   The following three theorems are due to Hammer and Rudeanu [22].

Theorem 5-12   *For every vector* $(x_1, \ldots, x_{i-1}, p_i, x_{i+1}, \ldots, x_n) \in B_2{}^n$, *if*

$$x_i = \Omega(x_1, \ldots, x_{i-1}, p_i, x_{i+1}, \ldots, x_n)$$

then the vector $(x_1, \ldots, x_i, \ldots, x_n) \in B_2{}^n$ satisfies Equation (5-71) and conversely, if $(x_1, \ldots, x_i, \ldots, x_n) \in B_2{}^n$ is a solution of Equation (5-71), then there exists a p_i (bivalent parameter ϵB_2) such that Equation (5-73) holds.

The construction of the Boolean function $\Omega_i(x_1, \ldots, x_{i-1}, p_i, x_{i+1}, \ldots, x_n)$ can be easily carried out as follows. Let Ω_i' denote the characteristic function of $g_i(x_1, \ldots, x_{i-1}, x_{i+1}, \ldots, x_n) < 0$, and let Ω_i'' denote the characteristic function of

$$g_i(x_1, \ldots, x_{i-1}, x_{i+1}, \ldots, x_n) = 0$$

Then

$$\Omega_i(x_1, \ldots, x_{i-1}, p_i, x_{i+1}, \ldots, x_n) = \Omega_i' \cup (p_i \cap \Omega_i'') \qquad (5\text{-}75)$$

since

$$\Omega_i' = \begin{cases} 1 & \text{if } g_i < 0 \\ 0 & \text{if } g_i \geq 0 \end{cases}$$

$$\Omega_i'' = \begin{cases} 1 & \text{if } g_i = 0 \\ 0 & \text{otherwise} \end{cases}$$

From Theorem 5-12 and relation (5-71), one obtains the following necessary and sufficient condition for x^* to be a minimizing point.

Theorem 5-13 *The vector $x^* = (x_1^*, \ldots, x_n^*)$ is a minimizing point of the function $f(x_1, \ldots, x_n)$ if and only if the following two conditions hold:*

a. *There exist a $p_i^* \in B_2$ such that*

$$x_i^* = \Omega_i(x_i^*, \ldots, x_{i-1}^*, p_i^*, x_{i+1}^*, \ldots, x_n^*) \qquad (5\text{-}76)$$

b. *The vector $(x_1^*, \ldots, x_{i-1}^*, x_{i+1}^*, \ldots, x_n^*)$ is a minimizing point of the function $(\Omega_i$ considered a pseudo-Boolean function)*

$$\Omega_i(x_1, \ldots, x_{i-1}, p_i, x_{i+1}, \ldots, x_n)g_i(x_1, \ldots, x_{i-1}, x_{i+1}, \ldots, x_n) + h(x_1, \ldots, x_{i-1}, x_{i+1}, \ldots, x_n) \qquad (5\text{-}77)$$

Exercise 5-18 Prove Theorem 5-13.
  Hint: Use Theorem 5-12, and the definition of a minimizing point.

By repeated applications of Theorem 5-13, one can exhibit an algorithm for finding the minimum of $f(x_1, \ldots, x_n)$, using the following theorem.

Theorem 5-14 *The vector $x^* = (x_1^*, \ldots, x_n^*)$ is a minimizing point of the pseudo-Boolean function $f(x_1, \ldots, x_n)$ if and only if there exist* *values $p_1^*, \ldots, p_n^*$ such that*

$$x_1^* = \Omega_1(p_1^*, x_2^*, \ldots, x_n^*)$$
$$x_2^* = \Omega_2(p_2^*, x_3^*, \ldots, x_n^*)$$
. . . .
$$x_n^* = \Omega_n(p_n^*)$$

and $f(x_1^*, \ldots, x_n^*) = f(\Omega_1, \Omega_2, \ldots, \Omega_n)$ is the minimum of $f(x_1, \ldots, x_n)$.

ALGORITHM FOR FINDING THE MINIMIZATION POINTS AND THE MINIMUM OF A PSEUDO–BOOLEAN FUNCTION

Step 1 If $f_i = $ constant, then $\min f = f_i$. Go to step 4. If $f_i \neq$ constant, go to step 2.

Step 2 Find g_i, h_i such that $f_i = x_i g_i + h_i$ and construct Ω_i' and Ω_i''. Set $x_i = \Omega_i' \cup p_i \Omega_i''$, where $\Omega_i' \cup p_i \Omega_i''$ is expressed as a pseudo-Boolean function. Go to step 3.

Step 3 Form $f_{i+1} = f_i[\Omega_i'(x_{i+1}, \ldots, x_n), x_{i+1}, \ldots, x_n]$. Set $i = i + 1$, and go to step 1.

Step 4 If $i = 1$, then all the x_i's are arbitrary $i = 1, \ldots, n$. If $i \neq 1$, then say $i = m$ and

$$x_m = \Omega_m(p_m)$$
$$x_{m-1} = \Omega_{m-1}(p_{m-1}, x_m)$$
. . . .
$$x_1 = \Omega_1(p_1, x_2, \ldots, x_m)$$

If $m < n$, then $x_{m+1}, \ldots, x_n$ are arbitrary. If $m = n$, then $x_1, \ldots, x_n$ are defined above.

In the above algorithm one could have used Ω_i instead of Ω_i' in finding the minimum value of f. In the algorithm Ω_i' was used since one only wanted to construct the minimum of $f(x_1, \ldots, x_n)$; hence p_i was set to zero.

Example 5-7 Find the minimum of the function

$$-5x_1x_2x_3 + 10x_1x_2 + 3x_1x_3 + 3x_2x_3 - 3x_1 - 8x_2 - 3x_3 + 3 \tag{5-78}$$

One writes:

$$f_1(x_1,x_2,x_3) = x_1(-5x_2x_3 + 10x_2 + 3x_3 - 3) + 3x_2x_3 - 8x_2 - 3x_3 + 3 \tag{5-79}$$

and solves

$$-5x_2x_3 + 10x_2 + 3x_3 - 3 \leq 0$$

Let

$$y_1 = x_2 x_3 \qquad y_2 = \bar{x}_2 \qquad y_3 = \bar{x}_3$$

Then one must solve

$$10y_2 + 5y_1 + 3y_3 \geq 10 \tag{5-79a}$$

The solution to Inequality (5-79a) is $y_2 = 1$, $y_1 = y_3 = 0$ (basic solution), and $\Omega'_1 = \bar{x}_2\bar{x}_3$, $\Omega''_1 = 0$.

$$f_2(x_2,x_3) = f_1(\Omega'_1,x_2,x_3) = -5x_2$$

Hence $g_2 = 1$, which implies that $\Omega'_2 = 1$ and $\Omega''_2 = 0$. Therefore, $f_3 = f_2(\Omega'_2,x_3) = -5 = \min f(x_1,x_2,x_3)$. The minimizing points are found to be

$$x_2 = 1$$
$$x_1 = \bar{x}_2\bar{x}_3 = 0\bar{x}_3 = 0$$
$$x_3 = p \qquad \text{(arbitrary bivalent parameter)}$$

Exercise 5-19   Minimize the following function, f, and find all of the minimizing points:

$$f = 2x_1 + 3x_2 - 7x_3 - 5x_1x_2x_3 + 3x_2x_4 + 9x_4x_5 - 2x_1x_5$$

Solution $x_1 = x_2 = x_3 = x_5 = 1$, $x_4 = 0$, $\min f = -9$.

MINIMIZATION OF AN ARBITRARY OBJECTIVE FUNCTION SUBJECT TO CONSTRAINTS

Consider the following minimization problem. Minimize the pseudo-Boolean function $f(x_1, \ldots, x_n)$, subject to the system of constraints $G(x_1, \ldots, x_n) \geq 0$.

Let $F = (\Omega(\alpha^1, K_1), \ldots, \Omega(\alpha^p, K_p))$ be the set of all distinct basic solutions of $G(x_1, \ldots, x_n) \geq 0$. One can then solve the above minimization problem as a series of at most p minimization problems using the following algorithm.

ALGORITHM

Step 1   Form the pseudo-Boolean functions $f_j, j = 1, \ldots, p$, defined by substituting z_i into $f(x_1, \ldots, x_n)$ for x_i, where

$$z_i = \begin{cases} \alpha_i & \text{if } i \in K = \text{the index of } \Omega(\alpha^j, K_j) \\ x_i & \text{if } i \notin K = \text{the index of } \Omega(\alpha^j, K_j) \end{cases}$$

Go to step 2.

Step 2   Minimize each $f_j, j = 1, \ldots, p$, using the method in part III, and denote the minima by $\delta^1, \ldots, \delta^p$. Go to step 3.

Step 3   Find $\min_{h=1,\ldots,p} \delta^j = \min f$. The minimizing points of $f(x_1, \ldots, x_n)$ are those points x^* such that $f(x_1^*, \ldots, x_n^*) = \min f$.

Exercise 5-20   Minimize the function

$$f = 3x_1\bar{x}_2 - 8\bar{x}_1x_3x_6 + 4x_2x_5\bar{x}_6 - 7\bar{x}_5x_6 + 3x_4 - 5x_4x_5x_6$$

subject to

$$2x_1 - 3x_2 + 5x_3 - 4x_4 + 2x_5 - x_6 \leq 2$$
$$4x_1 + 2x_2 + x_3 - 8x_4 - x_5 - 3x_6 \geq 4$$

Solution $\min f = -12$, $x = (0,1,1,1,0,1)$ and $(0,0,1,1,0,1)$.

Further techniques for minimizing pseudo-Boolean functions with constraints can be found in Ref. 22.

REFERENCES†

1. Balas, E.: An Additive Algorithm for Solving Linear Programs with Zero-One Variables, *Operations Res.*, vol. 13, pp. 517–546, 1965.
1a. Balas, E.: Duality in Discrete Programming, Stanford Univ. Technical Report No. 67-5, November, 1967.
1b. Balas, E.: Discrete Programming by the Filter Method, *Operations Res.*, vol. 15, pp. 915–957, 1967.
2. Balinski, M. L.: Integer Programming: Methods, Uses, Computation, *Management Sci.*, vol. 12, pp. 253–313, November, 1965.
3. Balinski, M. L.: On Finding Integer Solutions to Linear Programs, H. Koenig, ed., *Proc. IBM Sci. Symp. Combinatorial Problems*, pp. 225–248, 1965.
4. Balinski, M. L.: Some General Methods in Integer Programming, in "Nonlinear Programming" (NATO Summer School, Menton 1964), chap. 9, pp. 221–247, North-Holland Publishing Company, Amsterdam, 1967.
4a. Basin, Stanley: Algebraic Formulation of the Minimum Crossing Problem for Complete Graphs, private communication, 1967 (to be published).
4b. Benders, J. F., C. A. R. Catchpole, and C. Kuiken: Discrete Variables, Optimization Problems, The Rand Corp., Symposium on Mathematical Programming, March 16–20, 1959.
5. Ben-Israel, Adi, and A. Charnes: On Some Problems of Diophantine Programming, *Cahiers Centr. d'Etud. Rech. Operation. (Bruxelles)*, vol. 4, pp. 215–280, 1962.
5a. Birkhoff, G., and S. MacLane: "A Survey of Modern Algebra," The Macmillan Company, New York, 1953.
6. Bradley, Gordon H.: Equivalent Integer Programs I: Basic Theory, *Operations Research House, Stanford University, Tech. Rept. No. 68-4*, March 28, 1968.
7. Bradley, Gordon H.: Equivalent Integer Programs II: The Special Problem, *Operations Research House, Stanford University, Tech. Rept. No. 68-6*, April 18, 1968.
8. Breuer, M. A.: The Minimization of Boolean Functions Containing Unequal and Nonlinear Cost Functions, Electronics Res. Lab., University of California, ser. 60, no. 431, January 22, 1962.
9. Cooper, L., and C. Drebes: An Approximate Solution Method for the Fixed Charge Problem, *Naval Res. Log. Quart.*, vol. 14, no. 1, pp. 101–113, March, 1967.

† For a more complete list, see the bibliographies of Balinski, Ben-Israel and Charnes, and Young.

10. Dantzig, George B.: "Linear Programming and Extensions," Princeton University Press, Princeton, N.J., 1963.

11. Dantzig, George B.: On the Significance of Solving Linear Programming Problems with Some Integer Variables, *Economet.*, vol. 28, no. 1, pp. 30–34, January, 1960.

12. Fox, Bennett: Discrete Optimization Via Marginal Analysis, *Management Sci.*, vol. 13, pp. 210–216, November, 1966.

13. Gass, Saul I.: "Linear Programming Methods and Applications," 3d ed., McGraw-Hill Book Company, New York, 1969.

14. Gass, S. I.: Recent Developments in Linear Programming, in "Advances in Computers," Academic Press, Inc., New York, vol. 2, pp. 295–377, 1961.

15. Geoffrion, Arthur M.: Integer Programming by Implicit Enumeration and Balas' Method, *SIAM Rev.*, vol. 9, no. 2, pp. 178–190, April, 1967.

16. Gilmore, P., and R. E. Gomory: The Theory and Computation of Knapsack Functions, *Operations Res.*, vol. 14, pp. 1045–1074, 1966.

16a. Gilmore, P., and R. E. Gomory: A Linear Programming Approach to the Cutting Stock Problem—Part II, *Operations Res.*, pp. 863–888, 1963.

17. Glover, F.: A Multiphase-dual Algorithm for the Zero-One Integer Programming Problem, *Operations Res.*, vol. 13, pp. 879–919, 1965.

18. Glover, Fred: Generalized Cuts in Diophantine Programming, *Management Sci.*, vol. 13, pp. 254–268, November, 1966.

19. Gomory, R. E.: All Integer–Integer Programming Algorithm, *IBM Research Center, RC-189*, January, 1960.

20. Gomory, R. E.: Outline of an Algorithm for Integer Solutions to Linear Programs, *Bull. Am. Math. Soc.*, vol. 64, pp. 275–278, 1958.

21. Gordon, Robert B.: Selecting Different Dropping Variables in the Simplex Algorithm, *Operations Research House, Stanford University, Tech. Rept. No. 68-3*, March, 1968.

22. Hammer (Ivănescu), Peter L., and Sergiu Rudeanu: "Pseudo-Boolean Methods for Bivalent Programming," Springer-Verlag OHG, Berlin, 1966.

23. Hammer (Ivănescu), Peter L., and Sergiu Rudeanu: "Boolean Methods in Operations Research and Related Areas," Springer-Verlag OHG, Berlin, 1968.

24. Heller, I., and C. B. Tompkins: An Extension of a Theorem of Dantzig's, in H. W. Kuhn and A. W. Tucker (eds.), "Linear Inequalities and Related Systems," Princeton University Press, Princeton, N.J., 1956.

25. Heller, I., and A. J. Hoffman: On Unimodular Matrices, *Pacific J. Math.*, vol. 12, no. 4, pp. 1321–1327, 1962.

26. Heller, I.: On Linear Systems with Integral Valued Solutions, *Bull. Am. Math. Soc.*, pp. 1351–1364, October, 1956.

27. Heller, I.: On Unimodular Sets of Vectors, in R. L. Graves and P. Wolfe (eds.), "Recent Advances in Mathematical Programming," McGraw-Hill Book Company, New York, 1963.

28. Hoffman, A. J.: On Simple Linear Programming Problems, *IBM Research Center, RC-541*, September, 1961.

29. House, R. W., L. D. Nelson, and T. Rado: Computer Studies of a Certain Class of Linear Integer Problems; chapter in A. Lavi and T. P. Vogl (eds.), "Recent Advances in Optimization Techniques," John Wiley & Sons, Inc., New York, 1966.

30. Kaplan, Seymour: Solution of the Lorie-Savage and Similar Integer Programming Problems by the Generalized Lagrange Multiplier Method, *Operations Res.*, vol. 14, no. 6, pp. 1130–1136, November–December, 1966.

31. Lawler, E. L., and M. D. Bell: A Method for Solving Discrete Optimization Problems, *Operations Res.*, vol. 14, no. 6, pp. 1098–1112, November–December, 1966.

31a. Miller, C. E., A. W. Tucker, and R. A. Zemlin: Integer Programming Formulation of Traveling Salesman Problems, *Journal of the A.C.M.*, vol. 7, no. 4, October, 1960.

32. Rockafellar, R. T.: A Combinatorial Algorithm for Linear Programs in the General Mixed Form, *J. Soc. Ind. Appl. Math.*, vol. 12, no. 1, March, 1964.

33. Saaty, T. L., and G. Suzuki: A Nonlinear Programming Model in Optimum Communication Satellite Use, *SIAM Rev.*, vol. 7, pp. 403–407, July, 1965.

34. Saaty, T. L., and Joseph Bram: Nonlinear Programming, in "Nonlinear Mathematics," chap. 3, McGraw-Hill Book Company, New York, 1964.

35. Shapiro, Jeremy F., and Harvey M. Wagner: A Finite Renewal Algorithm for the Knapsack and Turnpike Models, *Operations Res.*, vol. 15, no. 2, pp. 319–341, March–April, 1967.

35a. Simmonard, Michel: "Linear Programming," Prentice-Hall, Inc., Englewood Cliffs, N.J., 1966.

36. Veinott, Jr., Arthur F., and George B. Dantzig: Integral Extreme Points, *SIAM Rev.*, vol. 10, no. 3, July, 1968.

37. Wagner, Harvey, M.: An Integer Linear-Programming Model for Machine Scheduling, *Naval Res. Log. Quart.*, vol. 6, no. 2, pp. 131–140, June, 1959.

38. Wegner, P., and A. Doig: Symmetric Solutions of the Postage Stamp Problem, *Rev. Franc. Rech. Operation.*, vol. 41, pp. 353–374, 1966.

39. Weissman, John: Boolean Algebra, Map Coloring, and Interconnections, *Am. Math. Monthly*, vol. 69, no. 7, pp. 608–613, August–September, 1962.

40. Witzgall, Christoph: An All Integer Programming Algorithm with Parabolic Constraints, *J. Soc. Ind. Appl. Math.*, vol. 11, pp. 855–871, December, 1963.

41. Young, Richard D.: A Primal (All-Integer) Integer Programming Algorithm, *J. Res. Nat. Bur. Standards (U.S.)*, vol. 69B, pp. 213–249, September, 1965.

Indexes

Name Index

Subject Index

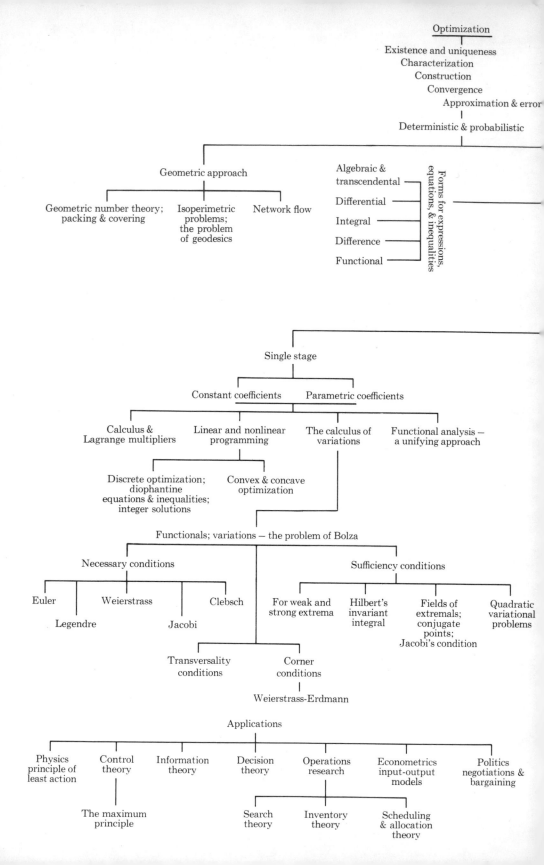

Optimization

Existence and uniqueness
Characterization
Construction
Convergence
Approximation & error

Deterministic & probabilistic

Geometric approach

Geometric number theory; packing & covering   Isoperimetric problems; the problem of geodesics   Network flow

Algebraic & transcendental

Differential

Integral

Difference

Functional

Forms for expressions, equations, & inequalities

Single stage

Constant coefficients   Parametric coefficients

Calculus & Lagrange multipliers   Linear and nonlinear programming   The calculus of variations   Functional analysis — a unifying approach

Discrete optimization; diophantine equations & inequalities; integer solutions   Convex & concave optimization

Functionals; variations — the problem of Bolza

Necessary conditions   Sufficiency conditions

Euler   Weierstrass   Clebsch   For weak and strong extrema   Hilbert's invariant integral   Fields of extremals; conjugate points; Jacobi's condition   Quadratic variational problems

Legendre   Jacobi

Transversality conditions   Corner conditions

Weierstrass-Erdmann

Applications

Physics principle of least action   Control theory   Information theory   Decision theory   Operations research   Econometrics input-output models   Politics negotiations & bargaining

The maximum principle   Search theory   Inventory theory   Scheduling & allocation theory